SOLUTIONS MANUAL

DIFFERENTIAL EQUATIONS AND BOUNDARY VALUE PROBLEMS
COMPUTING AND MODELING
SECOND EDITION

C. HENRY EDWARDS

DAVID E. PENNEY

PRENTICE HALL, UPPER SADDLE RIVER, NJ 07458

Executive Editor: George Lobell
Editorial Assistant: Gale A. Epps
Special Projects Manager: Barbara A. Murray
Production Editor: Jonathan Boylan
Supplement Cover Manager: Paul Gourhan
Supplement Cover Designer: PM Workshop Inc.
Manufacturing Buyer: Alan Fischer

Printed in the United States of America

10 9 8 7 6 5 4 3 2 1

ISBN 0-13-040123-4

Prentice-Hall International (UK) Limited, London
Prentice-Hall of Australia Pty. Limited, Sydney
Prentice-Hall Canada, Inc., Toronto
Prentice-Hall Hispanoamericana, S.A., Mexico
Prentice-Hall of India Private Limited, New Delhi
Prentice-Hall (Singapore) Pte. Ltd.
Prentice-Hall of Japan, Inc., Tokyo
Editora Prentice-Hall do Brazil, Ltda., Rio de Janeiro

CONTENTS

PREFACE

This is a solutions manual to accompany the textbook **DIFFERENTIAL EQUATIONS AND BOUNDARY VALUE PROBLEMS: Computing and Modeling** (1999) by C. Henry Edwards and David E. Penney. We provide here either the answer or a solution to essentially every problem in the text. In some cases only the answer is given to a problem that is entirely routine or involves only a standard elementary technique, but otherwise at least an outline of the principal steps in a complete solution is offered.

In every case our goal is to provide just that amount of detail in the way of answers, hints, and suggestions that will supplement the textbook discussion most instructively. In most cases we believe that giving the highlights to an argument or computation, but leaving something for the student to do, is better than including a complete solution that students could simply transcribe. Many of the sections in this manual begin with comments on the priority of topics within the corresponding section of the text.

The purpose of this manual is assistance in the teaching and learning of the subject of elementary differential equations. To this end we invite suggestions from those who use it (both instructors and students) as to what features might be added or improved to increase its usefulness in future editions.

Henry Edwards & David Penney
Department of Mathematics
University of Georgia
Athens, GA   30602

hedwards@math.uga.edu
dpenney@math.uga.edu

CHAPTER 1

FIRST-ORDER DIFFERENTIAL EQUATIONS

SECTION 1.1

DIFFERENTIAL EQUATIONS AND MATHEMATICAL MODELING

The main purpose of Section 1.1 is simply to introduce the basic notation and terminology of differential equations, and to tell the student what is meant by a solution of a differential equation. Also, the use of differential equations in the mathematical modeling of real-world phenomena is outlined.

Problems 1-12 are routine verifications by direct substitution of the indicated solutions into the given differential equations. As an example we include the solution of Problem 11.

11. If $y = y_1 = x^{-2}$ then

$$y' = -2x^{-3} \quad \text{and} \quad y'' = 6x^{-4},$$

so

$$x^2 y'' + 5xy' + 4y = x^2(6x^{-4}) + 5x(-2x^{-3}) + 4(x^{-2})$$

$$= 6x^{-2} - 10x^{-2} + 4x^{-2} = 0.$$

If $y = y_2 = x^{-2} \ln x$ then

$$y' = x^{-3} - 2x^{-3} \ln x \quad \text{and} \quad y'' = -5x^{-4} + 6x^{-4} \ln x,$$

so

$$x^2 y'' + 5xy' + 4y = x^2(-5x^{-4} + 6x^{-4}\ln x) + 5x(x^{-3} - 2x^{-3}\ln x) + 4(x^{-2}\ln x)$$

$$= (-5x^{-2} + 5x^{-2}) + (6x^{-2} - 10x^{-2} + 4x^{-2})\ln x = 0.$$

13. $r = 2/3$ **14.** $r = \pm 1/2$

15. $r = -2, 1$

16. If $y = e^{rx}$ then $y' = r e^{rx}$ and $y'' = r^2 e^{rx}$, so

$$3y'' + 3y' - 4y = (3r^2 + 3r - 4)e^{rx} = 0.$$

The solutions of the quadratic equation $3r^2 + 3r - 4 = 0$ are $r = (-3 \pm \sqrt{57})/6$.

17. $C = 2$ **18.** $C = 3$

19. $C = 6$ **20.** $C = 11$

21. $C = 7$

22. Substitution of $x = y = 0$ in $y(x) = \ln(x + C)$ yields $0 = \ln C$, so $C = 1$.

23. $C = -56$ **24.** $C = 17$

25. $C = \pi / 4$

26. Substitution of $x = \pi$ and $y = 0$ in $y(x) = (x + C) \cos x$ yields
$0 = (\pi + C)(-1)$, so $C = -\pi$.

27. $y' = x + y$

28. $y' = (y - 0) / (x - 2x) = 2y / x$

29. If m is the slope of the tangent line and m' the slope of the normal line at (x, y), then $mm' = -1$ yields

$$m' = -\frac{1}{y'} = \frac{y-1}{x-0}.$$

Therefore $y' = x / (1 - y)$.

30. $D_x(k + x^2) = 2x$, so the orthogonality relation $mm' = -1$ implies that $y = g(x)$ satisfies the differential equation $y' = -1/2x$.

31. $y' = (y - x) / (x + y)$ **32.** $dP / dt = k\sqrt{P}$

33. $dv/dt = kv^2$ **34.** $dv/dt = k(250 - v)$

35. $dN/dt = k(P - N)$ **36.** $dN/dt = kN(P - N)$

37. $y = 1$ or $y = x$ **38.** $y = e^x$

39. $y = x^2$ **40.** $y = 1$ or $y = -1$

41. $y = e^x / 2$ **42.** $y = \cos x$ or $y = \sin x$

43. (a) $y(10) = 10$ yields $10 = 1/(C - 10)$, so $C = 101/10$.

(b) There is no such value of C, but the constant function $y(x) = 0$ satisfies the conditions $y' = y^2$ and $y(0) = 0$.

(c) It is visually obvious that one and only one solution curve passes through each point (a, b) of the xy-plane, so it follows that there exists a unique solution to the initial value problem $y' = y^2$, $y(a) = b$.

44. **(b)** Obviously the functions $u(x) = -x^4$ and $v(x) = +x^4$ satisfy $xy' = 4y$. But $u'(x) = -4x^3$ and $v'(x) = +4x^3$ match at $x = 0$, where both are zero. Hence the given piecewise-defined function $y(x)$ is differentiable, and therefore satisfies the differential equation because $u(x)$ and $v(x)$ do so, for $x \leq 0$ and $x \geq 0$, respectively.

(c) If $a \geq 0$ (for instance), choose C_0 so that $C_0 a^4 = b$. Then the function

$$y(x) = \begin{cases} Cx^4 & \text{if } x \leq 0, \\ C_0 x^4 & \text{if } x \geq 0 \end{cases}$$

satisfies the differential equation for every value of C.

SECTION 1.2

INTEGRALS AS GENERAL AND PARTICULAR SOLUTIONS

This section introduces **general solutions** and **particular solutions** in the very simplest situation — a differential equation of the form $y' = f(x)$ — where only direct integration and evaluation of the constant of integration are involved. Students should review carefully the elementary concepts of velocity and acceleration, as well as the fps and cgs unit systems.

1. If $y' = 2x + 1$ then integration yields

$$y(x) = \int (2x+1)\, dx = x^2 + x + C.$$

Then substitution of $x = 0$, $y = 3$ gives $3 = 0 + 0 + C = C$, so

$$y(x) = x^2 + x + 3.$$

The solutions in Problems 2–9 follow the pattern of Problem 1, and only the answers are given.

2. $y = (x - 2)^4 / 4 + 1$

3. $y = (2x^{3/2} - 16)/3$

4. $y = -1/x + 6$

5. $y = 2(x + 2)^{1/2} - 5$

6. $y = [(x^2 + 9)^{3/2} - 125]/3$

7. $y = 10 \tan^{-1} x$

8. $y = (1/2)\sin 2x + 1$ **9.** $y = \sin^{-1}x$

10. $y = -(1 + x)e^{-x} + 2$

11.   If $a(t) = 50$ then

$$v = \int 50\,dt = 50t + v_0 = 50t + 10.$$

Hence

$$x = \int (50t + 10)\,dt = 25t^2 + 10t + x_0 = 25t^2 + 10t + 20.$$

12. $x = -10t^2 - 15t + 5$ **13.** $x = t^3/2 + 5t$

14. $x = t^3/3 + t^2/2 - 7t + 4$

15. $x = (1/3)(t + 3)^4 - 37t - 26$

16. $x = (4/3)(t + 4)^{3/2} - 5t - 29/3$

17. $x = [1/(t + 1) + t - 1]$

18. $x = 10 - 2\sin 5t$

19. $v = -9.8t + 49$, so the ball reaches its maximum height $(v = 0)$ after $t = 5$ seconds. Its maximum height then is $y(5) = -4.9(5)^2 + 49(5) = 122.5$ meters.

20. $v = -32t$ and $y = -16t^2 + 400$, so the ball hits the ground $(y = 0)$ when $t = 5$ sec, and then $v = -32(5) = -160$ ft/sec.

21. $a = -10$ m/s^2 and $v_0 = 100$ km/h ≈ 27.78 m/s, so $v = -10t + 27.78$, and hence

$$x(t) = -5t^2 + 27.78t.$$

The car stops when $v = 0$, $t \approx 2.78$, and thus the distance traveled before stopping is $x(2.78) \approx 38.59$ meters.

22. $v = -9.8t + 100$ and $y = -4.9t^2 + 100t + 20$.

(a) $v = 0$ when $t = 100/9.8$ so the projectile's maximum height is $y(100/9.8) = -4.9(100/9.8)^2 + 100(100/9.8) + 20 \approx 530$ meters.

(b)   It passes the top of the building when $y(t) = -4.9t^2 + 100t + 20 = 20$, and hence after $t = 100/4.9 \approx 20.41$ seconds.

(c)   The roots of the quadratic equation $y(t) = -4.9t^2 + 100t + 20 = 0$ are

$t = -0.20,\ 20.61$. Hence the projectile is in the air 20.61 seconds.

23. $a = -9.8\ \text{m/s2}$ so $v = -9.8\,t - 10$ and

$$y = -4.9\,t^2 - 10\,t + y_0.$$

The ball hits the ground when $y = 0$ and

$$v = -9.8\,t - 10 = -60,$$

so $t \approx 5.10$ s. Hence

$$y_0 = 4.9(5.10)^2 + 10(5.10) \approx 178.57\ \text{m}.$$

24. $v = -32t - 40$ and $y = -16t^2 - 40t + 555$. The ball hits the ground $(y = 0)$ when $t \approx 4.77$ sec, with velocity $v = v(4.77) \approx -192.64$ ft/sec, an impact speed of about 131 mph.

25.   Integration of $dv/dt = 0.12\,t^3 + 0.6\,t,\ v(0) = 0$ gives $v(t) = 0.3\,t^2 + 0.04\,t^3$. Hence $v(10) = 70$. Then integration of $dx/dt = 0.3\,t^2 + 0.04\,t^3,\ x(0) = 0$ gives $x(t) = 0.1\,t^3 + 0.04\,t^4$, so $x(10) = 200$. Thus after 10 seconds the car has gone 200 ft and is traveling at 70 ft/sec.

26.   Taking $x_0 = 0$ and $v_0 = 60\ \text{mph} = 88\ \text{ft/sec}$, we get

$$v = -at + 88,$$

and $v = 0$ yields $t = 88/a$. Substituting this value of t and $x = 176$ in

$$x = -at^2/2 + 88t,$$

we solve for $a = 22\ \text{ft/sec}^2$. Hence the car skids for $t = 88/22 = 4$ sec.

27.   If $a = -20\ \text{m/sec}^2$ and $x_0 = 0$ then the car's velocity and position at time t are given by

$$v = -20t + v_0, \quad x = -10\,t^2 + v_0 t.$$

It stops when $v = 0$ (so $v_0 = 20t$), and hence when

$$x = 75 = -10\,t^2 + (20t)t = 10\,t^2.$$

Thus $t = \sqrt{7.5}$ sec so

$$v_0 = 20(\sqrt{7.5}) \approx 54.77\ \text{m/sec} \approx 197\ \text{km/hr}.$$

28.   Starting with $x_0 = 0$ and $v_0 = 50\ \text{km/h} = 5 \times 10^4\ \text{m/h}$, we find by the method of

Problem 24 that the car's deceleration is $a = (25/3)\times10^7$ m/h^2. Then, starting with $x_0 = 0$ and $v_0 = 100$ km/h $= 10^5$ m/h, we substitute $t = v_0/a$ into

$$x = -at^2 + v_0 t$$

and find that $x = 60$ m when $v = 0$. Thus doubling the initial velocity quadruples the distance the car skids.

29.   If $v_0 = 0$ and $y_0 = 20$ then

$$v = -at \text{ and } y = -0.5at^2 + 20.$$

Substitution of $t = 2$, $y = 0$ yields $a = 10$ ft/sec^2. If $v_0 = 0$ and $y_0 = 200$ then

$$v = -10t \text{ and } y = -5t^2 + 200.$$

Hence $y = 0$ when $t = \sqrt{40} = 2\sqrt{10}$ sec and $v = -20\sqrt{10} \approx -63.25$ ft/sec.

30.   **On Earth:** $v = -32t + v_0$, so $t = v_0/32$ at maximum height (when $v = 0$). Substituting this value of t and $y = 144$ in

$$y = -16t^2 + v_0 t,$$

we solve for $v_0 = 96$ ft/sec as the initial speed with which the person can throw a ball straight upward.

On Planet Gzyx: From Problem 27, the surface gravitational acceleration on planet Gzyx is $a = 10$ ft/sec^2, so

$$v = -10t + 96 \quad \text{and} \quad y = -5t^2 + 96t.$$

Therefore $v = 0$ yields $t = 9.6$ sec, and thence $y_{max} = y(9.6) = 460.8$ ft is the height a ball will reach if its initial velocity is 96 ft/sec.

31.   If $v_0 = 0$ and $y_0 = h$ then the stone's velocity and height are given by

$$v = -gt, \quad y = -0.5\, gt^2 + h.$$

Hence $y = 0$ when $t = \sqrt{(2h/g)}$ so

$$v = -g\sqrt{(2h/g)} = -\sqrt{(2gh)}$$

32.   The method of solution is precisely the same as that in Problem 30. We find first that, on Earth, the woman must jump straight upward with initial velocity $v_0 = 12$ ft/sec to reach a maximum height of 2.25 ft. Then we find that, on the Moon, this initial velocity yields a maximum height of about 13.58 ft.

33. We use units of miles and hours. If $x_0 = v_0 = 0$ then the car's velocity and position after t hours are given by

$$v = at, \quad x = 0.5\, t^2.$$

Since $v = 60$ when $t = 5/6$, the velocity equation yields $a = 72 \text{ mi/hr}^2$. Hence the distance traveled by 12:50 pm is

$$x = (0.5)(72)(5/6)^2 = 25 \text{ miles.}$$

34. Again we have

$$v = at, \quad x = 0.5\, t^2.$$

But now $v = 60$ when $x = 35$. Substitution of $a = 60/t$ (from the velocity equation) into the position equation yields

$$35 = (0.5)(60/t)(t^2) = 30t,$$

whence $t = 7/6$ hr, that is, 1:10 p.m.

35. Integration of $y' = (9/v_S)(1 - 4x^2)$ yields

$$y = (3/v_S)(3x - 4x^3) + C,$$

and the initial condition $y(-1/2) = 0$ gives $C = 3/v_S$. Hence the swimmer's trajectory is

$$y(x) = (3/v_S)(3x - 4x^3 + 1).$$

Substitution of $y(1/2) = 1$ now gives $v_S = 6$ mph.

36. Integration of $y' = 3(1 - 16x^4)$ yields

$$y = 3x - (48/5)x^5 + C,$$

and the initial condition $y(-1/2) = 0$ gives $C = 6/5$. Hence the swimmer's trajectory is

$$y(x) = (1/5)(15x - 48x^5 + 6),$$

so his downstream drift is $y(1/2) = 2.4$ miles.

SECTION 1.3

SLOPE FIELDS AND SOLUTION CURVES

As pointed out in the text, the instructor may choose to delay covering Section 1.3 until later in Chapter 1. However, before proceeding to Chapter 2, it is important that students come to grips at some point with the question of the existence of a unique solution of a differential equation — and realize that it makes no sense to look for the solution without knowing in advance that it exists. The instructor may prefer to combine existence and uniqueness by simplifying the statement of the existence-uniqueness theorem as follows:

> Suppose that the function $f(x, y)$ and the partial derivative $\partial f/\partial y$ are both continuous in some neighborhood of the point (a, b). Then the initial value problem
> $$\frac{dy}{dx} = f(x, y), \qquad y(a) = b$$
> has a unique solution in some neighborhood of the point a.

Slope fields and geometrical solution curves are introduced in this section as a concrete aid in visualizing solutions and existence-uniqueness questions. Solution curves corresponding to the slope fields in Problems 1–10 are included in the answers section of the text and will not be duplicated here.

11.   Each isocline $x - 1 = C$ is a vertical straight line.

12.   Each isocline $x + y = C$ is a straight line with slope $m = -1$.

13.   Each isocline $y^2 = C \geq 0$, that is, $y = \sqrt{C}$ or $y = -\sqrt{C}$, is a horizontal straight line.

14.   Each isocline $y^{1/3} = C$, that is, $y = C^3$, is a horizontal straight line.

15.   Each isocline $y/x = C$, or $y = Cx$, is a straight line through the origin.

16.   Each isocline $x^2 - y^2 = C$ is a hyperbola that opens along the x-axis if $C > 0$, along the y-axis if $C < 0$.

17.   Each isocline $xy = C$ is a rectangular hyperbola that opens along the line $y = x$ if $C > 0$, along $y = -x$ if $C < 0$.

18.   Each isocline $x - y^2 = C$, or $y^2 = x - C$, is a translated parabola that opens along the x–axis.

19.   Each isocline $y - x^2 = C$, or $x^2 = y - C$, is a translated parabola that opens along the y–axis.

20. Each isocline is an exponential graph of the form $y = Ce^x$.

21. Because both $f(x, y) = 2x^2y^2$ and $\partial f/\partial y = 4x^2y$ are continuous everywhere, the existence-uniqueness theorem of Section 1.3 in the text guarantees the existence of a unique solution in some neighborhood of $x = 1$.

22. Both $f(x, y) = x \ln y$ and $\partial f/\partial y = x/y$ are continuous in a neighborhood of $(1, 1)$, so the theorem guarantees the existence of a unique solution in some neighborhood of $x = 1$.

23. Both $f(x, y) = y^{1/3}$ and $\partial f/\partial y = (1/3)y^{-2/3}$ are continuous near $(0, 1)$, so the theorem guarantees the existence of a unique solution in some neighborhood of $x = 0$.

24. $f(x, y) = y^{1/3}$ is continuous in a neighborhood of $(0, 0)$, but $\partial f/\partial y = (1/3)y^{-2/3}$ is not, so the theorem guarantees existence but not uniqueness in some neighborhood of $x = 0$.

25. $f(x, y) = (x - y)^{1/2}$ is not continuous at $(2, 2)$ because it is not even defined if $y > x$. Hence the theorem guarantees neither existence nor uniqueness in any neighborhood of the point $x = 2$.

26. $f(x, y) = (x - y)^{1/2}$ and $\partial f/\partial y = -(1/2)(x - y)^{-1/2}$ are continuous in a neighborhood of $(2, 1)$, so the theorem guarantees both existence and uniqueness of a solution in some neighborhood of $x = 2$.

27. Both $f(x, y) = (x - 1/y$ and $\partial f/\partial y = -(x - 1)/y^2$ are continuous near $(0, 1)$, so the theorem guarantees both existence and uniqueness of a solution in some neighborhood of $x = 0$.

28. Neither $f(x, y) = (x - 1)/y$ nor $\partial f/\partial y = -(x - 1)/y^2$ is continuous near $(1, 0)$, so the existence-uniqueness theorem guarantees nothing.

29. Both $f(x, y) = \ln(1 + y^2)$ and $\partial f/\partial y = 2y/(1 + y^2)$ are continuous near $(0, 0)$, so the theorem guarantees the existence of a unique solution near $x = 0$.

30. Both $f(x, y) = x^2 - y^2$ and $\partial f/\partial y = -2y$ are continuous near $(0, 1)$, so the theorem guarantees both existence and uniqueness of a solution in some neighborhood of $x = 0$.

31. If $f(x, y) = -(1 - y^2)^{1/2}$ then $\partial f/\partial y = y(1 - y^2)^{-1/2}$ is not continuous when $y = 1$, so the theorem does not guarantee uniqueness.

32. The two solutions are $y_1(x) = 0$ (constant) and $y_2(x) = x^3$.

35. The isoclines of $y' = y/x$ are the straight lines $y = Cx$ through the origin, and $y' = C$ at points of $y = Cx$, so it appears that these same straight lines are the solution curves of $xy' = y$. Then we observe that there is

(i)   a unique one of these lines through any point not on the y-axis;
(ii)   no such line through any point on the y-axis other than the origin; and
(iii)   infinitely many such lines through the origin.

36. $f(x,y) = 4xy^{1/2}$ and $\partial f/\partial y = 2xy^{-1/2}$ are continuous if $y > 0$, so for all a and all $b > 0$ there exists a unique solution near $x = a$ such that $y(a) = b$. If $b = 0$ then the theorem guarantees neither existence nor uniqueness. For any a, both $y_1(x) = 0$ and $y_2(x) = (x^2 - a^2)^2$ are solutions with $y(a) = 0$. Thus we have existence but not uniqueness near points on the x-axis.

SECTION 1.4

SEPARABLE EQUATIONS AND APPLICATIONS

Of course it should be emphasized to students that the possibility of separating the variables is the first one you look for. The general concept of natural growth and decay is important for all differential equations students, but the particular applications in this section are optional. Torricelli's law in the form of Equation (24) in the text leads to some nice concrete examples and problems.

1. $y = C\exp(-x^2)$ **2.** $y = 1/(x^2 + C)$

3. $y = C\exp(-\cos x)$ **4.** $y = C(1+x)^4$

5. $y = \sin(\sqrt{x} + C)$ **6.** $y = (x^{3/2} + C)^2$

7. $y = (2x^{4/3} + C)^{3/2}$ **8.** $y = \sin^{-1}(x^2 + C)$

9.   The partial fraction decomposition

$$\frac{2}{1-x^2} = \frac{1}{1+x} + \frac{1}{1-x}$$

leads to

$$y = C\frac{1+x}{1-x}$$

10. $y = [x - C(1+x)] / [1 + C(1+x)]$

11. $y = (C - x^2)^{-1/2}$ **12.** $y^2 + 1 = C\exp(x^2)$

13. $(1/4)\ln(y^4 + 1) = \sin x + C$ **14.** $3y + 2y^{3/2} = 3x + 2x^{3/2} + C$

15. $1/3y^3 - 2/y = 1/x + \ln|x| + C$ **16.** $\sec y = C(x^2 + 1)^{1/2}$

17. $\ln|1 + y| = x + \frac{1}{2}x^2 + C$ **18.** $y = \tan(C - x - 1/x)$

19. $y = 2\exp(e^x)$ **20.** $y = \tan(x^3 + \pi x)$

21. $y^2 = 1 + (x^2 - 16)^{1/2}$ **22.** $y = -3\exp(x^4 - x)$

23. $y = \dfrac{1}{2}\left(1 + e^{2x-2}\right)$ **24.** $y = (\pi/2)\sin x$

25. $y = x\exp(x^2 - 1)$ **26.** $y = 1/(1 - x^2 - x^3)$

27. $y = \ln|3e^{2x} - 2|$ **28.** $y = \tan^{-1}(\sqrt{x} - 1)$

29. About 51,840 persons **30.** About 3.87 hours

31. About 14,735 years

32. The purported relic is about 686 years old.

33. \$21,103.48 **34.** \$44.52

35. 2585 mg **36.** About 35 years

37. Taking $t = 0$ when the body was formed and $t = T$ now, the amount $Q(t)$ of lead in the body at time t (in years) is given by $Q(t) = Q_0 e^{-kt}$, where $k = (\ln 2)/(4.51\times10^9)$. The given information tells us that

$$\frac{Q(T)}{Q_0 - Q(T)} = 0.9.$$

After substituting $Q(T) = Q_0 e^{-kT}$, we solve readily for $e^{kT} = 19/9$, so

$$t = (1/k)\ln(19/9) \approx 4.86\times10^9.$$

Thus the body was formed approximately 4.86 billion years ago.

38. Taking $t = 0$ when the rock contained only potassium and $t = T$ now, the amount $Q(t)$ of potassium in the rock at time t (in years) is given by $Q(t) = Q_0 e^{-kt}$, where $k = (\ln 2)/(1.28\times10^9)$. The given information tells us that the amount $A(t)$ of argon at time t is

$$A(t) = \tfrac{1}{9}[Q_0 - Q(t)]$$

and also that $A(T) = Q(T)$. Thus

$$Q_0 - Q(T) = 9\,Q(T).$$

After substituting $Q(T) = Q_0 e^{-kT}$ we readily solve for

$$T = (\ln 10 / \ln 2)(1.28 \times 10^9) \approx 4.25 \times 10^9.$$

Thus the age of the rock is about 1.25 billion years.

39.   Because $A = 0$ the differential equation reduces to $T' = kT$, so $T(t) = 25e^{-kt}$. The fact that $T(20) = 15$ yields $k = (1/20)\ln(5/3)$, and finally we solve

$$5 = 25e^{-kt} \quad \text{for} \quad t = (\ln 5)/k \approx 63 \text{ min.}$$

40.   About 2.41 minutes

41.   **(a)**   0.495 m   **(b)** $(8.32 \times 10^{-7})I_0$ **(c)**   3.29 m

42.   **(a)**   20.486 inches; 9.604 inches
           (b)   3.45 miles, or about 18,200 feet

43.   **(a)** $A' = rA + Q$
           (b)   The solution of the differential equation with $A(0) = 0$ is given by

$$rA + Q = Qe^{rt}.$$

When we substitute $A = 40$ (thousand), $r = 0.11$, and $t = 18$, we find that $Q = 0.70482$, that is, \$704.82 per year.

44.   The answer is about 5.99 billion years. For a complete solution see Example 3 in Section 7.5 of Edwards & Penney, *Calculus with Analytic Geometry* (5th edition, Prentice-Hall, 1998).

45.   After 66 min 40 sec; this problem is just like Example 6 in the text.

46.   **(b)**   By separating the variables we solve the differential equation for

$$c - r\,P(t) = (c - r\,P_0)\,e^{rt}.$$

With $P(t) = 0$ this yields

$$c = r\,P_0\,e^{rt} / (e^{rt} - 1).$$

With $P_0 = 10,800$, $t = 60$, and $r = 0.010$ we get $239.37 for the monthly payment at 12% annual interest. With $r = 0.015$ we get $272.99 for the monthly payment at 18% annual interest.

47. If $N(t)$ denotes the number of people (in thousands) who have heard the rumor after t days, then the initial value problem is

$$N' = k(100 - N), \quad N(0) = 0$$

and we are given that $N(7) = 10$. The answer is $t \approx 46$ days.

48. With $A(y)$ constant, Equation (19) in the text takes the form

$$\frac{dy}{dt} = k\sqrt{y}$$

We readily solve this equation for

$$2\sqrt{y} = kt + C.$$

The condition $y(0) = 9$ yields $C = 6$, and then $y(1) = 4$ yields $k = 2$. Thus the depth at time t (in hours) is $y(t) = (3 - t)^2$, and hence it takes 3 hours for the tank to empty.

49. With $A = \pi(3)^2$ and $a = \pi(1/12)^2$, and taking $g = 32$ ft/sec^2, Equation (20) reduces to $162\, y' = -\sqrt{y}$. The solution such that $y = 9$ when $t = 0$ is given by

$$324\sqrt{y} = -t + 972.$$

Hence $y = 0$ when $t = 972$ sec $= 16$ min 12 sec.

50. The radius of the cross-section of the cone at height y is proportional to y, so $A(y)$ is proportional to y^2. Therefore Equation (20) takes the form

$$y^2 y' = -k\sqrt{y},$$

and a general solution is given by

$$2y^{5/2} = -5kt + C.$$

The initial condition $y(0) = 16$ yields $C = 2048$, and then $y(1) = 9$ implies that $5k = 1562$. Hence $y = 0$ when

$$t = C/5k = 2048/1562 \approx 1.31 \text{ hr.}$$

51.   The solution of $y' = -k\sqrt{y}$ is given by

$$2\sqrt{y} = -kt + C.$$

The initial condition $y(0) = h$ (the height of the cylinder) yields $C = 2\sqrt{h}$. Then substitution of $t = T$, $y = 0$ gives $k = (2\sqrt{h})/T$. It follows that

$$y = h(1 - t/T)^2.$$

If r denotes the radius of the cylinder, then

$$V(y) = \pi r^2 y = \pi r^2 h(1 - t/T)^2 = V_0(1 - t/T)^2.$$

52.   Since $x = y^{3/4}$, the cross-sectional area is $A(y) = \pi x^2 = \pi y^{3/2}$. Hence the general equation $A(y)y' = -a\sqrt{2gy}$ reduces to the differential equation $yy' = -k$ with general solution

$$(1/2)y^2 = -kt + C.$$

The initial condition $y(0) = 12$ gives $C = 72$, and then $y(1) = 6$ yields $k = 54$. It follows that the depth at time t is

$$y(t) = \sqrt{(144 - 108t)},$$

so the tank is empty after $t = 4/3$ hr, that is, at 1:20 p.m.

53.   **(a)**   Since $x^2 = by$, the cross-sectional area is $A(y) = \pi x^2 = \pi by$. Hence the equation $A(y)y' = -a\sqrt{2gy}$ reduces to the differential equation

$$y^{1/2}y' = -k = -(a/\pi b)\sqrt{2g}$$

with the general solution

$$(2/3)y^{3/2} = -kt + C.$$

The initial condition $y(0) = 4$ gives $C = 16/3$, and then $y(1) = 1$ yields $k = 14/3$. It follows that the depth at time t is

$$y(t) = (8 - 7t)^{2/3}.$$

(b)   The tank is empty after $t = 8/7$ hr, that is, at 1:08:34 p.m.

(c)   We see above that $k = (a/\pi b)\sqrt{(2g)} = 14/3$. Substitution of $a = \pi r^2$, $b = 1$, $g = (32)(3600)^2$ ft/hr^2 yields $r = (1/60)\sqrt{(7/12)}$ ft ≈ 0.15 in for the radius of the bottom-hole.

54. With $g = 32$ ft/sec^2 and $a = \pi(1/12)^2$, Equation (24) simplifies to

$$A(y)\frac{dy}{dt} = -\frac{\pi}{18}\sqrt{y}.$$

If z denotes the distance from the center of the cylinder down to the fluid surface, then $y = 3 - z$ and $A(y) = 10(9 - z^2)^{1/2}$. Hence the equation above becomes

$$10(9 - z^2)^{1/2}\frac{dz}{dt} = \frac{\pi}{18}(3 - z)^{1/2},$$

$$180(3 + z)^{1/2}dz = \pi\,dt,$$

and integration yields

$$120(3 + z)^{1/2} = \pi t + C.$$

Now $z = 0$ when $t = 0$, so $C = 120(3)^{3/2}$. The tank is empty when $z = 3$ (that is, when $y = 0$) and thus after

$$t = (120/\pi)(6^{3/2} - 3^{3/2}) \approx 362.90 \text{ sec}.$$

It therefore takes about 6 min 3 sec for the fluid to drain completely.

55. $A(y) = \pi(8y - y^2)$ as in Example 7 in the text, but now $a = \pi/144$ in Equation (24), so the initial value problem is

$$18(8y - y^2)y' = -\sqrt{y}, \qquad y(0) = 8.$$

We seek the value of t when $y = 0$. The answer is $t \approx 869$ sec $= 14$ min 29 sec.

56. The cross-sectional area function for the tank is $A = \pi(1 - y^2)$ and the area of the bottom-hole is $a = 10^{-4}\pi$, so Eq. (24) in the text gives the initial value problem

$$\pi(1 - y^2)\frac{dy}{dt} = -10^{-4}\pi\sqrt{2 \times 9.8y}, \quad y(0) = 1.$$

Simplification gives

$$\left(y^{-1/2} - y^{3/2}\right)\frac{dy}{dt} = -1.4 \times 10^{-4}\sqrt{10}$$

so integration yields

$$2y^{1/2} - \frac{2}{5}y^{5/2} = -1.4 \times 10^{-4}\sqrt{10}\,t + C.$$

The initial condition $y(0) = 1$ implies that $C = 2 - 2/5 = 8/5$, so $y = 0$ after $t = (8/5)/(1.4 \times 10^{-4}\sqrt{10}) \approx 3614$ seconds. Thus the tank is empty at about 14 seconds after 2 pm.

57. **(a)** As in Example 8, the initial value problem is

$$\pi(8y - y^2)\frac{dy}{dt} = -\pi k\sqrt{y}, \qquad y(0) = 4$$

where $k = 0.6r^2\sqrt{2g} = 4.8r^2$. Integrating and applying the initial condition just in the Example 8 solution in the text, we find that

$$\frac{16}{3}y^{3/2} - \frac{2}{5}y^{5/2} = -kt + \frac{448}{15}.$$

When we substitute $y = 2$ (ft) and $t = 1800$ (sec, that is, 30 min), we find that $k \approx 0.009469$. Finally, $y = 0$ when

$$t = \frac{448}{15k} \approx 3154 \text{ sec} = 53 \text{ min } 34 \text{ sec}.$$

Thus the tank is empty at 1:53:34 pm.

(b) The radius of the bottom-hole is

$$r = \sqrt{k/4.8} \approx 0.04442 \text{ ft} \approx 0.53 \text{ in, thus about a half inch.}$$

58. The given rate of fall of the water level is $dy/dt = -4$ in/hr $= -(1/10800)$ ft/sec. With $A = \pi x^2$ and $a = \pi r^2$, Equation (24) is

$$(\pi x^2)(1/10800) = -(\pi r^2)\sqrt{2gy} = -8\pi r^2\sqrt{y}.$$

Hence the curve is of the form $y = kx^4$, and in order that it pass through $(1, 4)$ we must have $k = 4$. Comparing $\sqrt{y} = 2x^2$ with the equation above, we see that

$$(8r^2)(10800) = 1/2,$$

so the radius of the bottom hole is $r = 1/(240\sqrt{3})$ ft $\approx 1/35$ in.

59. Let $t = 0$ at the time of death. Then the solution of the initial value problem

$$T' = k(70 - T), \qquad T(0) = 98.6$$

is

$$T(t) = 70 + 28.6 e^{-kt}.$$

If $t = a$ at 12 noon, then we know that

$$T(t) = 70 + 28.6 e^{-ka} = 80,$$

$$T(a+1) = 70 + 28.6 e^{-k(a+1)} = 75.$$

Hence

$$28.6 e^{-ka} = 10 \quad \text{and} \quad 28.6 e^{-ka} e^{-k} = 5.$$

It follows that $e^{-k} = 1/2$, so $k = \ln 2$. Finally the first of the previous two equations yields

$$a = (\ln 2.86)/(\ln 2) \approx 1.516 \text{ hr} \approx 1 \text{ hr } 31 \text{ min},$$

so the death occurred at 10:29 a.m.

60. Let $t = 0$ when it began to snow, and $t = t_0$ at 7:00 a.m. Let x denote distance along the road, with $x = 0$ where the snowplow begins at 7:00 a.m. If $y = ct$ is the snow depth at time t, w is the width of the road, and $v = dx/dt$ is the plow's velocity, then "plowing at a constant rate" means that the product wyv is constant. Hence our differential equation is of the form

$$k\frac{dx}{dt} = \frac{1}{t}.$$

The solution with $x = 0$ when $t = t_0$ is

$$t = t_0 e^{kx}.$$

We are given that $x = 2$ when $t = t_0 + 1$ and $x = 4$ when $t = t_0 + 3$, so it follows that

$$t_0 + 1 = t_0 e^{2k} \quad \text{and} \quad t_0 + 3 = t_0 e^{4k}.$$

Elimination of t_0 yields the equation

$$e^{4k} - 3e^{2k} + 2 = (e^{2k} - 1)(e^{2k} - 2) = 0,$$

so it follows (since $k > 0$) that $e^{2k} = 2$. Hence $t_0 + 1 = 2t_0$, so $t_0 = 1$. Thus it began to snow at 6 a.m.

61.   We still have $t = t_0 e^{kx}$, but now the given information yields the conditions

$$t_0 + 1 = t_0 e^{4k} \quad \text{and} \quad t_0 + 2 = t_0 e^{7k}$$

at 8 a.m. and 9 a.m., respectively. Elimination of t_0 gives the equation

$$2e^{4k} - e^{7k} - 1 = 0,$$

which we solve numerically for $k = 0.08276$. Using this value, we finally solve one of the preceding pair of equations for $t_0 = 2.5483$ hr $\approx$ 2 hr 33 min. Thus it began to snow at 4:27 a.m.

SECTION 1.5

LINEAR FIRST-ORDER EQUATIONS

In addition to learning to recognize and solve linear first order-equations, it is good preparation for Chapter 3 (higher order linear equations) for students to study carefully the existence-uniqueness theorem for first-order linear equations in this section. Although we recommend that students not memorize Equation (18) in the text, it's hard to deny that many students can set up mixture problems most easily by substituting in the equation

$$\frac{dx}{dt} = r_i c_i - r_o c_o,$$

where r_i and r_o are the incoming and outgoing flow rates, and c_i and $c_o = x/V$ are the incoming and outgoing concentrations.

In each of Problems 1–25 we give the integrating factor $\rho(x) = \exp\left[\int P(x)\,dx\right]$ as well as the desired general or particular solution. It is important to write the differential equation precisely in the form $y' + P(x)y = Q(x)$ before attempting to calculate the integrating factor $\rho(x)$.

1. $\rho = e^x$; $y = 2(1 - e^{-x})$

2. $\rho = e^{-2x}$; $y = 3xe^{2x}$

3. $\rho = e^{3x}$; $y = e^{-3x}(x^2 + C)$

4. $\rho = \exp(-x^2)$; $y = (x + C)\exp(-x^2)$

5. $\rho = x^2$; $y = x + 4/x^2$

6. $\rho = x^5;$ $y = x^2 + 32/x^5$

7. $\rho = x^{1/2};$ $y = 5x^{1/2} + Cx^{-1/2}$

8. $\rho = x^{1/3};$ $y = 3x + Cx^{-1/3}$

9. $\rho = 1/x;$ $y = x(7 + \ln x)$

10. $\rho = x^{-3/2};$ $y = 3x^3 + Cx^{3/2}$

11. $\rho = xe^{-3x};$ the general solution is $y(x) = Cx^{-1}e^{3x}.$ The particular solution such that $y(1) = 0$ is the constant function $y(x) = 0$ (obtained with $C = 0$).

12. $\rho = x^3;$ $y = x^5/4 - 56/x^3$

13. $\rho = e^x;$ $y = (e^x + e^{-x})/2$

14. $\rho = x^{-3};$ $y = x^3(10 + \ln x)$

15. $\rho = \exp(x^2);$ $y = [1 - 5\exp(-x^2)]/2$

16. $\rho = \exp(\sin x);$ $y = 1 + \exp(-\sin x)$

17. $\rho = 1 + x;$ $y = (1 + \sin x)/(1 + x)$

18. $\rho = x^{-2};$ $y = x^2(C + \sin x)$

19. $\rho = \sin x;$ $y = (1/2)\sin x + C \csc x$

20. $\rho = \exp(-x - x^2/2);$ $y = \exp(x + x^2/2) - 1$

21. $\rho = x^{-3};$ $y = x^3 \sin x$

22. $\rho = \exp(-x^2);$ $y = (x^3 + 5)\exp(x^2)$

23. $\rho = x^{-3}e^{2x};$ $y = x^3(2 + Ce^{-2x})$

24. $\rho = (x^2 + 4)^{3/2};$ $3y = 1 + 16(x^2 + 4)^{-3/2}$

25. First we calculate

$$\int \frac{3x^3\, dx}{x^2 + 1} = \int \left[3x - \frac{3x}{x^2 + 1}\right] dx = \frac{3}{2}\left[x^2 - \ln(x^2 + 1)\right].$$

It follows that

$$\rho = (x^2 + 1)^{-3/2}\exp(3x^2/2).$$

The desired particular solution is

$$y(x) = [\exp(-3x^2/2)][3(x^2 + 1)^{3/2} - 2].$$

26. With $x' = dx/dy$, the differential equation is

$$y^3x' + 4y^2x = 1.$$

With y as the independent variable we find that the integrating factor is $\rho(y) = y^4$; the general solution is

$$x(y) = 1/2y^2 + C/y^4.$$

27. $x' - x = ye^y$, $\qquad \rho(y) = e^{-y}$; $\quad x = e^y(C + y^2/2)$

28. $(1 + y^2)x' - 2yx = 1$

$\rho(y) = (1 + y^2)^{-1}$; $\quad 2x = y + (1 + y^2)(C + \tan^{-1}y)$

29. $y(x) = [\exp(x^2)][C + (\sqrt{\pi}/2)\text{erf}(x)]$

30. After division of the given equation by $2x$, multiplication by the integrating factor $\rho = x^{-1/2}$ yields

$$x^{-1/2}y' - \tfrac{1}{2}x^{-3/2}y = x^{-1/2}\cos x,$$

$$D_x(x^{-1/2}y) = x^{-1/2}\cos x,$$

$$x^{-1/2}y = C + \int_1^x t^{-1/2}\cos t\, dt.$$

The initial condition $y(1) = 0$ implies that $C = 0$, so the desired particular solution is

$$y(x) = x^{1/2}\int_1^x t^{-1/2}\cos t\, dt.$$

32. (a) $y_P(x) = \sin x - \cos x$
    (b) $y(x) = Ce^{-x} + \sin x - \cos x$
    (c) $y(x) = 2e^{-x} + \sin x - \cos x$

33. After about 7 min 41 sec

34. About 22.2 days. For a complete solution see Example 4 in Section 7.6 of Edwards and Penney, *Calculus with Analytic Geometry* (5th edition, Prentice-Hall, 1998).

35. The only difference from the Example 4 solution in the text is is that $V = 1640 \text{ km}^3$ and $r = 410 \text{ km}^3/\text{yr}$ for Lake Ontario, so the time required is

$$t = \frac{V}{r}\ln 4 = 4 \ln 4 \approx 5.5452 \text{ years.}$$

36. **(a)** The volume of brine in the tank after t min is $V(t) = 60 - t$ gal, so the initial value problem is

$$\frac{dx}{dt} = 2 - \frac{3x}{60-t}, \qquad x(0) = 0.$$

The solution is

$$x(t) = (60-t) - \frac{(60-t)^3}{3600}.$$

(b) The maximum amount ever in the tank is $40/\sqrt{3} \approx 23.09$ lb. This occurs after $t = 60 - 20\sqrt{3} \approx 25/36$ min.

37. The volume of brine in the tank after t min is $V(t) = 100 + 2t$ gal, so the initial value problem is

$$\frac{dx}{dt} = 5 - \frac{3x}{100+2t}, \qquad x(0) = 50.$$

The integrating factor $\rho(t) = (100 + 2t)^{3/2}$ leads to the solution

$$x(t) = (100+2t) - \frac{50000}{(100+2t)^{3/2}}.$$

such that $x(0) = 50$. The tank is full after $t = 150$ min, at which time $x(150) = 393.75$ lb.

38. **(a)** $x(t) = 50 e^{-t/20}$

(b) The solution of

$$\frac{dy}{dt} = \frac{5x}{100} - \frac{5y}{200} = \frac{5}{2}e^{-t/20} - \frac{1}{40}y$$

with $y(0) = 50$ is

$$y(t) = 150 e^{-t/40} - 100 e^{-t/20}.$$

(c) $y_{\text{max}} = 56.25$ lb when $t = 40 \ln(4/3) \approx 11.51$ min.

39. **(a)** The initial value problem

$$\frac{dx}{dt} = -\frac{x}{10}, \qquad x(0) = 100$$

for Tank 1 has solution $x(t) = 100\,e^{-t/10}$. Then the initial value problem

$$\frac{dy}{dt} = \frac{x}{10} - \frac{y}{10} = 10\,e^{-t/10} - \frac{y}{10}, \qquad y(0) = 0$$

for Tank 2 has solution $y(t) = 10t\,e^{-t/10}$.

(b) $y_{max} = y(10) = 100e^{-1} \approx 36.79$ gal.

40. **(b)** Assuming inductively that $x_n = t^n e^{-t/2} / \left(n!2^n\right)$, the equation for x_{n+1} is

$$\frac{dx_{n+1}}{dt} = \frac{1}{2}x_n - \frac{1}{2}x_{n+1} = \frac{t^n\,e^{-t/2}}{n!\,2^{n+1}} - \frac{1}{2}x_{n+1}.$$

We easily solve this first–order equation with $x_{n+1}(0) = 0$ and find that

$$x_{n+1} = \frac{t^{n+1}\,e^{-t/2}}{(n+1)!\,2^{n+1}},$$

thereby completing the proof by induction.

41. **(a)** $A'(t) = 0.06A + 0.12S = 0.06A + 3.6e^{0.05t}$

(b) The solution with $A(0) = 0$ is

$$A(t) = 360(e^{0.06t} - e^{0.05t}),$$

so $A(40) \approx 1308.283$ thousand dollars.

42. The mass of the hailstone at time t is $m = (4/3)\pi r^3 = (4/3)\pi k^3 t^3$. Then the equation $d(mv)/dt = mg$ simplifies to

$$tv' + 3v = gt.$$

The solution satisfying the initial condition $v(0) = 0$ is $v(t) = gt/4$, so $v'(t) = g/4$.

43. The solution of the initial value problem $y' = x - y, \ y(-5) = y_0$ is

$$y(x) = x-1+(y_0+6)e^{-x-5}.$$

Substituting $x = 5$, we therefore solve the equation $4+(y_0+6)e^{-10} = y_1$ with $y_1 = 3.998,\ 3.999,\ 4,\ 4.001,\ 4.002$ for the desired initial values $y_0 = -50.0529,\ -28.0265,\ -6.0000,\ 16.0265,\ 38.0529$, respectively.

44.   The solution of the initial value problem $y' = x+y,\ \ y(-5) = y_0$ is

$$y(x) = -x-1+(y_0-4)e^{x+5}.$$

Substituting $x = 5$, we therefore solve the equation $-6+(y_0-4)e^{10} = y_1$ with $y_1 = -10,\ -5,\ 0,\ 5,\ 10$ for the desired initial values $y_0 = 3.99982,\ 4.00005,\ 4.00027,\ 4.00050,\ 4.00073$, respectively.

SECTION 1.6

SUBSTITUTION METHODS AND EXACT EQUATIONS

It is traditional for every elementary differential equations text to include the particular types of equations that are found in this section. However, no one of them is vitally important solely in its own right. Their real purpose (at this point in the course) is to familiarize students with the technique of transforming a differential equation by substitution. The subsection on airplane flight trajectories (together with Problems 56–59) is optional material and may be omitted if the instructor desires.

The differential equations in Problems 1–15 are homogeneous, so we make the substitutions

$$v = \frac{y}{x}, \qquad y = vx, \qquad \frac{dy}{dx} = v+x\frac{dv}{dx}.$$

1. $x^2 - 2xy - y^2 = C$ 　　　　**2.** $y^2 = x^2(\ln x + C)$

3. $y = x(C + \ln|x|)^2$

4. $\tan^{-1}(y/x) + (1/2)\ln(1 + y^2/x^2) = \ln x + C$

5. $\ln|xy| = C + x/y$ 　　　　**6.** $x = 2y(\ln y + C)$

7. $y^3 = 3x^3(C + \ln|x|)$ 　　　　**8.** $y = -x\ln(C - \ln x)$

9. $y = x / (C - \ln|x|)$ 　　　　**10.** $x^2 + 2y^2 = Cx^6$

11. $y = C(x^2 + y^2)$ 　　　　**12.** $4x^2 + y^2 = x^2(\ln x + C)^2$

13. $y + (x^2 + y^2)^{1/2} = Cx^2$

14. If $x > 0$ then the substitution $y = vx$ leads to

$$\ln x = \int \frac{v \, dv}{(1+v^2)^{1/2} - (1+v^2)}$$

$$= \frac{1}{2} \int \frac{du}{u^{1/2}(1 - u^{1/2})} \qquad (u = 1 + v^2)$$

$$= -\int \frac{dw}{w} = -\ln W + \ln C$$

with $w = 1 - u^{1/2}$. Back-substitution and simplification finally yields the implicit solution

$$x - (x^2 + y^2)^{1/2} = C.$$

15. $x^2(2xy + y^2) = C$

16. The substitution $v = x + y + 1$ leads to

$$x = \int \frac{dv}{1 + v^{1/2}} = \int \frac{2u \, du}{1 + u} \qquad (v = u^2)$$

$$= 2u - 2\ln(1 + u) + C$$

$$x = 2(x + y + 1)^{1/2} - 2\ln(1 + (x + y + 1)^{1/2}) + C$$

17. The substitution $v = 4x + y$ yields

$$y = 2\tan(2x + C) - 4x.$$

18. The substitution $v = x + y$ leads to

$$y = \ln(x + y + 1) + C.$$

Problems 19–25 are Bernoulli equations. We indicate for each the appropriate substitution as specified in Equation (10) of this section.

19. $y^2 = x / (2 + Cx^5); \qquad v = y^{-2}$

20. $y = [3 + C \exp(-3x^2)]^{1/3}; \qquad v = y^3$

21. $y^2 = 1/(Ce^{-2x} - 1);$ $\qquad v = y^{-2}$

22. $y = (Cx^6 + 15/7x)^{-1/3};$ $\qquad v = y^{-3}$

23. $y = (x + Cx^2)^{-3};$ $\qquad v = y^{-1/3}$

24. $y^2 = e^{2x}/(C + \ln x);$ $\qquad v = y^{-2}$

25. $2x^3y^3 = 3(1 + x^4)^{1/2} + C;$ $\qquad v = y^3$

26. The substitution $v = y^3$ yields the linear equation $v' + v = e^{-x}$.
Solution: $y^3 = e^{-x}(x + C)$

27. The substitution $v = y^3$ yields the linear equation $xv' - v = 3x^4$.
Solution: $y = (x^4 + Cx)^{1/3}$

28. The substitution $v = e^y$ yields the linear equation $xv' - 2v = 2x^3e^{2x}$.
Solution: $y = \ln(Cx^2 + x^2e^{2x})$

29. The substitution $v = \sin y$ yields the homogeneous equation $2xvv' = 4x^2 + v^2$.
Solution: $\sin^2 y = 4x^2 - Cx$

30. First we multiply each side of the given equation by e^y. Then the substitution $v = e^y$ gives the homogeneous equation $(x + v)v' = x - v$ of Problem 1 above.
Solution: $x^2 - 2xe^y - e^{2y} = C$

The differential equations in Problems 31–42 are exact, and we give only the solutions that are found using the method of Example 9 in the text.

31. $x^2 + 3xy + y^2 = C$ $\qquad$ **32.** $2x^2 - xy + 3y^2 = C$

33. $x^3 + 2xy^2 + 2y^3 = C$ $\qquad$ **34.** $x^3 + x^2y^2 + y^4 = C$

35. $(1/4)x^4 + (1/3)y^3 + y \ln x = C$

36. $x + y^2 + e^{xy} = C$

37. $\sin x + x \ln y + e^y = C$

38. $x^2 + 2x \tan^{-1}y + \ln(1 + y^2) = C$

39. $x^3y^3 + xy^4 + (1/5)y^5 = C$

40. $e^x \sin y + x \tan y = C$

41. $x^2/y + y^2/x^3 + 2y^{1/2} = C$

42. $xy^{-2/3} + x^{-3/2}y = C$

46. The substitution $v = \ln y$, $y = e^v$, $y' = e^v v'$ yields the linear equation $x v' + 2v = 4x^2$.
Solution: $y = \exp(x^2 + C/x^2)$

47. Substitution: $x = u - 1$, $y = v - 2$
Solution: $x^2 - 2xy - y^2 - 2x - 6y = C$

48. The substitution $x = u + 3$, $y = v - 2$ yields the homogeneous equation

$$\frac{dv}{du} = \frac{-u + 2v}{4u - 3v}.$$

The substitution $v = pu$ leads to

$$\ln u = \int \frac{(4 - 3p)\, dp}{(3p + 1)(p - 1)}.$$

Evaluation of this integral by partial fractions finally yields the implicit solution

$$(x + 3y + 3)^5 = C(-x + y + 5).$$

49. The substitution $v = x - y$ yields the separable equation $v' = 1 - \sin v$. With the aid of the identity

$$\frac{1}{1 - \sin v} = \frac{1 + \sin v}{\cos^2 v} = \sec^2 v + \sec v \tan v$$

we obtain the solution

$$x = \tan(x - y) + \sec(x - y) + C.$$

52. $y = x + (2/\sqrt{\pi})[\exp(-x^2)]\,[C + \mathrm{erf}(x)]^{-1}$ in terms of the *error function* $\mathrm{erf}(x)$ defined in Problem 29 of Section 1.5.

53. $y = x + (C - x)^{-1}$

54. The substitution $y' = C$ in the Clairaut equation immediately yields the general solution $y = Cx + g(C)$.

55. Clearly the line $y = Cx - C^2/4$ and the tangent line at $(C/2, C^2/4)$ to the parabola $y = x^2$ both have slope C.

57. With $a = 100$ and $k = 1/10$, Equation (19) in the text is

$$y = 50[(x/100)^{9/10} - (x/100)^{11/10}].$$

The equation $y'(x) = 0$ then yields

$$(x/100)^{1/10} = (9/11)^{1/2},$$

so it follows that

$$y_{max} = 50[(9/11)^{9/2} - (9/11)^{11/2}] \approx 3.68 \text{ mi.}$$

59. **(a)** $y = 50[(x/100)^{1/2} - (x/100)^{3/2}]; \quad y(0) = 0$

   (b) $y = 50[1 - (x/100)^2]; \quad y(0) = 50$

   (c) $y = 50[(x/100)^{-1/2} - (x/100)^{5/2}];$

CHAPTER 1 Review Problems

1.   Linear: $y = x^3(C + \ln x)$

2.   Separable: $y = x / (3 - Cx - x \ln x)$

3.   Homogeneous: $y = x/(C - \ln x)$

4.   Exact: $x^2 y^3 + e^x - \cos y = C$

5.   Separable: $y = C \exp[(1 - x)/x^3]$

6.   Separable: $y = x / (1 + Cx + 2x \ln x)$

7.   Linear: $y = x^{-2}(C + \ln x)$

8.   Homogeneous: $y = 3Cx/(C - x^3)$

9.   Bernoulli: $y = (x^2 + C/x)^2$

10. Separable: $y = \tan(C + x + x^3/3)$

11. Homogeneous: $y = x / (C - 3 \ln x)$

12. Exact: $3x^2 y^3 + 2xy^4 = C$

13. Separable: $y = 1/(C + 2x^2 - x^5)$

14. Homogeneous: $y^2 = x^2/(C + 2\ln x)$

15. Linear: $y = (x^3 + C)e^{-3x}$

16. Substitution: $v = y - x$.
    Solution: $y - x - 1 = Ce^{2x}(y - x + 1)$

17. Exact: $e^x + e^y + e^{xy} = C$

18. Homogeneous: $y^2 = Cx^2(x^2 - y^2)$

19. Separable: $y = x^2/(x^5 + Cx^2 + 1)$

20. Linear: $y = 2x^{-3/2} + Cx^{-3}$

21. Linear: $y = [C + \ln(x - 1)]/(x + 1)$

22. Bernoulli: $y = (2x^4 + Cx^2)^3$

23. Exact: $xe^y + y\sin x = C$

24. Separable: $y = x^{1/2}/(6x^2 + Cx^{1/2} + 2)$

25. Linear: $y = (x + 1)^{-2}(x^3 + 3x^2 + 3x + C)$

26. Exact: $6x^{3/2}y^{4/3} - 10x^{6/5}y^{3/2} = C$

27. Bernoulli: $y = x^{-1}(C + \ln x)^{-1/3}$

28. Linear: $y = x^{-1}(C + e^{2x})$

29. Linear: $y = (x^2 + x + C)(2x + 1)^{-1/2}$

30. Substitution: $v = x + y$.
    Solution: $x = 2(x + y)^{1/2} - 2\ln[1 + (x + y)^{1/2}] + C$

31. Separable and linear

32. Separable and Bernoulli

33. Exact and homogeneous

34. Exact and homogeneous

35. Separable and linear

36. Separable and Bernoulli

CHAPTER 2

MATHEMATICAL MODELS
AND NUMERICAL METHODS

SECTION 2.1

POPULATION MODELS

Section 2.1 introduces the first of the two major classes of mathematical models studied in this text, and in particular is a prerequisite to the discussion of equilibrium solutions and stability in Section 2.2.

Problems 1–4 are fairly routine, so only the answers are given.

1. $x(t) = 40/(8 - 3e^{-15t})$

2. $x(t) = 10/(2 + 3e^{15t})$

3. $x(t) = 77/(11 - 4e^{-28t})$

4. $x(t) = 221/(17 - 4e^{91t})$

5.   Solution of the equation $P' = k\sqrt{P}$, with $k = 2$ because of the initial conditions, gives $P(t) = (t - C)^2$. Then $P(0) = 100$ implies $P(t) = (t + 10)^2$. Hence $P(12) = 484$.

6.   Given: $P' = -\delta P = -k\sqrt{P}$ and $P(0) = 900$, $P(6) = 441$.
Integration of the differential equation gives

$$2\sqrt{P} = -kt + C,$$

and then the given data yield $C = 60$ and $k = 3$. Thus $2\sqrt{P} = -3t + 60$, so $P = 0$ after $t = 20$ weeks.

7.   **(a)**   Starting with $dP/dt = k\sqrt{P}$, we separate the variables and integrate to get

$$P(t) = (kt/2 + C)^2.$$

Clearly $P(0) = P_0$ implies $C = \sqrt{P_0}$.

(b)   If $P(t) = (kt/2 + 10)^2$, then $P(6) = 169$ implies that $k = 1$. Hence $P(t) = (t/2 + 10)^2$, so there are 256 fish after 12 months.

8.   Solution of the equation $P' = kP^2$ gives $P(t) = 1/(C - kt)$. Now $P(0) = 12$ implies that $C = 12$, so now $P(t) = 12/(1 - 12\,kt)$. Then $P(10) = 24$ implies that $k = 1/240$, so finally $P(t) = 240/(20 - t)$. Hence $P = 48$ when $t = 15$, the year 2003, and obviously $P \to \infty$ as $t \to 20$.

9. (b) We find that $P(t) = 180/(30 - t)$, so $P \to \infty$ as $t \to 30$.

10. Now $dP/dt = -kP^2$ with $k > 0$, and separation of variables yields

$$P(t) = 1/(kt + C).$$

Clearly $C = 1/P_0$, so $P(t) = P_0/(1 + kP_0 t)$. Therefore $P(t) \to 0$ as $t \to \infty$.

11. If we write $P' = bP(a/b - P)$ we see that $M = a/b$. Hence

$$\frac{B_0 P_0}{D_0} = \frac{(aP_0)P_0}{bP_0^2} = \frac{a}{b} = M.$$

Note also (for Problems 12 and 13) that $a = B_0/P_0$ and $b = D_0/P_0^2 = k$.

12. The relations in Problem 11 give $k = 1/2400$ and $M = 160$. The solution is $P(t) = 19200/(120 + 40 e^{-t/15})$. We find that $P = 0.95M$ after about 27.69 months.

13. The relations in Problem 11 give $k = 1/2400$ and $M = 180$. The solution is $P(t) = 43200/(240 - 60 e^{-3t/80})$. We find that $P = 1.05M$ after about 44.22 months.

14. If we write $P' = aP(P - b/a)$ we see that $M = b/a$. Hence

$$\frac{D_0 P_0}{B_0} = \frac{(bP_0)P_0}{aP_0^2} = \frac{b}{a} = M.$$

Note also (for Problems 12 and 13) that $b = D_0/P_0$ and $a = B_0/P_0^2 = k$.

15. The relations in Problem 14 give $k = 1/1000$ and $M = 90$. The solution is $P(t) = 9000/(100 - 10 e^{9t/100})$. We find that $P = 10M$ after about 24.41 months.

16. The relations in Problem 14 give $k = 1/1100$ and $M = 120$. The solution is $P(t) = 13200/(110 + 10 e^{6t/55})$. We find that $P = 0.1M$ after about 42.12 months.

17. The only difference is that, if $P > M$, then

$$\int \frac{dP}{M - P} = -\ln|M - P| = -\ln(P - M)$$

so integration of the separated equation yields

$$\frac{P}{P-M} = A\,e^{kMt}.$$

This gives $A = P_0/(P_0 - M)$, so each side of the equation preceding Equation (4) in this section is simply multiplied by -1, and the result in Equation (4) is unchanged.

18.   We work in thousands of persons, so $M = 100$ for the total fixed population. We substitute $M = 100$, $P'(0) = 1$, and $P_0 = 50$ in the logistic equation, and thereby obtain

$$1 = k(50)(100 - 50), \qquad \text{so} \qquad k = 0.0004.$$

If t denotes the number of days until 80 thousand people have heard the rumor, then Eq. (4) gives

$$80 = \frac{50 \times 100}{50 + (100 - 50)e^{-0.04t}},$$

so that t is approximately 34.66. Thus the rumor will have spread to 80% of the population in a little less than 35 days.

19.   (a) $x' = 0.8x - 0.004x^2 = 0.004x(200 - x)$, so the maximum amount that will dissolve is $M = 200$ g.

(b)   With $M = 200$, $P_0 = 50$, and $k = 0.004$, Equation (4) in the text yields the solution

$$x(t) = 10{,}000/(50 + 150e^{-0.08t}).$$

We find that $x = 100$ when $t = 1.25 \ln 3 \approx 1.37$ sec.

20.   The differential equation for $N(t)$ is

$$N'(t) = kN(15 - N).$$

When we substitute $N(0) = 5$ (thousands) and $N'(0) = 0.5$ (thousands/day) we find that $k = 0.01$. With N in place of P, this is the logistic equation in (3), so its solution is given by Equation (4):

$$N(t) = \frac{15 \times 5}{5 + 10\exp[-(0.01)(15)t]} = \frac{15}{1 + 2\,e^{-0.15t}}.$$

From this equation we find that $N = 10$ after $t = (\ln 4)/(0.15) \approx 9.24$ days.

21.   Proceeding as in Example 4 in the text, we solve the equations

$$25.00k(M - 25.00) = 3/8, \qquad 47.54k(M - 47.54) = 1/2$$

for $M = 100$ and $k = 0.0002$. Then Equation (4) gives the population function

$$P(t) = \frac{2500}{25 + 75e^{-0.02t}}.$$

We find that $P = 75$ when $t = 50 \ln 9 \approx 110$, that is, in 2035 A. D.

22. The differential equation for $P(t)$ is

$$P'(t) = 0.001P^2 - \delta P.$$

When we substitute $P(0) = 100$ and $P'(0) = 8$ we find that $\delta = 0.02$, so

$$P'(t) = 0.001P^2 - 0.02P = 0.001P(P - 20).$$

This is the same as Equation (10) in the text with $k = 0.001$ and $M = 20$, so Equation (11) gives the solution

$$P(t) = \frac{20C\, e^{-0.02t}}{C\, e^{-0.02t} - 1}.$$

$P(0) = 100$ yields $C = 5/4$, so

$$P(t) = \frac{100\, e^{-0.02t}}{5\, e^{-0.02t} - 4}.$$

From this equation we find that $P = 200$ when $t = 50 \ln(9/8) \approx 5.89$ months.

23. We are given that

$$P' = kP^2 - 0.01P,$$

and the fact that $P = 200$ and $P' = 2$ when $t = 0$ implies that $k = 0.0001$, so

$$P' = 10^{-4}(P^2 - P).$$

The solution with $P(0) = 200$ is

$$P(t) = 100/(1 - 0.5e^{0.01\,t}).$$

(a) $P = 1000$ when $t = 100 \ln(9/5) \approx 58.78$.

(b) $P \to \infty$ as $t \to 100 \ln 2 \approx 69.31$

24. The situation here is similar to that in Problem 17, the only difference being that if $P < M$ then

$$\int \frac{dP}{P-M} = \ln|P-M| = \ln(M-P)$$

so the second equation preceding Equation (11) in this section becomes

$$\ln[P/(M-P)] = -kMt + C_1.$$

26. If we substitute $P(0) = 10^6$ and $P'(0) = 3 \times 10^5$ into the differential equation

$$P'(t) = \beta_0 e^{-\alpha t} P,$$

we find that $\beta_0 = 0.3$. Hence the solution given in Problem 17 is

$$P(t) = P_0 \exp[(0.3/\alpha)(1 - e^{-\alpha t})].$$

The fact that $P(6) = 2P_0$ now yields the equation

$$f(\alpha) = (0.3)(1 - e^{-6\alpha}) - \alpha \ln 2 = 0$$

for α. We apply Newton's iterative formula

$$\alpha_{n+1} = \alpha_n - \frac{f(\alpha_n)}{f'(\alpha_n)}$$

with $f'(\alpha) = 1.8 e^{-6\alpha} - \ln 2$ and initial guess $\alpha_0 = 1$, and find that $\alpha \approx 0.3915$. Therefore the limiting cell population as $t \to \infty$ is

$$P_0 \exp(\beta_0/\alpha) = 10^6 \exp(0.3/0.3915) \approx 2.15 \times 10^6.$$

Thus the tumor does not grow much further after 6 months.

27. Any way you look at it, you should see that, the larger the parameter $k > 0$ is, the faster the logistic population $P(t)$ approaches its limiting population M.

Problem 28 is just straightforward (though tedious) algebra and arithmetic leading to the logistic solution shown in Eq. (8) of the text. In Problems 29 and 30 we give just the values of k and M, the resulting logistic solution, and the predicted year 2000 population.

29. $k = 0.0000668717$ and $M = 338.027$, so $P(t) = \dfrac{25761.7}{76.212 + 261.815 e^{-0.0226045 t}}$,

predicting $P = 192.525$ in the year 2000.

30. $k = 0.000146679$ and $M = 208.250$, so $P(t) = \dfrac{4829.73}{23.192 + 185.058\, e^{-0.0305458\, t}}$,

predicting $P = 248.856$ in the year 2000.

SECTION 2.2

EQUILIBRIUM SOLUTIONS AND STABILITY

In Problems 1–12 we identify the stable and unstable critical points as well as the funnels and spouts along the equilibrium solutions, and then the explicit solution satisfying $x(0) = x_0$.

1.   Unstable critical point: $x = 4$
Spout: Along the equilibrium solution $x(t) = 4$

     Solution: $x(t) = 4 + (x_0 - 4)e^t$

2.   Stable critical point: $x = 3$
Funnel: Along the equilibrium solution $x(t) = 3$

     Solution: $x(t) = 3 + (x_0 - 3)e^{-t}$

3.   Stable critical point: $x = 0$
Unstable critical point: $x = 4$
Funnel: Along the equilibrium solution $x(t) = 0$
Spout: Along the equilibrium solution $x(t) = 4$

     Solution: $x(t) = 4x_0 / \left(x_0 + (4 - x_0)e^{4t} \right)$

4.   Stable critical point: $x = 3$
Unstable critical point: $x = 0$
Funnel: Along the equilibrium solution $x(t) = 3$
Spout: Along the equilibrium solution $x(t) = 0$

     Solution: $x(t) = 3x_0 / \left(x_0 + (3 - x_0)e^{-3t} \right)$

5.   Stable critical point: $x = -2$
Unstable critical point: $x = 2$
Funnel: Along the equilibrium solution $x(t) = -2$
Spout: Along the equilibrium solution $x(t) = 2$

     Solution: $x(t) = 2\left[(x_0 + 2) + (x_0 - 2)e^{4t} \right] / \left[(x_0 + 2) - (x_0 - 2)e^{4t} \right]$

6.   Stable critical point: $x = 3$
Unstable critical point: $x = -3$

Funnel: Along the equilibrium solution $x(t) = 3$
Spout: Along the equilibrium solution $x(t) = -3$

Solution: $x(t) = 3\left[(x_0 - 3) + (x_0 + 3)e^{6t}\right] / \left[(3 - x_0) + (x_0 + 3)e^{6t}\right]$

7. Critical point: $x = 2$

This single critical point is *semi-stable*, meaning that solutions with $x_0 > 2$ go to infinity as t increases, while solutions with $x_0 < 2$ approach 2.

Solution: $x(t) = \left[x_0(2t - 1) - 4t\right] / \left[t x_0 - 2t - 1\right]$

8. Critical point: $x = 3$

This single critical point is *semi-stable*, meaning that solutions with $x_0 < 3$ go to minus infinity as t increases, while solutions with $x_0 > 3$ approach 3.

Solution: $x(t) = \left[x_0(3t + 1) - 9t\right] / \left[t x_0 - 3t + 1\right]$

9. Stable critical point: $x = 1$
Unstable critical point: $x = 4$
Funnel: Along the equilibrium solution $x(t) = 1$
Spout: Along the equilibrium solution $x(t) = 4$

Solution: $x(t) = \left[4(1 - x_0) + (x_0 - 4)e^{3t}\right] / \left[1 - x_0 + (x_0 - 4)e^{3t}\right]$

10. Stable critical point: $x = 5$
Unstable critical point: $x = 2$
Funnel: Along the equilibrium solution $x(t) = 5$
Spout: Along the equilibrium solution $x(t) = 2$

Solution: $x(t) = \left[2(5 - x_0) + 5(x_0 - 2)e^{3t}\right] / \left[(5 - x_0) + (x_0 - 2)e^{3t}\right]$

11. Unstable critical point: $x = 1$
Spout: Along the equilibrium solution $x(t) = 1$

Solution: $(x(t) - 1)^{-2} = (x_0 - 1)^{-2} - 2t$

12. Stable critical point: $x = 2$
Funnel: Along the equilibrium solution $x(t) = 2$

Solution: $(2 - x(t))^{-2} = (2 - x_0)^{-2} + 2t$

13. **(a)** If $k = -a^2$ where $h > 0$ then $kx - x^3 = -a^2 x - x^3 = -x(a^2 + x^2)$ is positive if $x < 0$, negative if $x > 0$, and is 0 only if $x = 0$.

(b) If $k = +a^2$ where $h > 0$ then $kx - x^3 = +a^2 x - x^3 = -x(x + a)(x - a)$ is positive if $x < -a$, negative if $-a < x < 0$, positive if $0 < x < a$, and negative if $x > a$.

14.   **(a)**   If $h < kM$ then the differential equation is $x' = kx((M-h/k)-x)$, which is a logistic equation with the *reduced* limiting population $M - h/k$.

(b)   If $h > kM$ then the differential equation can be rewritten in the form $x' = -ax - bx^2$ with a and b both positive. The solution of this equation is

$$x(t) = \frac{ax_0}{(a+bx_0)e^{at} - bx_0}$$

so it is obvious that $x(t) \to 0$ as $t \to \infty$.

15.   Just do it.

16.   Just do it.

17.   **(i)** In the first alternative form that is given, all of the coefficients within parentheses are positive if $H < x_0 < N$. Hence it is obvious that $x(t) \to N$ as $t \to \infty$.

(ii) In the second alternative form that is given, all of the coefficients within parentheses are positive if $x_0 < H$. Hence the denominator is initially equal to $N - H > 0$, but decreases as t increases, and reaches the value 0 when

$$t = \frac{1}{N-H}\ln\frac{N-x_0}{H-x_0} > 0.$$

18.   If $4h = kM^2$ then Eqs. (13) and (14)in the text show that the differential equation takes the form $x' = -k(M/2 - x)^2$ with the single critical point $x = M/2$. This equation is readily solved by separation of variables, but clearly x' is negative whether x is less than or greater than $M/2$.

19.   Separation of variables in the differential equation $x' = -k((x-a)^2 + b^2)$ yields

$$x(t) = a - b\tan\left(bkt + \tan^{-1}\frac{a-x_0}{b}\right).$$

It therefore follows that $x(t)$ goes to minus infinity in a finite period of time.

20.   Aside from a change in sign, this calculation is the same as that indicated in Eqs. (13) and (14) in the text.

21.   This is simply a matter of analyzing the signs of x' in the cases $x < a$, $a < x < b$, $b < x < c$, and $c > x$.

SECTION 2.3

ACCELERATION-VELOCITY MODELS

This section consists of three essentially independent subsections that can be studied separately: resistance proportional to velocity, resistance proportional to velocity-squared, and inverse-square gravitational acceleration.

The integrations in Problems 2, 4, and 6 are quite elementary and the answers are provided in the text, so they are omitted here.

1. Equation: $v' = k(250 - v), \quad v(0) = 0, \quad v(10) = 100$

    Solution: $v(t) = 250(1 - e^{-kt})$ with $k = (1/10)\ln(5/3)$

    Answer: $v = 200$ when $t \approx 31.5$ sec

3. Equation: $v' = -kv, \quad v(0) = 40, \quad v(10) = 20$

    Solution: $v(t) = 40\, e^{-kt}$ with $k = (1/10)\ln 2$

    $x(t) = (40/k)(1 - e^{-kt})$

    Answer: $x(\infty) = v_0/k = 400/\ln 2 \approx 577$ ft

5. Equation: $v' = -kv^2, \quad v(0) = 40, \quad v(10) = 20$

    Solution: $v(t) = 400/(10 + t)$

    $x(t) = 400 \ln[(10 + t)/10]$

    Answer: $x(60) = 400 \ln 7 \approx 778$ ft

7. Equation: $v' = 10 - 0.1v, \quad x(0) = v(0) = 0$

    (a) $v(t) = 100(1 - e^{-t/10})$
    $v(\infty) = 100$ ft/sec

    (b) $x(t) = 100t - 1000(1 - e^{-t/10})$
    $v = 90$ ft/sec when $t = 23.0259$ sec and $x = 1402.59$ ft

8. Equation: $v' = 10 - 0.001v^2, \quad x(0) = v(0) = 0$

    (a) $v(t) = 100\tanh(t/10)$
    $v(\infty) = 100$ ft/sec

    (b) $x(t) = 1000\ln(\cosh(t/10))$
    $v = 90$ ft/sec when $t = 14.7222$ sec and $x = 830.366$ ft

9. The solution of the initial value problem

$$1000v' = 5000 - 100v, \qquad v(0) = 0$$

is

$$v(t) = 50(1 - e^{-t/10}).$$

Hence as $t \to \infty$, we see that $v(t)$ approaches $v_{max} = 50$ ft/sec ≈ 34 mph.

10. Before opening parachute:

$$v' = -32 - 0.15v, \quad v(0) = 0, \quad y(0) = 10000$$

$$v(t) = 213.333(e^{-0.15t} - 1), \qquad v(20) = -202.712 \text{ ft / sec}$$

$$y(t) = 11422.2 - 1422.22 \, e^{-0.15ty} - 213.333t, \quad y(20) = 7084.75 \text{ ft}$$

After opening parachute:

$$v' = -32 - 1.5v, \quad v(0) = -202.712, \quad y(0) = 7084.75$$

$$v(t) = -21.3333 - 181.379 \, e^{-1.5t}$$

$$y(t) = 6964.83 + 120.919 \, e^{-1.5t} - 21.3333t,$$

$$y = 0 \text{ when } t = 326.476$$

Thus she opens her parachute after 20 sec at a height of 7085 feet, and the total time of descent is $20 + 326.476 = 346.476$ sec, about 5 minutes and 46.5 seconds. Her impact speed is 21.33 ft/sec, about 15 mph.

11. If the paratrooper's terminal velocity was 100 mph = 440/3 ft/sec, then Equation (7) in the text yields $\rho = 12/55$. Then we find by solving Equation (9) numerically with $y_0 = 1200$ and $v_0 = 0$ that $y = 0$ when $t \approx 12.5$ sec. Thus the newspaper account is inaccurate.

12. With $m = 640/32 = 20$ slugs, $W = 640$ lb, $B = (8)(62.5) = 500$ lb, and $F_R = -v$ lb (F_R is upward when $v < 0$), the differential equation is

$$20 \, v'(t) = -640 + 500 - v = -140 - v.$$

Its solution with $v(0) = 0$ is

$$v(t) = 140\left(e^{-0.05t} - 1\right)$$

and integration with $y(0) = 0$ yields

$$y(t) = 2800\left(e^{-0.05t} - 1\right) - 140t.$$

Using these equations we find that $t = 20 \ln(28/13) \approx 15.35$ sec when $v = -75$ ft/sec, and that $y(15.35) \approx -648.31$ ft. Thus the maximum safe depth is just under 650 ft.

Given the hints and integrals provided in the text, Problems 13–16 are fairly straightforward integration problems.

17.   The solution of the initial value problem $v' = -9.8 - 0.0011v^2$, $v(0) = 49$ is

$$v(t) = 94.388 \tan(0.478837 - 0.103827t),$$

and integration with $y(0) = 0$ gives

$$y(t) = 108.465 + 909.091 \ln(\cos(0.478837 - 0.103827t)).$$

We solve $v(0) = 0$ for $t = 4.61189$, and then calculate $y(4.61189) = 108.465$.

18.   The solution of the initial value problem $v' = -9.8 + 0.0011v^2$, $v(0) = 0$ is

$$v(t) = -94.388 \tanh(0.103827t),$$

and integration with $y(0) = 0$ gives

$$y(t) = 108.465 - 909.091 \ln(\cosh(0.103827t)).$$

We solve $y(0) = 0$ for $t = 4.79895$, and then calculate $v(4.79895) = -43.489$.

19.   Equation: $v' = 4 - (1/400)v^2$, $v(0) = 0$

        Solution: $v(t) = 40 \tanh(t/10)$

        Answer: $v(10) \approx 30.46$ ft/sec, $v(\infty) = 40$ ft/sec

20.   Equation: $v' = -32 - (1/800)v^2$, $v(0) = 160$, $y(0) = 0$

        Solution: $v(t) = 160 \tan\left(\dfrac{\pi}{4} - \dfrac{t}{5}\right)$

$$y(t) = 800 \ln\left(\cos\left(\dfrac{\pi}{4} - \dfrac{t}{5}\right)\right) + 400 \ln 2$$

We solve $v(t) = 0$ for $t = 3.92699$ and then calculate $y(3.92699) = 277.26$ ft.

21.   Equation: $v' = -g - \rho v^2$, $v(0) = v_0$, $y(0) = 0$

        Solution: $v(t) = -\sqrt{\dfrac{g}{\rho}} \tan\left(t\sqrt{g\rho} - \tan^{-1}\left(v_0\sqrt{\dfrac{\rho}{g}}\right)\right)$

We solve $v(t) = 0$ for $t = \dfrac{1}{\sqrt{g\rho}} \tan^{-1}\left(v_0 \sqrt{\dfrac{\rho}{g}} \right)$ and then calculate $y(t)$.

22. The solution of the initial value problem $v' = -32 + 0.075 v^2$, $v(0) = 0$ is

$$v(t) = -20.666 \tanh(1.54919\,t),$$

so the terminal speed is 20.666 ft/sec, and integration with $y(0) = 0$ gives

$$y(t) = 10000 - 13.333 \ln(\cosh(1.54919\,t)).$$

We solve $y(0) = 0$ for $t = 484.57$. Thus the descent takes about 8 min 5 sec.

23. Before opening parachute:

$$v' = -32 + 0.00075 v^2, \quad v(0) = 0, \quad y(0) = 10000$$
$$v(t) = -206.559 \tanh(0.154919\,t) \quad v(30) = -206.521 \ \text{ft}\,/\,\text{sec}$$
$$y(t) = 10000 - 1333.33 \ln(\cosh(0.154919\,t)), \quad y(30) = 4727.30 \ \text{ft}$$

After opening parachute:

$$v' = -32 + 0.075 v^2, \quad v(0) = -206.521, \quad y(0) = 4727.30$$
$$v(t) = -20.6559 \tanh(1.54919\,t + 0.00519595)$$
$$y(t) = 4727.30 - 13.3333 \ln(\cosh(1.54919\,t + 0.00519595))$$
$$y = 0 \ \text{when} \quad t = 229.304$$

Thus she opens her parachute after 30 sec at a height of 4727 feet, and the total time of descent is $30 + 229.304 = 259.304$ sec, about 4 minutes and 19.3 seconds.

24. Let M denote the mass of the Earth. Then

(a) $\sqrt{2GM/R} = c$ implies $R = 0.884 \times 10^{-3}$ meters, about 0.88 cm;

(b) $\sqrt{2G(329320M)/R} = c$ implies $R = 2.91 \times 10^3$ meters, about 2.91 kilometers.

25. We get the desired formula when we set $v = 0$ in Eq. (23) and solve for r.

26. **(a)** Integration of $v v' = -GM/r^2$ gives

$$\frac{1}{2}v^2 = GM\left(\frac{1}{r} - \frac{1}{r_0} \right)$$

and we solve for

$$\frac{dr}{dt} = v = -\sqrt{2GM\left(\frac{1}{r}-\frac{1}{r_0}\right)}$$

taking the negative square root because $v < 0$ in descent. Hence

$$t = -\sqrt{\frac{r_0}{2GM}} \int \sqrt{\frac{r}{r_0-r}} \, dr \qquad (r = r_0 \cos^2 \theta)$$

$$= \sqrt{r_0/2GM} \int 2r_0 \cos^2 \theta \, d\theta$$

$$= \frac{r_0^{3/2}}{\sqrt{2GM}} (\theta + \sin \theta \cos \theta)$$

$$t = \sqrt{\frac{r_0}{2GM}} \left(\sqrt{rr_0-r^2} + r_0 \cos^{-1}\sqrt{\frac{r}{r_0}} \right)$$

(b) Substitution of $G = 6.6726 \times 10^{-11}$, $M = 5.975 \times 10^{24}$ kg, $r = R = 6.378 \times 10^6$ m, and $r_0 = R + 10^6$ yields $t = 616.742$, that is, about 10 min 17 sec. (Recall that we are ignoring air resistance.)

27. Integration of $v\dfrac{dv}{dy} = -\dfrac{GM}{(y+R)^2}$, $y(0) = 0$, $v(0) = v_0$ gives

$$\frac{1}{2}v^2 = \frac{GM}{y+R} - \frac{GM}{R} + \frac{1}{2}v_0^2$$

which simplifies to the desired formula for v^2. Then substitution of $G = 6.6726 \times 10^{-11}$, $M = 5.975 \times 10^{24}$ kg, $R = 6.378 \times 10^6$ m, $v = 0$, and $v_0 = 1$ yields an equation that we easily solve for $y = 51427.3$, that is, about 51.427 km.

28. When we integrate

$$v\frac{dv}{dr} = -\frac{GM_e}{r^2} + \frac{GM_m}{(S-r)^2}, \quad r(0) = R, \quad r'(0) = v_0$$

in the usual way and solve for v we get

$$v = \sqrt{\frac{2GM_e}{r} - \frac{2GM_e}{R} - \frac{2GM_m}{r-S} + \frac{2GM_m}{R-S} + v_0^2}.$$

The earth and moon attractions balance at the point where the right-hand side in the acceleration equation vanishes, which is when

$$r = \frac{\sqrt{M_e}\, S}{\sqrt{M_e} - \sqrt{M_m}}.$$

If we substitute this value of r, $M_m = 7.35 \times 10^{22}$ kg, $S = 384.4 \times 10^6$, and the usual values of the other constants involved, then set $v = 0$ (to just reach the balancing point), we can solve the resulting equation for $v_0 = 11109$ m/s. Note that this is only 71 m/s less than the earth escape velocity of 11180 m/s, so the moon really doesn't help much.

SECTION 2.4

NUMERICAL APPROXIMATION: EULER'S METHOD

Note: The typical problem in Sections 2.4–2.6 calls for a table of approximate values. Each of these tables was produced with a computer using programs similar to those listed in the text. In order to save space in this manual, we have chosen in most cases to give only data from the last line of the table -- that is, only the values at the final point of the interval in question. This will enable the reader to determine whether his or her results agree with ours (though answers produced with different hardware and/or software can be expected to differ slightly -- perhaps in the last digit or two -- because of differing methods of performing simple arithmetic).

1.   The iterative formula of Euler's method is

$$y_{n+1} = y_n + h(-y_n),$$

and the exact solution is $y(x) = 2 e^{-x}$. The resulting table of approximate and actual values is

x	y with $h = 0.1$	y with $h = 0.05$	y actual
0.0	2.0000	2.0000	2.0000
0.1	1.8000	1.8050	1.8097
0.2	1.6200	1.6290	1.6375
0.3	1.4580	1.4702	1.4816
0.4	1.3122	1.3268	1.3406
0.5	1.1810	1.1975	1.2131

2.   Iterative formula: $y_{n+1} = y_n + h(2y_n)$

Exact solution: $y(x) = (1/2)e^{2x}$

Approximate: $y(0.5) \approx 1.2442$ with $h = 0.1$,
                    1.2969 with $h = 0.05$

Actual: $y(0.5) \approx 1.3591$

3. Iterative formula: $y_{n+1} = y_n + h(y_n + 1)$

Exact solution: $y(x) = 2e^x - 1$

Approximate: $y(0.5) \approx 2.2210$ with $h = 0.1$,
2.2578 with $h = 0.05$

Actual: $y(0.5) \approx 2.2974$

4. Iterative formula: $y_{n+1} = y_n + h(x_n - y_n)$

Exact solution: $y(x) = 2e^{-x} + x - 1$

Approximate: $y(0.5) \approx 0.6810$ with $h = 0.1$,
0.6975 with $h = 0.05$

Actual: $y(0.5) \approx 0.7131$

5. Iterative formula: $y_{n+1} = y_n + h(y_n - x_n - 1)$

Exact solution: $y(x) = 2 + x - e^x$

Approximate: $y(0.5) \approx 0.8895$ with $h = 0.1$,
0.8711 with $h = 0.05$

Actual: $y(0.5) \approx 0.8513$

6. Iterative formula: $y_{n+1} = y_n + h(-2x_n y_n)$

Exact solution: $y(x) = 2\exp(-x^2)$

Approximate: $y(0.5) \approx 1.6272$ with $h = 0.1$,
1.5912 with $h = 0.05$

Actual: $y(0.5) \approx 1.5576$

7. Iterative formula: $y_{n+1} = y_n + h(-3x_n^2 y_n)$

Exact solution: $y(x) = 3\exp(-x^3)$

Approximate: $y(0.5) \approx 2.7373$ with $h = 0.1$,
2.6930 with $h = 0.05$

Actual: $y(0.5) \approx 2.6475$

8. Iterative formula: $y_{n+1} = y_n + h\exp(-y_n)$

Exact solution: $y(x) = \ln(x + 1)$

Approximate: $y(0.5) \approx 0.4198$ with $h = 0.1$,
0.4124 with $h = 0.05$

Actual: $y(0.5) \approx 0.4055$

9. Iterative formula: $y_{n+1} = y_n + h(1 + y_n^2)/4$

Exact solution: $y(x) = \tan[(x + \pi)/4]$

Approximate:	$y(0.5) \approx 1.2785$ with $h = 0.1,$		
	1.2828 with $h = 0.05$		
Actual:	$y(0.5) \approx 1.2874$		

10.

Iterative formula:	$y_{n+1} = y_n + h(2x_n y_n^2)$
Exact solution:	$y(x) = 1/(1 - x^2)$
Approximate:	$y(0.5) \approx 1.2313$ with $h = 0.1,$
	1.2776 with $h = 0.05$
Actual:	$y(0.5) \approx 1.3333$

The tables of approximate and actual values called for in Problems 11-16 were produced using a slight alteration of Program EULERANS, which is listed below preceding Problem 17.

11. The iterative formula of Euler's method is

$$y_{n+1} = y_n + h(y_n - 2),$$

and the exact solution is $y(x) = 2 - e^x$. The resulting table of approximate and actual values is

x	y with $h=0.01$	y with $h=0.005$	y actual
0.0	1.0000	1.0000	1.0000
0.2	0.7798	0.7792	0.7786
0.4	0.5111	0.5097	0.5082
0.6	0.1833	0.1806	0.1779
0.8	−0.2167	−0.2211	−0.2255
1.0	−0.7048	−0.7115	−0.7183

12.

Iterative formula:	$y_{n+1} = y_n + h(y_n - 1)^2/2$
Exact solution:	$y(x) = 1 + 2/(2 - x)$
Approximate:	$y(1) \approx 2.9864$ with $h = 0.01,$
	2.9931 with $h = 0.005$
Actual:	$y(1) \approx 3.0000$

13.

Iterative formula:	$y_{n+1} = y_n + 2hx_n^3/y_n$
Exact solution:	$y(x) = (8 + x^4)^{1/2}$
Approximate:	$y(2) \approx 4.8890$ with $h = 0.01,$
	4.8940 with $h = 0.005$
Actual:	$y(2) \approx 4.8990$

14. Iterative formula: $y_{n+1} = y_n + hy_n^2/x_n$

Exact solution: $y(x) = 1/(1 - \ln x)$

Approximate: $y(2) \approx 3.2031$ with $h = 0.01$,
3.2304 with $h = 0.005$

Actual: $y(2) \approx 3.2589$

15. Iterative formula: $y_{n+1} = y_n + h(3 - 2y_n/x_n)$

Exact solution: $y(x) = x + 4/x^2$

Approximate: $y(3) \approx 3.4422$ with $h = 0.01$,
3.4433 with $h = 0.005$

Actual: $y(3) \approx 3.4444$

16. Iterative formula: $y_{n+1} = y_n + 2hx_n^5/y_n^2$

Exact solution: $y(x) = (x^6 - 37)^{1/3}$

Approximate: $y(3) \approx 8.8440$ with $h = 0.01$,
8.8445 with $h = 0.005$

Actual: $y(3) \approx 8.8451$

The tables of approximate values called for in Problems 17–24 were produced using the following BASIC program, which upon execution first asks for the right-hand side in the differential equation $y' = f(x,y)$ to be edited into line 230.

```
100 REM Program EULERANS
110 REM Uses Euler's method to approximate the solution
120 REM of the equation y' = f(x,y) on the given interval.
130 REM The function f(x,y) is edited into line 230, and
140 REM and the number N of subintervals is input.
150 REM
160 REM Initialization:
165 REM
170       PRINT "EDIT IN YOUR FUNCTION, THEN RUN 210"
180       PRINT   :    EDIT 230
210       DEFDBL A,F,H,X,Y     :     DEFINT I,J,K,N,S
220       DIM A(4,20)
230       DEF FNF(X,Y)  =  X*X + Y*Y
245       INPUT "INITIAL X"; X0
250       INPUT "INITIAL Y"; Y0
260       INPUT "INITIAL NUMBER OF SUBINTERVALS"; N
270       K  =  1   :   H  =  .1
280       PRINT "      y with    y with    y with    y with"
290       PRINT " x     h=0.1     h=0.02    h=0.004   h=0.0008"
300       PRINT
310 REM
320 REM Euler's iteration:
325 REM
330       FOR I  =  1 TO 4
```

```
340              X  =  X0    :    Y  =  Y0
350            FOR J  =   0  TO N
360                IF J/K  =   J\K THEN A(I,J/K)  =   Y
370                Y  =  Y + H*FNF(X,Y)
380                X  =  X + H
390            NEXT J
400            H  =  H/5  :  K  =  5*K  :  N  =  5*N
410        NEXT I
420 REM
425 REM Print results:
430 REM
435        N  =  N/625  :  S  =  N/5
440        FOR J  =   0  TO N STEP S
445            X  =  X0 + J/10
450            PRINT USING
        "#.#   #.####   #.####   #.####   #.####";
        X,A(1,J), A(2,J),  A(3,J), A(4,J)
460        NEXT J
470        END
```

17. Here $f(x,y) = x^2 + y^2$ on [0,1]. A run of Program EULERANS results in the following display:

```
RUN
EDIT IN YOUR FUNCTION, THEN RUN 210
230        DEF FNF(X,Y)   =   X*X + Y*Y
RUN 210
INITIAL X? 0
INITIAL Y? 0
INITIAL NUMBER OF SUBINTERVALS? 10
```

x	y with h=0.1	y with h=0.02	y with h=0.004	y with h=0.0008
0.0	0.0000	0.0000	0.0000	0.0000
0.2	0.0010	0.0023	0.0026	0.0027
0.4	0.0140	0.0198	0.0210	0.0213
0.6	0.0551	0.0688	0.0717	0.0723
0.8	0.1413	0.1672	0.1727	0.1738
1.0	0.2925	0.3379	0.3477	0.3497

It seems apparent that $y(1) \approx 0.35$, in contrast with Example 4 in the text, where the initial condition is $y(0) = 1$.

In Problems 18–24 we give only the final approximate values of y obtained using Euler's method with step sizes $h = 0.1$, $h = 0.02$, $h = 0.004$, and $h = 0.0008$.

18. With $x_0 = 0$ and $y_0 = 1$, the approximate values of $y(2)$ obtained are:

h	0.1	0.02	0.004	0.0008
y	1.6680	1.6771	1.6790	1.6794

19. With $x_0 = 0$ and $y_0 = 1$, the approximate values of $y(2)$ obtained are:

h	0.1	0.02	0.004	0.0008
y	6.1831	6.3653	6.4022	6.4096

20. With $x_0 = 0$ and $y_0 = -1$, the approximate values of $y(2)$ obtained are:

h	0.1	0.02	0.004	0.0008
y	-1.3792	-1.2843	-1.2649	-1.2610

21. With $x_0 = 1$ and $y_0 = 2$, the approximate values of $y(2)$ obtained are:

h	0.1	0.02	0.004	0.0008
y	2.8508	2.8681	2.8716	2.8723

22. With $x_0 = 0$ and $y_0 = 1$, the approximate values of $y(2)$ obtained are:

h	0.1	0.02	0.004	0.0008
y	6.9879	7.2601	7.3154	7.3264

23. With $x_0 = 0$ and $y_0 = 0$, the approximate values of $y(1)$ obtained are:

h	0.1	0.02	0.004	0.0008
y	1.2262	1.2300	1.2306	1.2307

24. With $x_0 = -1$ and $y_0 = 1$, the approximate values of $y(1)$ obtained are:

h	0.1	0.02	0.004	0.0008
y	0.9585	0.9918	0.9984	0.9997

25. With step sizes $h = 0.15$, $h = 0.03$, and $h = 0.006$ we get the following results:

x	y with $h=0.15$	y with $h=0.03$	y with $h=0.006$
-1.0	1.0000	1.0000	1.0000
-0.7	1.0472	1.0512	1.0521
-0.4	1.1213	1.1358	1.1390
-0.1	1.2826	1.3612	1.3835
+0.2	0.8900	1.4711	0.8210
+0.5	0.7460	1.2808	0.7192

While the values for $h = 0.15$ alone are not conclusive, a comparison of the values of y for all three step sizes with $x > 0$ suggests some anomaly in the transition from negative to positive values of x.

26. With step sizes $h = 0.1$ and $h = 0.01$ we get the following results:

x	y with $h = 0.1$	y with $h = 0.01$
0.0	0.0000	0.0000
0.1	0.0000	0.0003
0.2	0.0010	0.0025
0.3	0.0050	0.0086
.	.	.
.	.	.
.	.	.
1.8	2.8200	4.3308
1.9	3.9393	7.9425
2.0	5.8521	28.3926

Clearly there is some difficulty near $x = 2$.

27.   With step sizes $h = 0.1$ and $h = 0.01$ we get the following results:

x	y with $h = 0.1$	y with $h = 0.01$
0.0	1.0000	1.0000
0.1	1.2000	1.2200
0.2	1.4428	1.4967
.	.	.
.	.	.
.	.	.
0.7	4.3460	6.4643
0.8	5.8670	11.8425
0.9	8.3349	39.5010

Clearly there is some difficulty near $x = 0.9$.

SECTION 2.5

A CLOSER LOOK AT THE EULER METHOD

The initial value problems in Problems 1–24 here are the same as those in Problems 1–24 of Section 2.4, so the answers here may be compared with those in the previous section to see how great an improvement is the improved Euler method over the original Euler method.

In each of Problems 1–10 we give first the predictor formula for u_{n+1}, next the improved Euler corrector for y_{n+1}, and finally the approximate and actual values of $y(0.5)$ obtained with step size $h = 0.1$.

1. $u_{n+1} = y_n - hy_n$

$y_{n+1} = y_n + (h/2)[-y_n - u_{n+1}]$

Approx value: 1.2142
Actual value: 1.2131

The complete table of results is

| | Improved | Actual |
x	Euler y	value
0.1	1.8100	1.8097
0.2	1.6381	1.6375
0.3	1.4824	1.4816
0.4	1.3416	1.3406
0.5	1.2142	1.2131

2. $u_{n+1} = y_n + 2hy_n$

$y_{n+1} = y_n + (h/2)[2y_n + 2u_{n+1}]$

Approx value: 1.3514
Actual value: 1.3591

3. $u_{n+1} = y_n + h(y_n + 1)$

$y_{n+1} = y_n + (h/2)[(y_n + 1) + (u_{n+1} + 1)]$

Approx value: 2.2949
Actual value: 2.2974

4. $u_{n+1} = y_n + h(x_n - y_n)$

$y_{n+1} = y_n + (h/2)[(x_n - y_n) + (x_n + h - u_{n+1})]$

Approx value: 0.7142
Actual value: 0.7131

5. $u_{n+1} = y_n + h(y_n - x_n - 1)$

$y_{n+1} = y_n + (h/2)[(y_n - x_n - 1) + (u_{n+1} - x_n - h - 1)]$

Approx value: 0.8526
Actual value: 0.8513

6. $u_{n+1} = y_n - 2x_ny_nh$

$y_{n+1} = y_n - (h/2)[2x_ny_n + 2(x_n + h)u_{n+1}]$

Approx value: 1.5575
Actual value: 1.5576

The complete table of results is

x	Improved Euler y	Actual value
0.1	1.9800	1.9801
0.2	1.9214	1.9216
0.3	1.8276	1.8279
0.4	1.7041	1.7043
0.5	1.5575	1.5576

7. $u_{n+1} = y_n - 3x_n^2 y_n h$

$y_{n+1} = y_n - (h/2)[3x_n^2 y_n + 3(x_n + h)^2 u_{n+1}]$

Approx value: 2.6405
Actual value: 2.6475

8. $u_{n+1} = y_n + h \exp(-y_n)$

$y_{n+1} = y_n + (h/2)[\exp(-y_n) + \exp(-u_{n+1})]$

Approx value: 0.4053
Actual value: 0.4055

9. $u_{n+1} = y_n + h(1 + y_n^2)/4$

$y_{n+1} = y_n + h[1 + y_n^2 + 1 + (u_{n+1})^2]/8$

Approx value: 1.2873
Actual value: 1.2874

10. $u_{n+1} = y_n + 2x_n y_n^2 h$

$y_{n+1} = y_n + h[x_n y_n^2 + (x_n + h)(u_{n+1})^2]$

Approx value: 1.3309
Actual value: 1.3333

The results given below for Problems 11–24 were computed using an improved Euler alteration of Program EULERANS, which was listed in Section 2.4 of this manual.

11. With $h = 0.01$: $y(1) \approx -0.71824$
With $h = 0.005$: $y(1) \approx -0.71827$
Actual: $y(1) \approx -0.71828$

The table of numerical results is

x	y with $h = 0.01$	y with $h = 0.005$	y exact

0.0	1.00000	1.00000	1.00000
0.2	0.77860	0.77860	0.77860
0.4	0.50819	0.50818	0.50818
0.6	0.17790	0.17789	0.17788
0.8	−0.22551	−0.22553	−0.22554
1.0	−0.71824	−0.71827	−0.71828

12. With $h = 0.01$: $y(1) \approx 2.99995$
With $h = 0.005$: $y(1) \approx 2.99999$
Actual: $y(1) \approx 3.00000$

13. With $h = 0.01$: $y(2) \approx 4.89901$
With $h = 0.005$: $y(2) \approx 4.89899$
Actual: $y(2) \approx 4.89898$

14. With $h = 0.01$: $y(2) \approx 3.25847$
With $h = 0.005$: $y(2) \approx 3.25878$
Actual: $y(2) \approx 3.25889$

15. With $h = 0.01$: $y(3) \approx 3.44445$
With $h = 0.005$: $y(3) \approx 3.44445$
Actual: $y(3) \approx 3.44444$

16. With $h = 0.01$: $y(3) \approx 8.84511$
With $h = 0.005$: $y(3) \approx 8.84509$
Actual: $y(3) \approx 8.84509$

17. With $h = 0.1$: $y(1) \approx 0.35183$
With $h = 0.02$: $y(1) \approx 0.35030$
With $h = 0.004$: $y(1) \approx 0.35023$
With $h = 0.0008$: $y(1) \approx 0.35023$

The table of numerical results is

x	y with $h = 0.1$	y with $h = 0.02$	y with $h = 0.004$	y with $h = 0.0008$
0.0	0.00000	0.00000	0.00000	0.00000
0.2	0.00300	0.00268	0.00267	0.00267
0.4	0.02202	0.02139	0.02136	0.02136
0.6	0.07344	0.07249	0.07245	0.07245
0.8	0.17540	0.17413	0.17408	0.17408
1.0	0.35183	0.35030	0.35023	0.35023

18.   With $h =$ 0.1: $y(2) \approx 1.68043$
             With $h =$ 0.02: $y(2) \approx 1.67949$
             With $h =$ 0.004: $y(2) \approx 1.67946$
             With $h = 0.0008$: $y(2) \approx 1.67946$

19.   With $h =$ 0.1: $y(2) \approx 6.40834$
             With $h =$ 0.02: $y(2) \approx 6.41134$
             With $h =$ 0.004: $y(2) \approx 6.41147$
             With $h = 0.0008$: $y(2) \approx 6.41147$

20.   With $h =$ 0.1: $y(2) \approx -1.26092$
             With $h =$ 0.02: $y(2) \approx -1.26003$
             With $h =$ 0.004: $y(2) \approx -1.25999$
             With $h = 0.0008$: $y(2) \approx -1.25999$

21.   With $h =$ 0.1: $y(2) \approx 2.87204$
             With $h =$ 0.02: $y(2) \approx 2.87245$
             With $h =$ 0.004: $y(2) \approx 2.87247$
             With $h = 0.0008$: $y(2) \approx 2.87247$

22.   With $h =$ 0.1: $y(2) \approx 7.31578$
             With $h =$ 0.02: $y(2) \approx 7.32841$
             With $h =$ 0.004: $y(2) \approx 7.32916$
             With $h = 0.0008$: $y(2) \approx 7.32920$

23.   With $h =$ 0.1: $y(1) \approx 1.22967$
             With $h =$ 0.02: $y(1) \approx 1.23069$
             With $h =$ 0.004: $y(1) \approx 1.23073$
             With $h = 0.0008$: $y(1) \approx 1.23073$

24.   With $h =$ 0.1: $y(1) \approx 1.00006$
             With $h =$ 0.02: $y(1) \approx 1.00000$
             With $h =$ 0.004: $y(1) \approx 1.00000$
             With $h = 0.0008$: $y(1) \approx 1.00000$

In the solutions for Problems 25 and 26 we illustrate the following general MATLAB ode solver.

```
function  [t,y] = ode(method, yp, t0,b, y0, n)
%  [t,y] = ode(method, yp, t0,b, y0, n)
%  calls the method described by 'method' for the
%  ODE 'yp' with function header
%
%                y' = yp(t,y)
%
%  on the interval  [t0,b]  with initial (column)
%  vector  y0.  Choices for method are 'euler',
%  'impeuler', 'rk' (Runge-Kutta), 'ode23', 'ode45'.
```

```
%   Results are saved at the endPoints of n subintervals,
%   that is, in steps of length  h = (b - t0)/n.  The
%   result  t  is an (n+1)-column vector from b to t1,
%   while  y  is a matrix with  n+1  rows (one for each
%   t-value) and one column for each dependent variable.

h = (b - t0)/n;                  % step size
t = t0 : h : b;
t = t';                          % col. vector of t-values
y = y0';                         % 1st row of result matrix
for  i = 2 : n+1                  % for i=2 to i=n+1
    t0 = t(i-1);                  % old t
    t1 = t(i);                    % new t
    y0 = y(i-1,:)';              % old y-row-vector
    [T,Y] = feval(method, yp, t0,t1, y0);
    y = [y;Y'];                  % adjoin new y-row-vector
end
```

To use the improved Euler method, we call as **'method'** the following function.

```
function [t,y] = impeuler(yp, t0,t1, y0)
%
%   [t,y] = impeuler(yp, t0,t1, y0)
%   Takes one improved Euler step for
%
%        y' = yprime( t,y ),
%
%   from t0  to  t1  with initial value  the
%   column vector  y0.

h = t1 - t0;
k1 = feval( yp, t0, y0        );
k2 = feval( yp, t1, y0 + h*k1 );
k  = (k1 + k2)/2;
t = t1;
y = y0 + h*k;
```

25. Here our differential equation is described by the MATLAB function

```
function  vp = vpbolt1(t,v)
vp = -0.04*v - 9.8;
```

Then the commands

```
n = 50;
[t1,v1] = ode('impeuler','vpbolt1',0,10,49,n);
n = 100;
[t2,v2] = ode('impeuler','vpbolt1',0,10,49,n);
t = (0:10)';
ve = 294*exp(-t/25)-245;
[t, v1(1:5:51), v2(1:10:101), ve]
```

generate the table

t	with $n = 50$	with $n = 100$	actual v
0	49.0000	49.0000	49.0000
1	37.4722	37.4721	37.4721
2	26.3964	26.3963	26.3962
3	15.7549	15.7547	15.7546
4	5.5307	5.5304	5.5303
5	-4.2926	-4.2930	-4.2932
6	-13.7308	-13.7313	-13.7314
7	-22.7989	-22.7994	-22.7996
8	-31.5115	-31.5120	-31.5122
9	-39.8824	-39.8830	-39.8832
10	-47.9251	-47.9257	-47.9259

We notice first that the final two columns agree to 3 decimal places (each difference being than 0.0005). Scanning the $n = 100$ column for sign changes, we suspect that $v = 0$ (at the bolt's apex) occurs just after $t = 4.5$ sec. Then interpolation between $t = 4.5$ and $t = 4.6$ in the table

[t2(40:51),v2(40:51)]

3.9000	6.5345
4.0000	5.5304
4.1000	4.5303
4.2000	3.5341
4.3000	2.5420
4.4000	1.5538
4.5000	0.5696
4.6000	-0.4108
4.7000	-1.3872
4.8000	-2.3597
4.9000	-3.3283
5.0000	-4.2930

indicates that $t = 4.56$ at the bolt's apex. Finally, interpolation in

[t2(95:96),v2(95:96)]

9.4000	-43.1387
9.5000	-43.9445

gives the impact velocity $v(9.41) \approx -43.22$ m/s.

26. Now our differential equation is described by the MATLAB function

```
function  vp = vpbolt2(t,v)
vp = -0.0011*v.*abs(v) - 9.8;
```

Then the commands

```
n = 100;
[t1,v1] = ode('impeuler','vpbolt2',0,10,49,n);
n = 200;
[t2,v2] = ode('impeuler','vpbolt2',0,10,49,n);
t = (0:10)';
[t, v1(1:10:101), v2(1:20:201)]
```

generate the table

t	with $n = 100$	with $n = 200$
0	49.0000	49.0000
1	37.1547	37.1547
2	26.2428	26.2429
3.	15.9453	15.9455
4	6.0041	6.0044
5	-3.8020	-3.8016
6	-13.5105	-13.5102
7	-22.9356	-22.9355
8	-31.8984	-31.8985
9	-40.2557	-40.2559
10	-47.9066	-47.9070

We notice first that the final two columns agree to 2 decimal places (each difference being less than 0.005). Scanning the $n = 200$ column for sign changes, we suspect that $v = 0$ (at the bolt's apex) occurs just after $t = 4.6$ sec. Then interpolation between $t = 4.61$ and $t = 4.65$ in the table

```
[t2(91:101),v2(91:101)]
```

4.5000	1.0964
4.5500	0.6063
4.6000	0.1163
4.6500	-0.3737
4.7000	-0.8636
4.7500	-1.3536
4.8000	-1.8434
4.8500	-2.3332
4.9000	-2.8228
4.9500	-3.3123
5.0000	-3.8016

indicates that $t = 4.61$ at the bolt's apex. Finally, interpolation in

```
[t2(189:190),v2(189:190)]
```

9.4000	-43.4052
9.4500	-43.7907

gives the impact velocity $v(9.41) \approx -43.48$ m/s.

SECTION 2.6

THE RUNGE-KUTTA METHOD

1. The actual solution is $y(x) = 2e^{-x}$. The following table of values is obtained by applying the Runge-Kutta method with step size $h = 0.25$:

x	Approx y	Actual y
0.25	1.55762	2.55760
0.50	1.21309	1.21306

2. Actual solution: $y(x) = (1/2)e^{2x}$
    Approx $y(0.5) \approx 1.35867$
    Actual $y(0.5) \approx 1.35914$

3. Actual solution: $y(x) = 2e^{x} - 1$
    Approx $y(0.5) \approx 2.29740$
    Actual $y(0.5) \approx 2.29744$

4. Actual solution: $y(x) = 2e^{-x} + x - 1$
    Approx $y(0.5) \approx 0.71309$
    Actual $y(0.5) \approx 0.71306$

5. Actual solution: $y(x) = -e^{x} + x + 2$
    Approx $y(0.5) \approx 0.85130$
    Actual $y(0.5) \approx 0.85128$

6. Actual solution: $y(x) = 2 \exp(-x^2)$
    Approx $y(0.5) \approx 1.55759$
    Actual $y(0.5) \approx 1.55760$

7. Actual solution: $y(x) = 3 \exp(-x^3)$
    Approx $y(0.5) \approx 2.64745$
    Actual $y(0.5) \approx 2.64749$

8. Actual solution: $y(x) = \ln(x + 1)$
    Approx $y(0.5) \approx 0.40547$
    Actual $y(0.5) \approx 0.40547$

9. Actual solution: $y(x) = \tan[(x + \pi)/4]$
    Approx $y(0.5) \approx 1.28743$
    Actual $y(0.5) \approx 1.28743$

10. Actual solution: $y(x) = 1/(1 - x^2)$
Approx $y(0.5) \approx 1.33337$
Actual $y(0.5) \approx 1.33333$

11. Actual solution: $y(x) = 2 - e^x$
With $h = 0.2$: $y(1) \approx -0.71825$
With $h = 0.1$: $y(1) \approx -0.71828$
Actual: $y(1) \approx -0.71828$

The table of numerical results is

x	y with $h = 0.2$	y with $h = 0.1$	y exact
0.0	1.00000	1.00000	1.00000
0.2	0.77860	0.77860	0.77860
0.4	0.50818	0.50818	0.50818
0.6	0.17789	0.17788	0.17788
0.8	−0.22552	−0.22554	−0.22554
1.0	−0.71825	−0.71828	−0.71828

12. Actual solution: $y(x) = 1 + 2/(2 - x)$
With $h = 0.2$: $y(1) \approx 2.99996$
With $h = 0.1$: $y(1) \approx 3.00000$
Actual: $y(1) \approx 3.00000$

13. Actual solution: $y(x) = (8 + x^4)^{1/2}$
With $h = 0.2$: $y(2) \approx 4.89900$
With $h = 0.1$: $y(2) \approx 4.89898$
Actual: $y(2) \approx 4.89898$

14. Actual solution: $y(x) = 1/(1 - \ln x)$
With $h = 0.2$: $y(2) \approx 3.25795$
With $h = 0.1$: $y(2) \approx 3.25882$
Actual: $y(2) \approx 3.25889$

15. Actual solution: $y(x) = x + 4/x^2$
With $h = 0.2$: $y(3) \approx 3.44445$
With $h = 0.1$: $y(3) \approx 3.44444$
Actual: $y(3) \approx 3.44444$

16. Actual solution: $y(x) = (x^6 - 37)^{1/3}$
With $h = 0.2$: $y(3) \approx 8.84515$
With $h = 0.1$: $y(3) \approx 8.84509$
Actual: $y(3) \approx 8.84509$

17.	With $h = 0.2$:	$y(1) \approx 0.350258$
	With $h = 0.1$:	$y(1) \approx 0.350234$
	With $h = 0.05$:	$y(1) \approx 0.350232$
	With $h = 0.025$:	$y(1) \approx 0.350232$

The table of numerical results is

x	y with $h = 0.2$	y with $h = 0.1$	y with $h = 0.05$	y with $h = 0.025$
0.0	0.000000	0.000000	0.000000	0.000000
0.2	0.002667	0.002667	0.002667	0.002667
0.4	0.021360	0.021359	0.021359	0.021359
0.6	0.072451	0.072448	0.072448	0.072448
0.8	0.174090	0.174081	0.174080	0.174080
1.0	0.350258	0.350234	0.350232	0.350232

18.	With $h = 0.2$:	$y(2) \approx 1.679513$
	With $h = 0.1$:	$y(2) \approx 1.679461$
	With $h = 0.05$:	$y(2) \approx 1.679459$
	With $h = 0.025$:	$y(2) \approx 1.679459$

19.	With $h = 0.2$:	$y(2) \approx 6.411464$
	With $h = 0.1$:	$y(2) \approx 6.411474$
	With $h = 0.05$:	$y(2) \approx 6.411474$
	With $h = 0.025$:	$y(2) \approx 6.411474$

20.	With $h = 0.2$:	$y(2) \approx -1.259990$
	With $h = 0.1$:	$y(2) \approx -1.259992$
	With $h = 0.05$:	$y(2) \approx -1.259993$
	With $h = 0.025$:	$y(2) \approx -1.259993$

21.	With $h = 0.2$:	$y(2) \approx 2.872467$
	With $h = 0.1$:	$y(2) \approx 2.872468$
	With $h = 0.05$:	$y(2) \approx 2.872468$
	With $h = 0.025$:	$y(2) \approx 2.872468$

22.	With $h = 0.2$:	$y(2) \approx 7.326761$
	With $h = 0.1$:	$y(2) \approx 7.328452$
	With $h = 0.05$:	$y(2) \approx 7.328971$
	With $h = 0.025$:	$y(2) \approx 7.329134$

23.	With $h = 0.2$:	$y(1) \approx 1.230735$
	With $h = 0.1$:	$y(1) \approx 1.230731$
	With $h = 0.05$:	$y(1) \approx 1.230731$
	With $h = 0.025$:	$y(1) \approx 1.230731$

24.   With $h = 0.2$: $y(1) \approx 1.000000$
With $h = 0.1$: $y(1) \approx 1.000000$
With $h = 0.05$: $y(1) \approx 1.000000$
With $h = 0.025$: $y(1) \approx 1.000000$

In the solutions for Problems 25 and 26 we use the general MATLAB solver **ode** that was listed prior to the Problem 25 solution in Section 2.5. To use the Runge-Kutta method, we call as **'method'** the following function.

```
function [t,y] = rk(yp, t0,t1, y0)

%   [t, y] = rk(yp, t0, t1, y0)
%   Takes one Runge-Kutta step for
%
%        y' = yp( t,y ),
%
%   from t0  to  t1  with initial value  the
%   column vector  y0.
h = t1 - t0;
k1 = feval(yp, t0          , y0              );
k2 = feval(yp, t0 + h/2, y0 + (h/2)*k1 );
k3 = feval(yp, t0 + h/2, y0 + (h/2)*k2 );
k4 = feval(yp, t0 + h    ,y0 +      h *k3 );
k  = (1/6)*(k1 + 2*k2 + 2*k3 + k4);
t = t1;
y = y0 + h*k;
```

25.   Here our differential equation is described by the MATLAB function

```
function  vp = vpbolt1(t,v)
vp = -0.04*v - 9.8;
```

Then the commands

```
n = 100;
[t1,v1] = ode('rk','vpbolt1',0,10,49,n);
n = 200;
[t2,v] = ode('rk','vpbolt1',0,10,49,n);
t = (0:10)';
ve = 294*exp(-t/25)-245;
[t, v1(1:n/20:1+n/2), v(1:n/10:n+1), ve]
```

generate the table

t	with $n = 100$	with $n = 200$	actual v
0	49.0000	49.0000	49.0000
1	37.4721	37.4721	37.4721
2	26.3962	26.3962	26.3962

```
3      15.7546     15.7546     15.7546
4       5.5303      5.5303      5.5303
5      -4.2932     -4.2932     -4.2932
6     -13.7314    -13.7314    -13.7314
7     -22.7996    -22.7996    -22.7996
8     -31.5122    -31.5122    -31.5122
9     -39.8832    -39.8832    -39.8832
10    -47.9259    -47.9259    -47.9259
```

We notice first that the final three columns agree to the 4 displayed decimal places. Scanning the last column for sign changes in v, we suspect that $v = 0$ (at the bolt's apex) occurs just after $t = 4.5$ sec. Then interpolation between $t = 4.55$ and $t = 4.60$ in the table

[t2(91:95),v(91:95)]

```
4.5000      0.5694
4.5500      0.0788
4.6000     -0.4109
4.6500     -0.8996
4.7000     -1.3873
```

indicates that $t = 4.56$ at the bolt's apex. Now the commands

```
y = zeros(n+1,1);
h = 10/n;
for j = 2:n+1
    y(j) = y(j-1) + v(j-1)*h +
                0.5*(-.04*v(j-1) - 9.8)*h^2;
end
ye = 7350*(1 - exp(-t/25)) - 245*t;
[t, y(1:n/10:n+1), ye]
```

generate the table

t	Approx y	Actual y
0	0	0
1	43.1974	43.1976
2	75.0945	75.0949
3	96.1342	96.1348
4	106.7424	106.7432
5	107.3281	107.3290
6	98.2842	98.2852
7	79.9883	79.9895
8	52.8032	52.8046
9	17.0775	17.0790
10	-26.8540	-26.8523

We see at least 2-decimal place agreement between approximate and actual values of y. Finally, interpolation between $t = 9$ and $t = 10$ here suggests that $y = 0$ just after $t = 9.4$. Then interpolation between $t = 9.40$ and $t = 9.45$ in the table

```
[t2(187:191),y(187:191)]
```

```
9.3000      4.7448
9.3500      2.6182
9.4000      0.4713
9.4500     -1.6957
9.5000     -3.8829
```

indicates that the bolt is aloft for about 9.41 seconds.

26.   Now our differential equation is described by the MATLAB function

```
function  vp = vpbolt2(t,v)
vp = -0.0011*v.*abs(v) - 9.8;
```

Then the commands

```
n = 200;
[t1,v1] = ode('rk','vpbolt2',0,10,49,n);
n = 2*n;
[t2,v] = ode('rk','vpbolt2',0,10,49,n);
t = (0:10)';
ve = zeros(size(t));
ve(1:5)= 94.388*tan(0.478837 - 0.103827*t(1:5));
ve(6:11)= -94.388*tanh(0.103827*(t(6:11)-4.6119));
[t, v1(1:n/20:1+n/2), v(1:n/10:n+1), ve]
```

generate the table

t	with $n = 200$	with $n = 400$	actual v
0	49.0000	49.0000	49.0000
1	37.1548	37.1548	37.1547
2	26.2430	26.2430	26.2429
3	15.9456	15.9456	15.9455
4	6.0046	6.0046	6.0045
5	-3.8015	-3.8015	-3.8013
6	13.5101	-13.5101	-13.5100
7	-22.9354	-22.9354	-22.9353
8	-31.8985	-31.8985	-31.8984
9	-40.2559	-40.2559	-40.2559
10	-47.9071	-47.9071	-47.9071

We notice first that the final three columns almost agree to the 4 displayed decimal places. Scanning the last colmun for sign changes in v, we suspect that $v = 0$ (at the bolt's apex) occurs just after $t = 4.6$ sec. Then interpolation between $t = 4.600$ and $t = 4.625$ in the table

```
[t2(185:189),v(185:189)]
```

```
4.6000     0.1165
4.6250    -0.1285
4.6500    -0.3735
4.6750    -0.6185
4.7000    -0.8635
```

indicates that $t = 4.61$ at the bolt's apex. Now the commands

```
y = zeros(n+1,1);
h = 10/n;
for j = 2:n+1
    y(j) = y(j-1) + v(j-1)*h + 0.5*(-.04*v(j-1) -
9.8)*h^2;
end
ye = zeros(size(t));
ye(1:5)= 108.465+909.091*log(cos(0.478837 -
0.103827*t(1:5)));
ye(6:11)= 108.465-909.091*log(cosh(0.103827
                  *(t(6:11)-4.6119)));
[t, y(1:n/10:n+1), ye]
```

generate the table

t	Approx y	Actual y
0	0	0.0001
1	42.9881	42.9841
2	74.6217	74.6197
3	95.6719	95.6742
4	106.6232	106.6292
5	107.7206	107.7272
6	99.0526	99.0560
7	80.8027	80.8018
8	53.3439	53.3398
9	17.2113	17.2072
10	-26.9369	-26.9363

We see almost 2-decimal place agreement between approximate and actual values of y.
Finally, interpolation between $t = 9$ and $t = 10$ here suggests that $y = 0$ just after $t = 9.4$.
Then interpolation between $t = 9.400$ and $t = 9.425$ in the table

```
[t2(377:381),y(377:381)]
```

```
9.4000     0.4740
9.4250    -0.6137
9.4500    -1.7062
9.4750    -2.8035
9.5000    -3.9055
```

indicates that the bolt is aloft for about 9.41 seconds.

CHAPTER 3

LINEAR EQUATIONS OF HIGHER ORDER

SECTION 3.1

INTRODUCTION: SECOND-ORDER LINEAR EQUATIONS

In this section the central ideas of the theory of linear differential equations are introduced and illustrated concretely in the context of **second-order** equations. These key concepts include superposition of solutions (Theorem 1), existence and uniqueness of solutions (Theorem 2), linear independence, the Wronskian (Theorem 3), and general solutions (Theorem 4). This discussion of second-order equations serves as preparation for the treatment of nth order linear equations in Section 3.2. Although the concepts in this section may seem somewhat abstract to students, the problems set is quite tangible and largely computational.

In each of Problems 1–16 the verification that y_1 and y_2 satisfy the given differential equation is a routine matter. As in Example 2, we then impose the given initial conditions on the general solution $y = c_1 y_1 + c_2 y_2$. This yields two linear equations that determine the values of the constants c_1 and c_2.

1. $y = 5(e^x - e^{-x})/2$ 2. $y = 2e^{3x} - 3e^{-3x}$

3. $y = 3 \cos 2x + 4 \sin 2x$ 4. $y = 10 \cos 5x - 2 \sin 5x$

5. $y = 2e^x - e^{2x}$ 6. $y = 4e^{2x} + 3e^{-3x}$

7. $y = 6 - 8e^{-x}$ 8. $y = (14 - 2e^{3x})/3$

9. $y = 2e^{-x} + xe^{-x}$ 10. $y = 3e^{5x} - 2xe^{5x}$

11. $y = 5e^x \sin x$

12. If $y(x) = Ae^{-3x} \cos 2x + Be^{-3x} \sin 2x$, then

$$y'(x) = -3e^{-3x}(A \cos 2x + B \sin 2x) + e^{-3x}(-2A \sin 2x + 2B \cos 2x).$$

The initial conditions are $y(0) = A = 2$, $y'(0) = -3A + 2B = 0$, so the particular solution is

$$y(x) = e^{-3x}(2 \cos 2x + 3 \sin 2x).$$

13. $y = 5x - 2x^2$ 14. $y = 3x^2 - 16/x^3$

15. $\quad y = 7x - 5x \ln x$ 　　　　　　　　　　**16.** $\quad y = 2\cos(\ln x) + 3\sin(\ln x)$

20. Linearly dependent, because

$$f(x) = \pi = \pi(\cos^2 x + \sin^2 x) = \pi\, g(x)$$

21. Linearly independent, because $x^3 = +x^2|x|$ if $x > 0$, whereas $x^3 = -x^2|x|$ if $x < 0$.

22. Linearly independent, because $1 + x = c(1 + |x|)$ would require that $c = 1$ with $x = 0$, but $c = 0$ with $x = -1$. Thus there is no such constant c.

23. Linearly independent, because $f(x) = +g(x)$ if $x > 0$, whereas $f(x) = -g(x)$ if $x < 0$.

24. Linearly dependent, because $g(x) = 2f(x)$.

25. $f(x) = e^x \sin x$ and $g(x) = e^x \cos x$ are linearly independent, because $f(x) = k\, g(x)$ would imply that $\sin x = k \cos x$, whereas $\sin x$ and $\cos x$ are linearly independent.

26. To see that $f(x)$ and $g(x)$ are linearly independent, assume that $f(x) = c\, g(x)$, and then substitute both $x = 0$ and $x = \pi/2$.

27. Let $L[y] = y'' + py' + qy$. Then $L[y_c] = 0$ and $L[y_p] = f$, so

$$L[y_c + y_p] = L[y_c] + [y_p] = 0 + f = f.$$

28. If $y(x) = 1 + c_1 \cos x + c_2 \sin x$ then

$$y'(x) = -c_1 \sin x + c_2 \cos x,$$

so the initial conditions $y(0) = y'(0) = -1$ yield $c_1 = -2, c_2 = -1$. Hence $y = 1 - 2\cos x - \sin x$.

29. There is no contradiction because if the given differential equation is divided by x^2 to get the form in Equation (8) in the text, then the resulting functions $p(x) = -4/x$ and $q(x) = 6/x^2$ are not continuous at $x = 0$.

30. **(a)** $\quad y_2 = x^3$ and $y_2 = |x^3|$ are linearly independent because $x^3 = c|x^3|$ would require that $c = 1$ with $x = 1$, but $c = -1$ with $x = -1$.

(b) The fact that $W(y_1, y_2) = 0$ everywhere does not contradict Theorem 3, because when the given equation is written in the required form

$$y'' - (3/x)y' + (3/x^2)y = 0,$$

the coefficient functions $p(x) = -3/x$ and $q(x) = 3/x^2$ are not continuous at $x = 0$.

31. $W(y_1, y_2) = -2x$ vanishes at $x = 0$, whereas if y_1 and y_2 were (linearly independent) solutions of an equation $y'' + py' + qy = 0$ with p and q both continuous on an open interval I containing $x = 0$, then Theorem 3 would imply that $W \neq 0$ on I.

32. **(a)** $W = y_1y_2' - y_1'y_2$, so

$$AW' = A(y_1'y_2' + y_1y_2'' - y_1''y_2 - y_1'y_2')$$
$$= y_1(Ay_2'') - y_2(Ay_1'')$$
$$= y_1(-By_2' - Cy_2) - y_2(-By_1' - Cy_1)$$
$$= -B(y_1y_2' - y_1'y_2)$$

and thus $AW' = -BW$.

(b) Just separate the variables.

(c) Because the exponential factor is never zero.

33. $y(x) = c_1e^x + c_2e^{2x}$ **34.** $y(x) = c_1e^{-5x} + c_2e^{3x}$

35. $y(x) = c_1 + c_2e^{-5x}$ **36.** $y(x) = c_1 + c_2e^{-3x/2}$

37. $y(x) = c_1e^{-x/2} + c_2e^x$ **38.** $y(x) = c_1e^{-x/2} + c_2e^{-3x/2}$

39. $y(x) = (c_1 + c_2x)e^{-x/2}$ **40.** $y(x) = (c_1 + c_2x)e^{2x/3}$

41. $y(x) = c_1e^{-4x/3} + c_2e^{5x/2}$ **42.** $y(x) = c_1e^{-4x/7} + c_2e^{3x/5}$

43. $y'' + 10y' = 0$ **44.** $y'' - 100y = 0$

45. $y'' + 20y' + 100y = 0$ **46.** $y'' + 110y' + 1000y = 0$

47. $y'' = 0$ **48.** $y'' - 2y' - y = 0$

49. The solution curve with $y(0) = 1$, $y'(0) = 6$ is $y(x) = 8e^{-x} - 7e^{-2x}$. We find that $y'(x) = 0$ when $x = \ln(7/4)$ so $e^{-x} = 4/7$ and $e^{-2x} = 16/49$. It follows that $y(\ln(7/4)) = 16/7$, so the high point on the curve is $(\ln(7/4)), 16/7) \approx (0.56, 2.29)$, which looks consistent with Fig. 3.1.6.

50. The two solution curves with $y(0) = a$ and $y(0) = b$ (as well as $y'(0) = 1$) are

$$y = (2a+1)e^{-x} - (a+1)e^{-2x},$$
$$y = (2b+1)e^{-x} - (b+1)e^{-2x}.$$

Subtraction and then division by $a - b$ gives $2e^{-x} = e^{-2x}$, so it follows that $x = -\ln 2$. Now substitution in either formula gives $y = -2$, so the common point of intersection is $(-\ln 2, -2)$.

SECTION 3.2

GENERAL SOLUTIONS OF LINEAR EQUATIONS

Students should check each of Theorems 1 through 4 in this section to see that, in the case $n = 2$, it reduces to the corresponding theorem in Section 3.1. Similarly, the computational problems for this section largely parallel those for the previous section. By the end of Section 3.2 students should understand that, although we do not prove the existence-uniqueness theorem now, it provides the basis for everything we do with linear differential equations.

1. $(5/2)(2x) + (-8/3)(3x^2) + (-1)(5x - 8x^2) = 0$

2. $(-4)(5) + (5)(2 - 3x^2) + (1)(10 + 15x^2) = 0$

3. $(1)(0) + (0)(\sin x) + (0)(e^x) = 0$

4. $(1)(17) + (-17/2)(2 \sin^2 x) + (-17/3)(3 \cos^2 x) = 0$, because $\sin^2 x + \cos^2 x = 1$.

5. $(1)(17) + (-34)(\cos^2 x) + (17)(\cos 2x) = 0$, because $2 \cos^2 x = 1 + \cos 2x$.

6. $(-1)(e^x) + (1)(\cosh x) + (1)(\sinh x) = 0$, because $\cosh x = (e^x + e^{-x})/2$ and $\sinh x = (e^x - e^{-x})/2$.

7. $W = \begin{vmatrix} 1 & x & x^2 \\ 0 & 1 & 2x \\ 0 & 0 & 2 \end{vmatrix} = 2$ is nonzero everywhere.

8. $W = \begin{vmatrix} e^x & e^{2x} & e^{3x} \\ e^x & 2e^{2x} & 3e^{3x} \\ e^x & 4e^{2x} & 9e^{3x} \end{vmatrix} = 2e^{6x}$ is never zero.

9. $W = e^x(\cos^2 x + \sin^2 x) = e^x \neq 0$

10. $W = x^{-7}e^x(x + 1)(x + 4)$ is nonzero for $x > 0$.

11. $W = x^3 e^{2x}$ is nonzero if $x \neq 0$.

12. $W = x^{-2}[2\cos^2(\ln x) + 2\sin^2(\ln x)] = 2x^{-2}$ is nonzero for $x > 0$.

In each of Problems 13–20 we first form the general solution

$$y(x) = c_1 y_1(x) + c_2 y_2(x) + c_3 y_3(x),$$

then calculate $y'(x)$ and $y''(x)$, and finally impose the given initial conditions to determine the values of the coefficients c_1, c_2, c_3.

13. $y = (4e^x - e^{-2x})/3$

14. $y = (3e^x - 6e^{2x} + 3e^{3x})/2$

15. $y = (2 - 2x + x^2)e^x$

16. $y = -12e^x + 13e^{2x} - 10xe^{2x}$

17. $y = (29 - 2\cos 3x - 3\sin 3x)/9$

18. $y = e^x(2 - \cos x - \sin x)$

19. $y = x + 2x^2 + 3x^3$

20. $y = 2x - x^{-2} + x^{-2}\ln x$

In each of Problems 21–24 we first form the general solution

$$y(x) = y_c(x) + y_p(x) = c_1 y_1(x) + c_2 y_2(x) + y_p(x),$$

then calculate $y'(x)$, and finally impose the given initial conditions to determine the values of the coefficients c_1 and c_2.

21. $y = 2\cos x - 5\sin x + 3x$

22. $y = 4e^{2x} - e^{-2x} - 3$

23. $y = e^{-x} + 4e^{3x} - 2$

24. $y = e^x(3\cos x + 4\sin x) + x + 1$

25. $L[y] = L[y_1 + y_2] = L[y_1] + L[y_2] = f + g$

26. **(a)** $y_1 = 2$ and $y_2 = 3x$ **(b)** $y = 2 + 3x$

27. The equations

$$c_1 + c_2 x + c_3 x^2 = 0, \qquad c_2 + 2c_3 x + 0, \qquad 2c_3 = 0$$

(the latter two obtained by successive differentiation of the first one) evidently **imply that** $c_1 = c_2 = c_3 = 0$.

29. If $c_0 e^{rx} + c_1 x e^{rx} + \cdots + c_n x^n e^{rx} = 0$, then division by e^{rx} yields

$$c_0 + c_1 x + \cdots + c_n x^n = 0.$$

30. When the equation $x^2 y'' - 2xy' + 2y = 0$ is rewritten in standard form

$$y'' + (-2/x)y' + (2/x^2)y = 0,$$

the coefficient functions $p_1(x) = -2/x$ and $p_2(x) = 2/x^2$ are not continuous at $x = 0$. Thus the hypotheses of Theorem 3 are not satisfied.

31. **(b)** If $y(0) = 1$ and $y'(0) = 0$, then the equation

$$y'' - 2y' - 5y = 0$$

implies that $y''(0) = 2y'(0) + 5y(0) = 5$.

32. Let the functions $y_1, y_2, \cdots, y_n$ be chosen as indicated. Then evaluation at $x = a$ of the $(k-1)$st derivative of the equation $c_1 y_1 + c_2 y_2 + \cdots c_n y_n = 0$ **yields** $c_k = 0$. Thus $c_1 = c_2 = \cdots = c_n = 0$, so the functions are linearly **independent**.

33. This follows from the fact that

$$\begin{vmatrix} 1 & 1 & 1 \\ a & b & c \\ a^2 & b^2 & c^2 \end{vmatrix} = (b-a)(c-b)(c-a).$$

34. $W(f_1, f_2, \cdots, f_n) = V \exp(r_i x)$, and neither V nor $\exp(r_i x)$ vanishes.

SECTION 3.3

HOMOGENEOUS EQUATIONS WITH CONSTANT COEFFICIENTS

This is a purely computational section devoted to the single most widely applicable **type of** higher order differential equations -- linear ones with constant coefficients. We include explanatory comments only when the solution of the characteristic equation is not **routine.**

1. $y = c_1e^{2x} + c_2e^{-2x}$ 2. $y = c_1 + c_2e^{3x/2}$

3. $y = c_1e^{2x} + c_2e^{-5x}$ 4. $y = c_1e^{x/2} + c_2e^{3x}$

5. $y = c_1e^{-3x} + c_2xe^{-3x}$

6. $y = e^{-5x/2}[c_1\exp(x\sqrt{5/2}) + c_2\exp(-x\sqrt{5/2})]$

7. $y = c_1e^{3x/2} + c_2xe^{3x/2}$

8. $y = e^{3x}(c_1\cos 2x + c_2\sin 2x)$ 9. $y = e^{-4x}(c_1\cos 3x + c_2\sin 3x)$

10. $y = c_1 + c_2x + c_3x^2 + c_4e^{-3x/5}$ 11. $y = c_1 + c_2x + c_3e^{4x} + c_4xe^{4x}$

12. $y = c_1 + c_2e^x + c_3xe^x + c_4x^2e^x$ 13. $y = c_1 + c_2e^{-2x/3} + c_3xe^{-2x/3}$

14. $y = c_1e^x + c_2e^{-x} + c_3\cos 2x + c_4\sin 2x$

15. $y = c_1e^{2x} + c_2xe^{2x} + c_3e^{-2x} + c_4xe^{-2x}$

16. $y = (c_1 + c_2x)\cos 3x + (c_3 + c_4x)\sin 3x$

17. $y = c_1\cos(x/\sqrt{2}) + c_2\sin(x/\sqrt{2}) + c_3\cos(2x/\sqrt{3}) + c_4\sin(2x/\sqrt{3})$

18. $y = c_1e^{2x} + c_2e^{-2x} + c_3\cos 2x + c_4\sin 2x$

19. $y = c_1e^x + c_2e^{-x} + c_3xe^{-x}$

20. $r^4 + 2r^3 + 3r^2 + 2r + 1 = (r^2 + r + 1)^2$, so

        $y = e^{-x/2}(c_1 + c_2x)\cos(x\sqrt{3/2}) + e^{-x/2}(c_3 + c_4x)\sin(x\sqrt{3/2})$

21. $y = 5e^x + 2e^{3x}$

22. $y = e^{-x/3}(3\cos x/\sqrt{3} + 5\sqrt{3}\sin x/\sqrt{3})$

23. $y = e^{3x}(3\cos 4x - 2\sin 4x)$

24. $y = (-7 + e^{2x} + 8e^{-x/2})/2$

25. $y = (-13 + 6x + 9e^{-2x/3})/4$

26. $y = (24 - 9e^{-5x} - 25xe^{-5x})/5$

27. $y = c_1e^x + c_2e^{-2x} + c_3xe^{-2x}$

28.   First we spot the root $r = 2$. Then long division of $2r^3 - r^2 - 5r - 2$ by $r - 2$ yields the quadratic factor

$$2r^2 + 3r + 1 = (2r + 1)(r + 1)$$

with roots $r = -1, -1/2$. Hence the general solution is

$$y = c_1e^{2x} + c_2e^{-x} + c_3e^{-x/2}.$$

29. $y = c_1e^{-3x} + e^{3x/2}[c_2\cos(3x\sqrt{3}/2) + c_3 \sin(3x\sqrt{3}/2)$

30.   First we spot the root $r = -1$. Then long division of

$$r^4 - r^3 + r^2 - 3r - 6$$

by $r + 1$ yields the cubic factor $r^3 - 2r^2 + 3r - 6$. Next we spot the root $r = 2$, and another long division yields the factor $r^2 + 3$ with roots $r = \pm i\sqrt{3}$. Hence the general solution is

$$y = c_1e^{-x} + c_2e^{2x} + c_3\cos x\sqrt{3} + c_4\sin x\sqrt{3}.$$

31.   The characteristic equation $r^3 + 3r^2 + 4r - 8 = 0$ has the evident root $r = 1$, and long division then yields the quadratic factor $r^2 + 4r + 8 = (r + 2)^2 + 4$ corresponding to the complex conjugate roots $-2 \pm 2i$. Hence the general solution is

$$y = c_1e^x + e^{-2x}(c_2\cos 2x + c_3\sin 2x).$$

32.   The characteristic equation $r^4 + r^3 - 3r^2 - 5r - 2 = 0$ has root $r = 2$ that is readily found by trial and error, and long division then yields the factorization

$$(r - 2)(r + 1)^3 = 0.$$

Thus we obtain the general solution

$$y = c_1e^{2x} + (c_2 + c_3x + c_4x^2)e^{-x}.$$

33.   Knowing that $y = e^{3x}$ is one solution, we divide the characteristic polynomial $r^3 + 3r^2 - 54$ by $r - 3$ and get the quadratic factor

$$r^2 + 6r + 18 = (r + 3)^2 + 9.$$

Hence the general solution is

$$y = c_1 e^{3x} + e^{-3x}(c_2 \cos 3x + c_3 \sin 3x).$$

34. Knowing that $y = e^{2x/3}$ is one solution, we divide the characteristic polynomial $3r^3 - 2r^2 + 12r - 8$ by $3r - 2$ and get the quadratic factor $r^2 + 4$. Hence the general solution is

$$y = c_1 e^{2x/3} + c_2 \cos 2x + c_3 \sin 2x.$$

35. $y = c_1 e^{-x/2} + c_2 e^{-x/3} + c_3 \cos 2x + c_4 \sin 2x$

36. The fact that $y = e^{-x} \sin x$ is one solution tells us that

$$(r+1)^2 + 1 = r^2 + 2r + 2$$

is a factor of the characteristic polynomial

$$9r^3 + 11r^2 + 4r - 14.$$

Then long division yields the linear factor $9r - 7$. Hence the general solution is

$$y = c_1 e^{7x/9} + e^{-x}(c_2 \cos x + c_3 \sin x).$$

37. The characteristic equation is $r^4 - r^3 = r^3(r-1) = 0$, so the general solution is

$$y(x) = A + Bx + Cx^2 + De^x.$$

The desired particular solution is

$$y(x) = 11 + 5x + 3x^2 + 7e^x.$$

38. Given that $r = 5$ is one characteristic root, we divide $(r-5)$ into the characteristic polynomial $r^3 - 5r^2 + 100r - 500$ and get the remaining factor $r^2 + 100$. Thus the general solution is

$$y(x) = Ae^{5x} + B\cos 10x + C\sin 10x.$$

The desired particular solution is

$$y(x) = 2e^{5x} - 2\cos 10x.$$

39. $(r-2)^3 = r^3 - 6r^2 + 12r - 8$, so the differential equation is

$$y''' - 6y'' + 12y' - 8y = 0.$$

40. $(r-2)(r^2 + 4) = r^3 - 2r^2 + 4r - 8$, so the differential equation is

$$y''' - 2y'' + 4y' - 8y = 0.$$

41. $(r^2 + 4)(r^2 - 4) = r^4 - 16$, so the differential equation is $y^{(4)} - 16y = 0$.

42. $(r^2 + 4)^3 = r^6 + 12r^4 + 48r^2 + 64$, so the differential equation is

$$y^{(6)} + 12y^{(4)} + 48y'' + 64y = 0.$$

44. (a) $x = i, -2i$

(b) $x = -i, 3i$

45. $y = c_1 e^{-ix} + c_2 e^{3ix}$

46. $y = c_1 e^{3ix} + c_2 e^{-2ix}$

47. $y = c_1 \exp[(1 + i\sqrt{3})x] + c_2 \exp[(-1 - i\sqrt{3})x]$

48. The general solution is

$$y(x) = Ae^x + Be^{\alpha x} + Ce^{\beta x}$$

where $\alpha = (-1 + i\sqrt{3})/2$ and $\beta = (-1 - i\sqrt{3})/2$. Imposition of the given initial conditions yields the equations

$$\begin{aligned}
A + B + C &= 1 \\
A + \alpha B + \beta C &= 0 \\
A + \alpha^2 B + \beta^2 C &= 0
\end{aligned}$$

that we solve for $A = B = C = 1/3$.

49. The general solution is

$$y = Ae^{2x} + Be^{-x} + C \cos x + D \sin x.$$

Imposition of the given initial conditions yields the equations

$$\begin{aligned}
A + B + C \quad &= 0 \\
2A - B \quad + D &= 0 \\
4A + B - C \quad &= 0 \\
8A - B \quad - D &= 30
\end{aligned}$$

that we solve for $A = 2$, $B = -5$, $C = 3$, and $D = -9$. Thus

$$y = 2e^{2x} - 5e^{-x} + 3\cos x - 9\sin x.$$

50. $y_1(x) = \cos x$ if $x \geq 0$, $\cosh x$ if $x \leq 0$.

$y_2(x) = \sin x$ if $x \geq 0$, $\sinh x$ if $x \leq 0$.

SECTION 3.4

MECHANICAL VIBRATIONS

In this section we discuss four types of free motion of a mass on a spring -- undamped, underdamped, critically damped, and overdamped. However, the undamped and underdamped cases -- in which actual oscillations occur -- are emphasized because they are both the most interesting and the most important cases for applications.

1. Frequency: 2 rad/sec $= 1/\pi$ Hz; Period: π sec

2. With $m = 0.75$ and $k = 48$, we get the frequency $\omega_0 = [k/m]^{1/2} = [48/0.75]^{1/2} = 8$ rad/sec, and the period $T = 2\pi/\omega_0 = \pi/4$ sec.

3. The spring constant is $k = 15$ N/0.20 m $= 75$ N/m. The solution of $3x'' + 75x = 0$ with $x(0) = 0$ and $x'(0) = -10$ is $x(t) = -2\sin 5t$. Thus the amplitude is 2 m; the frequency is 5 rad/sec; and the period is $2\pi/5$ sec.

4. **(a)** With $m = 1/4$ kg and $k = (9$ N$)/(0.25$ m$) = 36$ N/m we find that $\omega_0 = 12$ rad/sec. The solution of $x'' + 144x = 0$ with $x(0) = 1$ and $x'(0) = -5$ is

$$x(t) = \cos 12t - (5/12)\sin 12t$$

$$= (13/12)[(12/13)\cos 12t - (5/13)\sin 12t]$$

$$x(t) = (13/12)\cos(12t - \alpha)$$

where $\alpha = 2\pi - \tan^{-1}(5/12) \approx 5.8884$.

(b) $C = 13/12 \approx 1.0833$ ft and $T = 2\pi/12 \approx 0.5236$ sec.

5. The gravitational acceleration at distance R from the center of the earth is $g = GM/R^2$. According to Equation (6) in the text the (circular) frequency ω of a pendulum is given by $\omega^2 = g/L = GM/R^2L$, so its period is $p = 2\pi/\omega = 2\pi R \sqrt{(L/GM)}$.

6.   If the pendulum in the clock executes n cycles per day (86400 sec) at Paris, then its period is $p_1 = 86400/n$ sec. At the equatorial location it takes 24 hr 2 min 40 sec = 86560 sec for the same number of cycles, so its period there is $p_2 = 86560/n$ sec. Now let $R_1 = 3956$ mi be the Earth's "radius" at Paris, and R_2 its "radius" at the equator. Then substitution in the equation $p_1/p_2 = R_1/R_2$ of Problem 5 (with $L_1 = L_2$) yields $R_2 = 3963.33$ mi. Thus this (rather simplistic) calculation gives 7.33 mi as the thickness of the Earth's equatorial bulge.

7.   The period equation

$$p = 3960\sqrt{(100.10)} = (3960 + x)\sqrt{100}$$

yields $x \approx 1.9795$ mi $\approx 10{,}450$ ft for the altitude of the mountain.

8.   Let n be the number of cycles of the pendulum required for the clock to register 24 hrs = 86400 sec. Then its period with length $L_1 = 30$ in is $p_1 = 86400/n$ sec. If L_2 denotes its length when its period is $p_2 = 87000/n$ sec, then the equation $p_1/p_2 = \sqrt{L_1}/\sqrt{L_2}$ of Problem 5 (with $R_1 = R_2$) yields $L_2 = 30.42$ in.

10.   The $F = ma$ equation $\rho\pi r^2 h x'' = \rho\pi r^2 hg - \pi r^2 xg$ simplifies to

$$x'' + (g/\rho h)x = g.$$

The solution of this equation with $x(0) = x'(0) = 0$

$$x(t) = \rho h(1 - \cos \omega_0 t)$$

where $\omega_0 = \sqrt{(g/\rho h)}$. With the given numerical values of ρ, h, and g, the amplitude of oscillation is $\rho h = 100$ cm and the period is $p = 2\pi\sqrt{(\rho h/g)} \approx 2.01$ sec.

11.   The fact that the buoy weighs 100 lb means that $mg = 100$ so $m = 100/32$ slugs. The weight of water is 62.4 lb/ft^3, so the $F = ma$ equation of Problem 10 is

$$(100/32)x'' = 100 - 62.4\pi r^2 x.$$

It follows that the buoy's circular frequency ω is given by

$$\omega^2 = (32)(62.4\pi)r^2/100.$$

But the fact that the buoy's period is $p = 2.5$ sec means that $\omega = 2\pi/2.5$. Equating these two results yields $r \approx 0.3173$ ft ≈ 3.8 in.

12.   **(a)**   Substitution of $M_r = (r/R)^3 M$ in $F_r = -GM_r m/r^2$ yields

$$F_r = -(GMm/R^3)r.$$

(b)   Because $GM/R^3 = g/R$, the equation $mr'' = F_r$ yields the differential equation

$$r'' + (g/R)r = 0.$$

(c)   The solution of this equation with $r(0) = R$ and $r'(0) = 0$ is $r(t) = R\cos \omega_0 t$ where $\omega_0 = \sqrt{(g/R)}$. Hence, with $g = 32.2$ ft/sec^2 and $R = (3960)(5280)$ ft, we find that the period of the particle's simple harmonic motion is

$$p = 2\pi/\omega_0 = 2\pi\sqrt{(R/g)} \approx 5063.10 \text{ sec} \approx 84.38 \text{ min}.$$

13.   (a) $x(t) = 50\left(e^{-2t/5} - e^{-t/2}\right)$

(b) $x'(t) = 25e^{-t/2} - 20e^{-2t/5} = 5e^{-2t/5}\left(5e^{-t/10} - 4\right) = 0$
when $t = 10\ln(5/4) \approx 2.23144$. Hence the mass's farthest distance to the right is $x(10\ln(5/4)) = 512/125 = 4.096$.

14.   (a) $x(t) = e^{-t/5}(20\cos 3t + 15\sin 3t) = 25e^{-t/5}\cos(3t - \alpha)$
where $\alpha = \tan^{-1}(3/4) \approx 0.6435$.

(b)   Thus the oscillations are "bounded" by the curves $x = \pm 25e^{-t/5}$ and the pseudoperiod of oscillation is $T = 2\pi/3$ (because $\omega = 3$).

15.   Overdamped motion: $x(t) = 4e^{-2t} - 2e^{-4t}$

16.   Overdamped motion: $x(t) = 4e^{-3t} - 2e^{-7t}$

17.   Critically damped: $x(t) = (5 + 10t)e^{-4t}$

18.   Underdamped motion: $x(t) = -2e^{-3t}\sin 4t = 2e^{-3t}\cos(4t - \pi/2)$

19.   Underdamped motion: $x(t) \approx (1/3)\sqrt{(313)}e^{-5t/2}\cos(6t - 0.8254)$

20.   Underdamped motion: $x(t) = e^{-4t}(5\cos 2t + 12\sin 2t)$
$$\approx 13e^{-4t}\cos(2t - 1.1760)$$

21.   Underdamped motion: $x(t) = e^{-5t}(6\cos 10t + 8\sin 10t)$
$$\approx 10e^{-5t}\cos(10t - 0.9273)$$

22.   (a)   With $m = 12/32 = 3/8$ slug, $c = 3$ lb-sec/ft, and $k = 24$ lb/ft, the differential equation is equivalent to

$$3x'' + 24x' + 192x = 0.$$

The solution with $x(0) = 1$ and $x'(0) = 0$ is

$$x(t) = e^{-4t}[\cos 4t\sqrt{3} + (1/\sqrt{3})\sin 4t\sqrt{3}]$$

$$= (2/\sqrt{3})e^{-4t}[(\sqrt{3}/2)\cos 4t\sqrt{3} + (1/2)\sin 4t\sqrt{3}]$$

$$x(t) = (2/\sqrt{3})e^{-4t}\cos(4t\sqrt{3} - \pi/6).$$

(b)   The time-varying amplitude is $2/\sqrt{3} \approx 1.15$ ft; the frequency is $4\sqrt{3} \approx 6.93$ rad/sec; and the phase angle is $\pi/6$.

23.   (a)   With $m = 100$ slugs we get $\omega = \sqrt{(k/100)}$. But we are given that

$$\omega = (80 \text{ cycles/min})(2\pi)(1 \text{ min/60 sec}) = 8\pi/3,$$

and equating the two values yields $k \approx 7018$ lb/ft.

(b)   With $\omega_1 = 2\pi(78/60)$ sec^{-1}, Equation (21) in the text yields $c \approx 372.31$ lb/(ft/sec). Hence $p = c/2m \approx 1.8615$. Finally $e^{-pt} = 0.01$ gives $t \approx 2.47$ sec.

30.   In the underdamped case we have

$$x(t) = e^{-pt}[A \cos \omega_1 t + B \sin \omega_1 t],$$

$$x'(t) = -pe^{pt}[A \cos \omega_1 t + B \sin \omega_1 t] + e^{-pt}[-A\omega_1\sin \omega_1 t + B\omega_1\cos \omega_1 t].$$

The conditions $x(0) = x_0$, $x'(0) = v_0$ yield the equations $A = x_0$ and $-pA + B\omega_1 = v_0$, whence $B = (v_0 + px_0)/\omega_1$.

32.   If $x(t) = Ce^{-pt}\cos(\omega_1 t - \alpha)$ then

$$x'(t) = -pCe^{-pt}\cos(\omega_1 t - \alpha) + C\omega_1 e^{-pt}\sin(\omega_1 t - \alpha) = 0$$

yields $\tan(\omega_1 t - \alpha) = -p/\omega_1$.

33.   If $x_1 = x(t_1)$ and $x_2 = x(t_2)$ are two successive local maxima, then $\omega_1 t_2 = \omega_1 t_1 + 2\pi$ so

$$x_1 = C\exp(-pt_1)\cos(\omega_1 t_1 - \alpha),$$

$$x_2 = C\exp(-pt_2)\cos(\omega_1 t_2 - \alpha) = C\exp(-pt_2)\cos(\omega_1 t_1 - \alpha).$$

Hence $x_1/x_2 = \exp[-p(t_1 - t_2)]$, and therefore

$$\ln(x_1/x_2) = -p(t_1 - t_2) = 2\pi p/\omega_1.$$

34.   With $t_1 = 0.34$ and $t_2 = 1.17$ we first use the equation $\omega_1 t_2 = \omega_1 t_1 + 2\pi$ from

Problem 31 to calculate $\omega_1 = 2\pi/(0.83) \approx 7.57$ rad/sec. Next, with $x_1 = 6.73$ and $x_2 = 1.46$, the result of Problem 33 yields

$$p = (1/0.83)\ln(6.73/1.46) \approx 1.84.$$

Then Equation (16) in this section gives

$$c = 2mp = 2(100/32)(1.84) \approx 11.51 \text{ lb-sec/ft},$$

and finally Equation (21) yields

$$k = (4m^2\omega_1^2 + c^2)/4m \approx 189.68 \text{ lb/ft}.$$

SECTION 3.5

NONHOMOGENEOUS EQUATIONS AND THE METHOD OF UNDETERMINED COEFFICIENTS

The method of undetermined coefficients is based on "educated guessing". If we can guess correctly the **form** of a particular solution of a nonhomogeneous linear equation with constant coefficients, then we can determine the particular solution explicitly by substitution in the given differential equation. Although it is pointed out at the end of Section 3.5 that this simple approach is not always successful -- in which case the method of variation of parameters is available if a complementary function is known -- it does turn out to work well with a surprisingly large number of the nonhomogeneous linear differential equations that arise in elementary scientific applications.

1. $y_p = (1/25)e^{3x}$

2. $y_p = -(5 + 6x)/4$

3. $y_p = (\cos 3x - 5 \sin 3x)/39$

4. $y_p = (-4e^x + 3xe^x)/9$

5. Substituting $\sin^2 x = (1 - \cos 2x)/2$ on the right-hand side leads to

$$y_p = (13 + 3 \cos 2x - 2 \sin 2x)/26.$$

6. $y_p = (4 - 56x + 49x^2)/343$

7. Substituting $\sinh x = (e^x - e^{-x})/2$ on the right-hand side leads to

$$y_p = (e^{-x} - e^x)/6 = -(1/3)\sinh x.$$

8. Because $\cosh 2x$ is part of the complementary function, we try

$$y_p = x(A \cosh 2x + B \sinh 2x)$$

and find that $y_p = (1/4)x \sinh 2x$.

9. $y_c = c_1e^x + c_2e^{-3x}$ so we try

$$y_p = A + x(B + Cx)e^x.$$

This gives $y_p = -(1/3) + (2x^2 - x)e^x/16$.

10. $y_p = (2x \sin 3x - 3x \cos 3x)/6$

11. $y_p = (3x^2 - 2x)/8$

12. $y_p = Ax + x(B \cos x + C \sin x) = 2x + (1/2)x \sin x$

13. $y_p = e^x(7 \sin x - 4 \cos x)/65$

14. $y_p = x^2(A + Bx)e^x = (-3x^2e^x + x^3e^x)/24$

15. $y_p = -17$

16. $y_p = (15 - e^{3x} - 2xe^{3x} + 3x^2e^{3x})/27$

17. $y_p = (x^2 \sin x - x \cos x)/4$

18. $y_p = x(Ae^x) + x(B + Cx)e^{2x} = -(24xe^x - 19xe^{2x} + 6x^2e^{2x})/144$

19. $y_p = x^2(A + Bx + Cx^2) = (10x^2 - 4x^3 + x^4)/8$

20. $y_p = -7 + (1/3)xe^x$

21. $y_p = xe^x(A \cos x + B \sin x)$

22. $y_p = Ax^3 + Bx^4 + Cx^5 + Dxe^x$

23. $y_p = (Ax + Bx^2)\cos 2x + (Cx + Dx^2)\sin 2x$

24. $y_p = Ax + Bx^2 + Cxe^{-3x} + Dx^2e^{-3x}$

25. $y_p = (Ax + Bx^2)e^{-x} + (Cx + Dx^2)e^{-2x}$

26. $y_p = e^{3x}[(Ax + Bx^2)\cos 2x + (Cx + Dx^2)\sin 2x]$

27. $y_p = Ax \cos x + Bx \sin x + Cx \cos 2x + Dx \sin 2x$

28. $y_p = (Ax + Bx^2 + Cx^3)\cos 3x + (Dx + Ex^2 + Fx^3)\sin 3x$

29. $y_p = (Ax^3 + Bx^4)e^x + Cxe^{2x} + Dxe^{-2x}$

30. $y_p = (A + Bx + Cx^2)\cos x + (D + Ex + Fx^2)\sin x$

31. $y = \cos 2x + (3/4)\sin 2x + x/2$

32. $y = (15e^{-x} - 16e^{-2x} + e^x)/6$

33. $y = \cos 3x - (2/15)\sin 3x + (1/5)\sin 2x$

34. $y = \cos x - \sin x + (1/2)x \sin x$

35. $y = 1 + x/2 + e^x(4\cos x - 5\sin x)/2$

36. $y = (234 + 240x - 12x^2 - 4x^4 - 33e^{2x} - 9e^{-2x})/192$

37. $y = 4 + x - 4e^x + 3xe^x - (1/2)x^2e^x + (1/6)x^3e^x$

38. $y = (176e^{-x}\cos x + 197e^{-x}\sin x - 6\cos 3x - 7\sin 3x)/85$

39. $y = -3 + 3x - (1/2)x^2 + (1/6)x^3 + 4e^{-x} + xe^{-x}$

40. $y = (5e^x + 5e^{-x} + 10\cos x - 20)/4$

41. $y_p = 255 - 450x + 30x^2 + 20x^3 + 10x^4 - 4x^5$

42. $y = y_c + y_p$ where y_p is given in Problem 41 and

$$y_c = -96\cos x + 288\sin x + e^{2x} - 160e^{-x}$$

43. **(b)** $y = c_1\cos 2x + c_2\sin 2x + (1/4)\cos x - (1/20)\cos 3x$

44. We use the identity

$$\sin x \sin 3x = (\cos 2x - \cos 4x)/2$$

and find that the general solution is

$$y = e^{-x/2}(c_1\cos x\sqrt{3}/2 + c_2\sin x\sqrt{3}/2)$$
$$+ (-3\cos 2x + 2\sin 2x)/26 + (-15\cos 4x + 4\sin 4x)/482$$

45. We substitute

$\frac{1}{2}x\cos x + \frac{1}{2}\sin x + -c_1\sin x + c_2\cos x$

$$\sin^4 x = (1 - \cos 2x)^2/4$$
$$= (1 - 2\cos 2x + \cos^2 2x)/4 = (3 - 4\cos 2x + \cos 4x)/8$$

on the right-hand side. The general solution is

$$y = c_1 \cos 3x + c_2 \sin 3x + 1/24 - (1/10)\cos 2x - (1/56)\cos 4x.$$

46. The complementary solution is $y_c = c_1 \cos x + c_2 \sin x$. We use the identity $\cos^3 x = (\cos 3x + 3\cos x)/4$ of Problem 43. The particular solution associated with $(1/4)x \cos 3x$ is

$$y_1 = (3\sin 3x - 4x\cos 3x)/128.$$

The particular solution associated with $(3/4)x \cos x$ is

$$y_2 = (3x\cos x + 3x^2 \sin x)/16.$$

The general solution is $y = y_c + y_1 + y_2$.

47. $y_1 = e^{-2x}, \qquad y_2 = e^{-x}, \qquad W = e^{-3x}$

$u_1 = -(4/3)e^{3x}, \qquad u_2 = 2e^{2x},$

$y_p = (2/3)e^x$

48. $y_1 = e^{-2x}, \qquad y_2 = e^{4x}, \qquad W = 6e^{2x}$

$u_1 = -x/2, \qquad u_2 = -e^{-6x}/12,$

$y_p = -(6x + 1)e^{-2x}/12$

49. $y_1 = e^{2x}, \qquad y_2 = xe^{2x}, \qquad W = e^{4x}$

$u_1 = -x^2, \qquad u_2 = 2x,$

$y_p = x^2 e^{2x}$

50. The complementary function is $y_1 = c_1 \cosh 2x + c_2 \sinh 2x$, so the Wronskian is

$$W = 2\cosh^2 2x - 2\sinh^2 2x = 2,$$

so when we solve Equations (31) simultaneously for u_1' and u_2', integrate each and substitute in $y_p = y_1 u_1 + y_2 u_2$, the result is

$$y_p = -(\cosh 2x)\int \tfrac{1}{2}(\sinh 2x)(\sinh 2x)\,dx + (\sinh 2x)\int \tfrac{1}{2}(\cosh 2x)(\sinh 2x)\,dx.$$

Using the identities $2\sinh^2 x = \cosh 2x - 1$ and $2\sinh x\cosh x = \sinh 2x$, we evaluate the integrals and find that

$$y_p = (4x \cosh 2x - \sinh 4x \cosh 2x + \cosh 4x \sinh 2x)/16$$

$$y_p = (4x \cosh 2x - \sinh 2x)/16$$

51. $\quad y_p = -(1/4)(\cos 2x \cos x - \sin 2x \sin x) + (1/20)(\cos 5x \cos 2x + \sin 5x \sin 2x)$

$\qquad = -(1/5)\cos 3x \quad (!)$

52. $\quad y_1 = \cos 3x, \quad y_2 = \sin 3x, \quad W = 3$

$\qquad y_p = (\sin 3x - 6x \cos 3x)/36$

53. $\quad y_1 = \cos 3x, \quad y_2 = \sin 3x, \quad W = 3$

$\qquad u_1' = -(2/3)\tan 3x, \quad u_2' = 2/3$

$\qquad y_p = (2/9)[3x \sin 3x + (\cos 3x)\ln|\cos 3x|]$

54. $\quad y_1 = \cos x, \quad y_2 = \sin x, \quad W = 1$

$\qquad u_1' = -\csc x, \quad u_2' = \cos x \csc^2 x$

$\qquad y_p = -1 - (\cos x)\ln|\csc x - \cot x|$

55. $\quad y_1 = \cos 2x, \quad y_2 = \sin 2x, \quad W = 2$

$\qquad u_1' = -(1/2)\sin^2 x \sin 2x = -(1/4)(1 - \cos 2x)\sin 2x$

$\qquad u_2' = (1/2)\sin^2 x \cos 2x = (1/4)(1 - \cos 2x)\cos 2x$

$\qquad y_p = (1 - x \sin 2x)/8$

56. $\quad y_1 = e^{-2x}, \quad y_2 = e^{2x}, \quad W = 4$

$\qquad u_1 = -(3x - 1)e^{3x}/36, \qquad u_2 = -(x + 1)e^{-x}/4$

$\qquad y_p = -e^x(3x + 2)/9$

57. With $y_1 = x$, $y_2 = x^{-1}$, and $f(x) = 72x^3$, Equations (31) in the text take the form

$$xu_1' + x^{-1}u_2' = 0,$$
$$u_1' - x^{-2}u_2' = 72x^3.$$

Upon multiplying the second equation by x and then adding, we readily solve first for

$$u_1' = 36x^3, \quad \text{so} \quad u_1 = 9x^4$$

and then

$$u_2' = -x^2 u_1' = -36x^5, \qquad \text{so} \qquad u_2 = -6x^6.$$

Then it follows that

$$y_p = y_1 u_1 + y_2 u_2 = (x)(9x^4) + (x^{-1})(-6x^6) = 3x^5.$$

58. Here it is important to remember that -- for variation of parameters -- the differential equation must be written in standard form with leading coefficient 1. We therefore rewrite the given equation with complementary function $y_c = c_1 x^2 + c_2 x^3$ as

$$y'' - (4/x)y' + (6/x^2)y = x.$$

Thus $f(x) = x$, and $W = x^4$, so simultaneous solution of Equations (31) as in Problem 50 (followed by integration of u_1' and u_2') yields

$$y_p = -x^2 \int x^3 \cdot x \cdot x^{-4} \, dx + x^3 \int x^2 \cdot x \cdot x^{-4} \, dx$$
$$= -x^2 \int dx + x^3 \int (1/x) \, dx = x^3(\ln x - 1).$$

59. $y_1 = x^2, \qquad y_2 = x^2 \ln x,$

$W = x^3, \qquad f(x) = x^2$

$u_1' = -x \ln x, \quad u_2' = x$

$y_p = x^4/4$

60. $y_c = c_1 x^{1/2} + c_2 x^{3/2}; \quad f(x) = 2x^{-2/3};$

$y_p = -72x^{4/3}/5$

61. $y_1 = \cos(\ln x), \qquad y_2 = \sin(\ln x), \qquad W = 1/x,$

$f(x) = (\ln x)/x^2$

$u_1 = (\ln x)\cos(\ln x) - \sin(\ln x)$

$u_2 = (\ln x)\sin(\ln x) + \cos(\ln x)$

$y_p = \ln x \quad (!)$

62. $y_1 = x, \qquad y_2 = 1 + x^2,$

$W = x^2 - 1, \quad f(x) = 1$

$u_1' = (1 + x^2)/(1 - x^2), \quad u_2' = x/(x^2 - 1)$

$y_p = -x^2 + x \ln|(1 + x)/(1 - x)| + (1/2)(1 + x^2)\ln|1 - x^2|$

63. This is simply a matter of solving the equations in (31) for the derivatives

$$u_1' = -\frac{y_2(x)f(x)}{W(x)} \quad \text{and} \quad u_2' = \frac{y_1(x)f(x)}{W(x)},$$

integrating each, and then substituting the results in (32).

64. Here we have $y_1(x) = \cos x$, $y_2(x) = \sin x$, $W(x) = 1$, $f(x) = 2\sin x$, so (33) gives

$$y_p(x) = -(\cos x)\int \sin x \cdot 2\sin x\,dx + (\sin x)\int \cos x \cdot 2\sin x\,dx$$

$$= -(\cos x)\int (1 - \cos 2x)\,dx + (\sin x)\int 2(\sin x)\cdot \cos x\,dx$$

$$= -(\cos x)(x - \sin x\cos x) + (\sin x)(\sin^2 x)$$

$$= -x\cos x + (\sin x)(\cos^2 x + \sin^2 x)$$

$$y_p(x) = -x\cos x + \sin x$$

But we can drop the term $\sin x$ because it satisfies the associated homogeneous equation $y'' + y = 0$.

SECTION 3.6

FORCED OSCILLATIONS AND RESONANCE

1. Trial of $x = A\cos 2t$ yields the particular solution $x_p = 2\cos 2t$. Hence the general solution is

$$x(t) = c_1\cos 3t + c_2\sin 3t + 2\cos 2t.$$

The initial conditions imply that $c_1 = -2$ and $c_2 = 0$, so $x = 2\cos 2t - 2\cos 3t$.

2. First we apply the method of undetermined coefficients to find the particular solution $x_p = -\sin 3t$. Then we impose the initial conditions $x(0) = x'(0) = 0$ on the general solution

$$x(t) = c_1\cos 2t + c_2\sin 2t - \sin 3t,$$

and find that $x = (3/2)\sin 2t - \sin 3t$.

3. First we apply the method of undetermined coefficients to find the particular solution

$$x_p = (3/15)\cos 5t + (4/15)\sin 5t = (1/3)\cos(5t - \beta)$$

where $\beta = \tan^{-1}(4/3) \approx 0.9273$. Hence the general solution is

$$x(t) = c_1\cos 10t + c_2\sin 10t + (3/15)\cos 5t + (4/15)\sin 5t.$$

The initial conditions $x(0) = 25$, $x'(0) = 0$ now yield $c_1 = 372/15$ and $c_2 = -2/15$, so the part of the solution with frequency $\omega = 10$ is

$$x_c = (1/15)(372 \cos 10t - 2 \sin 10t = (1/15)\sqrt{(138,388)} \cos(10t - \alpha)$$

where $\alpha = 2\pi - \tan^{-1}(1/186) \approx 6.2778$.

4. $x = [(-10/9)\cos 5t + 2 \sin 5t] + (10/9)\cos 4t = (2/9)\sqrt{106} \cos(5t - \alpha) + (10/9)\cos 4t$

where $\alpha = \pi - \tan^{-1}(9/5) \approx 2.07789$

5. $x(t) = (x_0 - C)\cos \omega_0 t + C \cos \omega t$ where $C = F_0/(k - m\omega^2)$

6. $x(t) = [(2mv_0\omega_0 + F_0)/2m\omega_0^2]\sin \omega_0 t - (F_0/2m\omega_0)t \cos \omega_0 t$

7.   When we substitute $x = A \cos 3t + B \sin 3t$ in the given differential equation we get the equations

$$-5A + 12B = 10, \quad -12A - 5B = 0$$

with solution $A = -50/169$, $B = 120/169$. Hence

$$x_{sp}(t) = (10/169)(-5 \cos 3t + 12 \sin 3t) = (10/13)\cos(3t - \alpha)$$

where $\alpha = \pi - \tan^{-1}(12/5) \approx 1.9656$.

8. $x_{sp} = (4/25)\cos(4t - \alpha); \quad \alpha = 2\pi - \tan^{-1}(3/4) \approx 5.6397$

9. $x_{sp} = (3/\sqrt{40,001})\cos(10t - \alpha)$ where $\alpha = \pi + \tan^{-1}(199/20) \approx 4.6122$

10. $x_{sp} \approx 0.09849 \cos(10t - \alpha)$ where $\alpha = \pi + \tan^{-1}(171/478) \approx 3.4851$

11. $x_{sp} = (1/4)\sqrt{(10)} \cos(3t - \alpha)$ where $\alpha = \pi - \tan^{-1}(3) \approx 1.8925$
        $x_{tr} = (1/4)\sqrt{(50)}e^{-2t}\cos(t - \beta)$ where $\beta = 2\pi - \tan^{-1}(7) \approx 4.8543$

12. $x = (75/522)e^{-3t}(2 \cos 2t + 5 \sin 2t) + (15/261)(-5 \cos 5t - 2 \sin 5t)$
        $\approx 0.77373\, e^{-3t}\cos(2t - 1.19029) + 0.30949 \cos(5t - 3.52210)$

13. $x_{sp} = (3/\sqrt{9236})\cos(10t - \alpha), \quad \alpha = \pi - \tan^{-1}(10/47) \approx 2.9288$
        $x_{tr} \approx 10.9761\, e^{-t}\cos(t\sqrt{5} - 0.4181)$

14. $x = (1/40)e^{-4t}(199 \cos 3t + 258 \sin 3t) + (1/40)(\cos t + 22 \sin t)$
        $\approx 8.14574\, e^{-4t}\cos(3t - 0.91379) + 0.55057 \cos(t - 1.52537)$

15. $C(\omega) = 2/\sqrt{4+\omega^4}$ begins with $C(0) = 1$ and steadily decreases as ω increases. Hence there is no practical resonance frequency.

16. $C(\omega) = 10/\sqrt{25+6\omega^2+\omega^4}$ begins with $C(0) = 2$ and steadily decreases as ω increases. Hence there is no practical resonance frequency.

17. $C(\omega) = 50/\sqrt{2025-54\omega^2+\omega^4}$ so

$$C'(\omega) = \frac{-100\,\omega(-27+\omega^2)}{(2025-54\omega^2+\omega^4)^{3/2}}.$$

Hence the practical resonance frequency is $\omega = \sqrt{27} = 3\sqrt{3}$.

18. $C(\omega) = 100/\sqrt{422500-1200\omega^2+\omega^4}$ so

$$C'(\omega) = \frac{-200\,\omega(-600+\omega^2)}{(422500-1200\omega^2+\omega^4)^{3/2}}.$$

Hence the practical resonance frequency is $\omega = \sqrt{600} = 10\sqrt{6}$.

19. $m = 100/32$ slugs and $k = 1200$ lb/ft so $\omega_0 = \sqrt{(k/m)} = \sqrt{(384)}$ rad/sec ≈ 3.12 Hz.

20. Let the machine have mass m. Then the force $F = mg$ (the machine's weight) causes a displacement of 0.5 cm $= 1/200$ m (meters), so the spring constant is $k = 200$ mg-N/m. Hence the resonance frequency is

$$\omega = \sqrt{(k/m)} = \sqrt{(200g)} = \sqrt{(200\times9.8)} \approx 44.27 \text{ rad/sec} \approx 423 \text{ rpm}.$$

21. If θ is the angular displacement from the vertical, then the (essentially horizontal) displacement of the mass is $x = L\theta$, so twice its total energy (KE + PE) is

$$m(x')^2 + kx^2 + 2mgh = mL^2(\theta')^2 + kL^2\theta^2 + 2mgL(1 - \cos\theta) = C.$$

Differentiation, substitution of $\theta \approx \sin\theta$, and simplification yields

$$\theta'' + (k/m + g/L)\theta = 0$$

so

$$\omega_0 = (k/m + g/L)^{1/2}.$$

22. Let x denote the displacement of the mass from its equilibrium position, $v = x'$ its velocity, and $\omega = v/a$ the angular velocity of the pulley. Then conservation of energy yields

$$mv^2/2 + I\omega^2/2 + kx^2/2 - mgx = C.$$

When we differentiate both sides with respect to t and simplify the result, we get the differential equation

$$(m + I/a^2)x'' + kx = mg.$$

Hence $\omega = [k/(m + I/a^2)]^{1/2}$.

23. **(a)** In ft-lb-sec units we have $m = 1000$ and $k = 10000$, so $\omega_0 = \sqrt{10}$ rad/sec ≈ 0.50 Hz.

(b) We are given that $\omega = 2\pi/2.25 \approx 2.79$ rad/sec, and the equation $mx'' + kx = F(t)$ simplifies to

$$x'' + 10x = (1/4)\omega^2\sin \omega t.$$

When we substitute $x(t) = A \sin \omega t$ we find that the amplitude is

$$A = \omega^2/4(10 - \omega^2) \approx 0.8854 \text{ ft} \approx 10.63 \text{ in.}$$

24. By the identity of Problem 43 in Section 3.5, the differential equation is

$$mx'' + kx = F_0(3 \cos \omega t + \cos 3\omega t)/4.$$

Hence resonance occurs when either ω or 3ω equals $\omega_0 = \sqrt{(k/m)}$, that is, when either $\omega = \omega_0$ or $\omega = \omega_0/3$.

25. Let $G_0 = \sqrt{E_0^2 + F_0^2}$ and $\rho = 1/\sqrt{(k - m\omega^2) + (c\omega)^2}$. Then

$$x_{sp}(t) = \rho E_0 \cos(\omega t - \alpha) + \rho F_0 \sin(\omega t - \alpha)$$

$$= \rho G_0 \left[\frac{E_0}{G_0}\cos(\omega t - \alpha) + \frac{F_0}{G_0}\sin(\omega t - \alpha)\right]$$

$$= \rho G_0 \left[\cos \beta \cos(\omega t - \alpha) + \sin \beta \sin(\omega t - \alpha)\right]$$

$$x_{sp}(t) = \rho G_0 \cos(\omega t - \alpha - \beta)$$

where $\tan \beta = F_0/E_0$. The desired formula now results when we substitute the value of ρ defined above.

28. The given differential equation corresponds to Equation (17) with $F_0 = mA\omega^2$. It therefore follows from Equation (21) that the amplitude of the stead*y* periodic vibrations at frequency ω is

$$C(\omega) = \frac{F_0}{\sqrt{(k - m\omega^2)^2 + (c\omega)^2}} = \frac{mA\omega^2}{\sqrt{(k - m\omega^2)^2 + (c\omega)^2}}.$$

SECTION 3.7

ELECTRICAL CIRCUITS

1. $5I' + 25I = 0$, $I(0) = 4$; $I(t) = 4e^{-5t}$

2. $5I' + 25I = 100$, $I(0) = 0$; $I(t) = 4(1 - e^{-5t})$

3. $5I' + 25I = 100 \cos 60t$, $I(0) = 0$

Substitution of the trial solution

$$I_p = A \cos 60t + B \sin 60t$$

yields

$$I_p = 4(\cos 60t + 12 \sin 60t)/145.$$

The complementary function is $I_c = ce^{-5t}$; the solution with $I(0) = 0$ is

$$I(t) = 4(\cos 60t + 12 \sin 60t - e^{-5t})/145.$$

4. $I(t) = 5(e^{-10t} - e^{-20t})$; we find that $I'(t) = 0$ when $t = (\ln 2)/10$, and then $I_{max} = 5/4$.

5. $2I' + 20I = 100e^{-10t}\cos 60t$, $I(0) = 0$

$I(t) = (5/6)e^{-10t}\sin 60t$

6. $I_{sp} = (1/37)(-21 \cos 60t + 22 \sin 60t) = (5/\sqrt{37})\cos(60t - \alpha)$

where $\alpha = \pi - \tan^{-1}(22/21)$

7. $RQ' + (1/C)Q = E_0$, $Q(0) = 0$

$Q(t) = E_0C(1 - e^{-t/RC})$

$I(t) = Q'(t) = (E_0/R)e^{-t/RC}$

8. (a) $Q(t) = 10te^{-5t}$ and $I(t) = 10(1 - 5t)e^{-5t}$.

(b) $I(t) = 0$ when $t = 1/5$, so $Q_{max} = 2e^{-1}$.

9. $Q(t) = (\cos 120t + 6 \sin 120t - e^{-20t})/1480$

$$I(t) = (36 \cos 120t - 6 \sin 120t + e^{-20t})/74$$

Steady state amplitude: $3/\sqrt{37}$

11. $I_{sp} = (1/37)(10 \cos 2t + 60 \sin 2t) = (10/\sqrt{37})\sin(2t - \delta)$ where $\delta = 2\pi - \tan^{-1}(1/6)$

12. $I_{sp} = (2/17)(\cos 10t + 4 \sin 10t) = (2/\sqrt{17})\sin(10t - \delta)$ where $\delta = 2\pi - \tan^{-1}(1/4)$

13. $I_{sp} = (20/13)(2 \cos 5t + 3 \sin 5t) = (20/\sqrt{13})\sin(5t - \delta)$ where $\delta = 2\pi - \tan^{-1}(2/3)$

14. Substitution of $I_{sp} = A \cos 100t + B \sin 100t$ in

$$I'' + 10I' + 40I = -6000 \sin 100t + 8000 \cos 100t$$

leads to the equations

$$-9.96A + \quad B = \quad 8$$
$$-A - 9.96B = -6,$$

whence we find that

$$I_{sp} \approx 0.67624 \sin 100t - 0.73532 \cos 100t \approx 0.99899 \sin(100t - 0.82723)$$

15. $I_{sp} = I_0 \sin(60\pi t - \delta)$ where

$$I_0 = 33\pi[(1000 - 36\pi^2)^2 + (30\pi)^2]^{-1/2} \approx 0.1591$$
$$\delta = 2\pi - \tan^{-1}[(1000 - 36\pi^2)/30\pi] \approx 4.8576$$

16. $I \approx 0.54168 \cos 377t + 1.51877 \sin 377t \approx 1.61247 \sin(377t + 0.34259)$

17. With $I(0) = 0$ and $Q(0) = 5$, Equation (16) in the text gives $I'(0) = -75$. The solution of $2I'' + 16I' + 50I = 0$ with these initial conditions is $I(t) = -25e^{-4t} \sin 3t$.

18. Our differential equation to solve is

$$2I'' + 60I' + 400I = -100e^{-t}.$$

We find the particular solution $I_p = (-50/171)e^{-t}$ by undetermined coefficients; the general solution is

$$I(t) = c_1 e^{-10t} + c_2 e^{-20t} - (50/171)e^{-t}.$$

The initial conditions are $I(0) = 0$ and $I'(0) = 50$, the latter found by substituting $L = 2, R = 60, 1/C = 400, I(0) = Q(0) = 0$, and $E(0) = 100$ into Equation (16). Imposition of these initial values on the general solution above yields

$$I(t) = (50/171)(19e^{-10t} - 18e^{-20t} - e^{-t}).$$

19. $2I'' + 60I' + 400I = -1000e^{-10t}$

$I(0) = 0, \quad I'(0) = -150$

$I(t) = 10e^{-20t} - 10e^{-10t} - 50te^{-10t}$

20.   The differential equation is $10I'' + 30I' + 50I = 100\cos 2t$, and the initial conditions are $I(0) = I'(0) = 0$. First we find separately the transient and steady periodic solutions

$$I_{tr} = e^{-3t/2}[c_1\cos(t/2)\sqrt{(11)} + c_2\sin(t/2)\sqrt{(11)}],$$

$$I_{sp} \approx 0.27027\cos 2t + 1.62162\sin 2t.$$

Then we impose the initial conditions and get

$$I(t) \approx 2.21676\, e^{-3t/2}\sin[(t/2)\sqrt{(11)} - 3.01937] + 1.64399\sin(2t + 0.16515).$$

21. $10I'' + 20I' + 100I = -1000\sin 5t$

$I(0) = 0, \quad I'(0) = -10$

$I(t) = (20/13)(2\cos 5t + 3\sin 5t) - (10/39)e^{-t}(12\cos 3t + 47\sin 3t)$

22. $I(t) \approx 0.15961\, e^{-25t}\sin[25t\sqrt{(159)} + 4.54718] + 0.15912\sin(60\pi t + 1.42563)$

23.   Critical frequency: $\omega_0 = 1/\sqrt{(LC)}$

24.   We need only observe that the roots

$$r = [-R \pm (R^2 - 4L/C)^{1/2}]/2L$$

necessarily have *negative* real parts.

SECTION 3.8

ENDPOINT PROBLEMS AND EIGENVALUES

The material on eigenvalues and endpoint problems in Section 3.8 is optional in a first course, and will not be needed until we discuss boundary value problems in the last three sections of Chapter 9 and in Chapter 10. However, after the concentration thus far on initial value problems, the inclusion of this section can give students a view of a new class of problems that have diverse and important applications (as illustrated by the subsection on the whirling string). If Section 3.8 is not covered at this point in the course, then it can be inserted just prior to Section 9.5.

1. If $\lambda = 0$ then $y'' = 0$ implies that $y(x) = A + Bx$. The endpoint conditions $y'(0) = 0$ and $y(1) = 0$ yield $B = 0$ and $A = 0$, respectively. Hence $\lambda = 0$ is *not* an eigenvalue.

    If $\lambda = \alpha^2 > 0$, then the general solution of $y'' + \alpha^2 y = 0$ is

    $$y(x) = A \cos \alpha x + B \sin \alpha x,$$

    so

    $$y'(x) = -A\alpha \sin \alpha x + B\alpha \cos \alpha x.$$

    Then $y'(0) = 0$ yields $B = 0$, so $y(x) = A \cos \alpha x$. Next $y(1) = 0$ implies that $\cos \alpha = 0$, so α is an odd multiple of $\pi/2$. Hence the positive eigenvalues are $\{(2n-1)^2 \pi^2/4\}$ with associated eigenfunctions $\{\cos(2n-1)\pi x/2\}$ for $n = 1, 2, 3, \cdots$.

2. If $\lambda = 0$ then $y'' = 0$ implies that $y(x) = A + Bx$. The endpoint conditions $y'(0) = y'(\pi) = 0$ imply only that $B = 0$, so $\lambda_0 = 0$ is an eigenvalue with associated eigenfunction $y_0(x) = 1$.

    If $\lambda = \alpha^2 > 0$, then the general solution of $y'' + \alpha^2 y = 0$ is

    $$y(x) = A \cos \alpha x + B \sin \alpha x.$$

    Then

    $$y'(x) = -A\alpha \sin \alpha x + B\alpha \cos \alpha x,$$

    so $y'(0) = 0$ implies that $B = 0$. Next, $y'(\pi) = 0$ implies that $\alpha\pi$ is an integral multiple of π. Hence the positive eigenvalues are $\{n^2\}$ with associated eigenfunctions $\{\cos nx\}$, $n = 1, 2, 3, \cdots$.

3. Much as in Problem 1 we see that $\lambda = 0$ is not an eigenvalue. Suppose that $\lambda = \alpha^2 > 0$, so

    $$y(x) = A \cos \alpha x + B \sin \alpha x.$$

    Then the conditions $y(-\pi) = y(\pi) = 0$ yield

    $$A \cos \alpha\pi + B \sin \alpha\pi = 0,$$

    $$A \cos \alpha\pi - B \sin \alpha\pi = 0.$$

    It follows that

    $$A \cos \alpha\pi = 0 = B \sin \alpha\pi.$$

    Hence either $A = 0$ and $B \neq 0$ with $\alpha\pi$ an even multiple of $\pi/2$, or $A \neq 0$ and $B = 0$ with $\alpha\pi$ an odd multiple of $\pi/2$. Thus the eigenvalues are $\{n^2/4\}$ for n a positive integer, and the nth eigenfunction is $y_n(x) = \cos(nx/2)$ if n is odd,

$y_n(x) = \sin(nx/2)$ if n is even.

4. Just as in Problem 2, $\lambda_0 = 0$ is an eigenvalue with associated eigenfunction $y_0(x) = 1$. If $\lambda = \alpha^2 > 0$ and

$$y(x) = A \cos \alpha x + B \sin \alpha x,$$

then the equations

$$y'(-\pi) = \alpha(A \sin \alpha\pi + B \cos \alpha\pi) = 0,$$

$$y'(\pi) = \alpha(-A \sin \alpha\pi + B \cos \alpha\pi) = 0$$

yield $A \sin \alpha\pi = B \cos \alpha\pi = 0$. If $A = 0$ and $B \neq 0$, then $\cos \alpha\pi = 0$ so $\alpha\pi$ must be an odd multiple of $\pi/2$. If $A \neq 0$ and $B = 0$, then $\sin \alpha\pi = 0$ so $\alpha\pi$ must be an even multiple of $\pi/2$. Therefore the positive eigenvalues are $\{n^2/4\}$ with associated eigenfunctions $y_n(x) = \cos(nx/2)$ if the integer n is even, $y_n(x) = \sin(nx/2)$ if n is odd.

5. If $\lambda = \alpha^2 > 0$ and

$$y(x) = A \cos \alpha x + B \sin \alpha x,$$

$$y'(x) = -A\alpha \sin \alpha x + B\alpha \cos \alpha x$$

then the conditions $y(-2) = y'(2) = 0$ yield

$$A \cos 2\alpha - B \sin 2\alpha = 0,$$

$$-A \sin 2\alpha + B \cos 2\alpha = 0.$$

It follows either that $A = B$ and $\cos 2\alpha = \sin 2\alpha$, or that $A = -B$ and $\cos 2\alpha = -\sin 2\alpha$. The former occurs if

$$2\alpha = \pi/4, 5\pi/4, 9\pi/4, \cdots,$$

the latter if

$$2\alpha = 3\pi/4, 7\pi/4, 11\pi/4, \cdots.$$

Hence the nth eigenvalue is

$$\lambda_n = \alpha_n^2 = (2n - 1)^2 \pi^2/64$$

for $n = 1, 2, 3, \cdots$, and the associated eigenfunction is

$$y_n(x) = \cos \alpha_n x + \sin \alpha_n x \quad (n \text{ odd})$$

or

$$y_n(x) = \cos \alpha_n x - \sin \alpha_n x \quad (n \text{ even}).$$

6. **(a)** If $\lambda = 0$ and $y(x) = A + Bx$, then $y'(0) = B = 0$, so $y(x) = A$. But then $y(1) + y'(1) = A = 0$ also, so $\lambda = 0$ is not an eigenvalue.

(b) If $\lambda = \alpha^2 > 0$ and

$$y(x) = A \cos \alpha x + B \sin \alpha x,$$

then

$$y'(x) = \alpha(-A \sin \alpha x + B \cos \alpha x),$$

so $y'(0) = B\alpha = 0$. Hence $B = 0$ so $y(x) = A \cos \alpha x$. Then

$$y(1) + y'(1) = A(\cos \alpha - \alpha \sin \alpha) = 0,$$

so α must be a positive root of the equation $\tan \alpha = 1/\alpha$.

7. **(a)** If $\lambda = 0$ and $y(x) = A + Bx$, then $y(0) = A = 0$, so $y(x) = Bx$. But then $y(1) + y'(1) = 2B = 0$, so $A = B = 0$ and $\lambda = 0$ is not an eigenvalue.

(b) If $\lambda = \alpha^2 > 0$ and $y(x) = A \cos \alpha x + B \sin \alpha x$, then $y(0) = A = 0$ so $y(x) = B \sin \alpha x$. Hence

$$y(1) + y'(1) = B(\sin \alpha + \alpha \cos \alpha) = 0.$$

so α must be a positive root of the equation $\tan \alpha = -\alpha$.

8. **(a)** If $\lambda = 0$ and $y(x) = A + Bx$, then $y(0) = A = 0$, so $y(x) = Bx$. But then $y(1) = y'(1)$ says only that $B = B$. Hence $\lambda_0 = 0$ is an eigenvalue with associated eigenfunction $y_0(x) = x$.

(b) If $\lambda = \alpha^2 > 0$ and $y(x) = A \cos \alpha x + B \sin \alpha x$, then $y(0) = A = 0$ so $y(x) = B \sin \alpha x$. Then $y(1) = y'(1)$ says that $B \sin \alpha = B\alpha \cos \alpha$, so α must be a positive root of the equation $\tan \alpha = \alpha$.

9. If $y'' + \lambda y = 0$ and $\lambda = -\alpha^2 < 0$, then

$$y(x) = Ae^{\alpha x} + Be^{-\alpha x}.$$

Then $y(0) = A + B = 0$, so $B = -A$ and therefore

$$y(x) = A(e^{\alpha x} - e^{-\alpha x}).$$

Hence

$$y'(L) = A\alpha(e^{\alpha L} + e^{-\alpha L}) = 0.$$

But $\alpha \neq 0$ and $e^{\alpha L} + e^{-\alpha L} > 0$, so $A = 0$. Thus $\lambda = -\alpha^2$ is not an eigenvalue.

12. **(a)** If $\lambda = 0$ and $y(x) = A + Bx$, then $y(-\pi) = y(\pi)$ means that $A + B\pi = A - B\pi$, so $B = 0$ and $y(x) = A$. But then $y'(-\pi) = y'(\pi)$ implies nothing about A. Hence $\lambda_0 = 0$ is an eigenvalue with $y_0(x) = 1$.

(b) If $\lambda = -\alpha^2 < 0$ and

$$y(x) = Ae^{\alpha x} + Be^{-\alpha x},$$

then the conditions $y(-\pi) = y(\pi)$ and $y'(-\pi) = y'(\pi)$ yield the equations

$$Ae^{\alpha\pi} + Be^{-\alpha\pi} = Ae^{-\alpha\pi} + Be^{\alpha\pi},$$

$$Ae^{\alpha\pi} - Be^{-\alpha\pi} = Ae^{-\alpha\pi} - Be^{\alpha\pi}.$$

Addition of these equations yields $2Ae^{\alpha\pi} = 2Ae^{-\alpha\pi}$. Since $e^{\alpha\pi} \neq e^{-\alpha\pi}$ because $\alpha \neq 0$, it follows that $A = 0$. Similarly $B = 0$. Thus there are no negative eigenvalues.

(c) If $\lambda = \alpha^2 > 0$ and

$$y(x) = A\cos\alpha x + B\sin\alpha x,$$

then the endpoint conditions yield the equations

$$A\cos\alpha\pi + B\sin\alpha\pi = A\cos\alpha\pi - B\sin\alpha\pi,$$

$$-A\sin\alpha\pi + B\cos\alpha\pi = A\sin\alpha\pi + B\cos\alpha\pi.$$

The first equation implies that $B\sin\alpha\pi = 0$, the second that $A\sin\alpha\pi = 0$. If A and B are not both zero, then it follows that $\sin\alpha\pi = 0$, so $\alpha = n$, an integer. In this case A and B are both arbitrary. Thus $\cos nx$ and $\sin nx$ are two different eigenfunctions associated with the single eigenvalue n^2.

13. **(a)** With $\lambda = 1$, the general solution of $y'' + 2y' + y = 0$ is

$$y(x) = Ae^{-x} + Bxe^{-x}.$$

But then $y(0) = A = 0$ and $y(1) = e^{-1}(A + B) = 0$. Hence $\lambda = 1$ is not an eigenvalue.

(b)   If $\lambda < 1$, then the equation $y'' + 2y' + \lambda y = 0$ has characteristic equation $r^2 + 2r + \lambda = 0$. This equation has the two distinct real roots $[2 \pm (4 - 4\lambda)^{1/2}]/2$; call them r and s. Then the general solution is

$$y(x) = Ae^{rx} + Be^{sx},$$

and the conditions $y(0) = y(1) = 0$ yield the equations

$$A + B = 0, \quad Ae^r + Be^s = 0.$$

If $A, B \neq 0$, then it follows that $e^r = e^s$. But $r \neq s$, so there is no eigenvalue $\lambda < 1$.

(c)   If $\lambda > 1$ let $\lambda - 1 = \alpha^2$, so $\lambda = 1 + \alpha^2$. Then the characteristic equation

$$r^2 + 2r + \lambda = (r + 1)^2 + \alpha^2 = 0$$

has roots $-1 \pm \alpha i$, so

$$y(x) = e^{-x}(A \cos \alpha x + B \sin \alpha x).$$

Now $y(0) = A = 0$, so $y(x) = Ae^{-x} \sin \alpha x$. Next, $y(1) = Ae^{-1} \sin \alpha = 0$, so $\alpha = n\pi$ with n an integer. Thus the nth positive eigenvalue is $\lambda_n = n^2\pi^2 + 1$. Because $\lambda = \alpha^2 + 1$, the eigenfunction associated with λ_n is

$$y_n(x) = e^{-x} \sin n\pi x.$$

14.   If $\lambda = 1 + \alpha^2$ then we first impose the condition $y(0) = 0$ on the solution

$$y(x) = e^{-x}(A \cos \alpha x + B \sin \alpha x)$$

found in Problem 13, and find that $A = 0$. Hence

$$y(x) = Be^{-x} \sin \alpha x,$$
$$y'(x) = B(- e^{-x} \sin \alpha x + e^{-x} \alpha \cos \alpha x),$$

so the condition $y'(1) = 0$ yields $-\sin \alpha + \alpha \cos \alpha = 0$, that is, $\tan \alpha = \alpha$.

15.   **(a)**   The endpoint conditions are

$$y(0) = y'(0) = y''(L) = y^{(3)}(L) = 0.$$

With these conditions, four successive integrations as in Example 5 yield the indicated shape function $y(x)$.

(b) The maximum value y_{max} of $y(x)$ on the closed interval $[0, L]$ must occur either at an interior point where $y'(x) = 0$ or at one of the endpoints $x = 0$ and $x = L$. Now

$$y'(x) = k(4x^3 - 12Lx^2 + 12L^2x) = 4kx(x^2 - 3Lx + 3L^2)$$

where $k = w/24EI$, and the quadratic factor has no real zero. Hence $x = 0$ is the only zero of $y'(x)$. But $y(0) = 0$, so it follows that $y_{max} = y(L)$.

16. **(a)** The endpoint conditions are

$$y(0) = y'(0) = 0 \text{ and } y(L) = y'(L) = 0.$$

(b) The derivative

$$y'(x) = k(4x^3 - 6Lx^2 + 2L^2x) = 2kx(2x - L)(x - L)$$

vanishes at $x = 0, L/2, L$. Because $y(0) = y(L) = 0$, the argument of Problem 15(b) implies that $y_{max} = y(L/2)$.

18. **(a)** The endpoint conditions are

$$y(0) = y'(0) = 0 \text{ and } y(L) = y''(L) = 0.$$

(b) The only zero of the derivative

$$y'(x) = 2kx(8x^2 - 15Lx + 6L^2)$$

interior to the interval $[0, L]$ is

$$x_m = (15 - \sqrt{33})L/16,$$

and $y(0) = y(L) = 0$, so it follows by the argument of Problem 15(b) that $y_{max} = y(x_m)$.

CHAPTER 4

INTRODUCTION TO SYSTEMS OF DIFFERENTIAL EQUATIONS

This chapter bridges the gap between the treatment of a single differential equation in Chapters 1–3 and the comprehensive treatment of linear and nonlinear systems in Chapters 5–6. It also is designed to offer some flexibility in the treatment of linear systems, depending on the background in linear algebra that students are assumed to have -- Sections 4.1 and 4.2 can stand alone as a very brief introduction to linear systems without the use of linear algebra and matrices. The final Section 4.3 of this chapter extends to systems the numerical approximation techniques of Chapter 2.

SECTION 4.1

FIRST-ORDER SYSTEMS AND APPLICATIONS

1. $x_1' = x_2 \qquad (x = x_1)$

    $x_2' = -7x_1 - 3x_2 + t^2$

2. $x_1' = x_2, \qquad x_2' = x_3, \qquad x_3' = x_4 \qquad (x = x_1)$

    $x_4' = -x_1 + 3x_2 - 6x_3 + \cos 3t$

3. $x_1' = x_2 \qquad (x = x_1)$

    $t^2 x_2' = (1 - t^2)x_1 - tx_2$

4. $x_1' = x_2, \qquad x_2' = x_3 \qquad (x = x_1)$

    $t^3 x_3' = -5x_1 - 3tx_2 + 2t^2 x_3 + \ln t$

5. $x_1' = x_2, \qquad x_2' = x_3 \qquad (x = x_1)$

    $x_3' = x_2^2 + \cos x_1$

6. $x_1' = x_2 \qquad (x = x_1)$

    $y_1' = y_2 \qquad (y = y_1)$

    $x_2' = 5x_1 - 4y_1$

    $y_2' = -4x_1 + 5y_1$

7. $x_1' = x_2$ $(x = x_1)$

       $y_1' = y_2$ $(y = y_1)$

       $x_2' = -kx_1(x_1^2 + y_1^2)^{-3/2}$

       $y_2' = -ky_1(x_1^2 + y_1^2)^{-3/2}$

8. $x_1' = x_2$ $(x = x_1)$

       $y_1' = y_2$ $(y = y_1)$

       $x_2' = -4x_1 + 2y_1 - 3x_2$

       $y_2' = 3x_1 - y_1 - 2y_2 + \cos t$

9. $x_1' = x_2$ $(x = x_1)$

       $y_1' = y_2$ $(y = y_1)$

       $z_1' = z_2$ $(z = z_1)$

       $x_2' = 3x_1 - y_1 + 2z_1$

       $y_2' = x_1 + y_1 - 4z_1$

       $z_2' = 5x_1 - y_1 - z_1$

10. $x_1' = x_2,$ $y_1' = y_2$

        $x_2' = x_1(1 - y_1)$

        $y_2' = y_1(1 - x_1)$

11. The computation $x'' = y' = -x$ yields the single linear second-order equation $x'' + x = 0$ with characteristic equation $r^2 + 1 = 0$ and general solution

$$x(t) = A \cos t + B \sin t.$$

Then the original first equation $y = x'$ gives

$$y(t) = B \cos t - A \sin t.$$

12. The computation $x'' = y' = x$ yields the single linear second-order equation $x'' - x = 0$ with characteristic equation $r^2 - 1 = 0$ and general solution

$$x(t) = A e^t + B e^{-t}.$$

Then the original first equation $y = x'$ gives

$$y(t) = A e^t - B e^{-t}.$$

13. The computation $x'' = -2y' = -4x$ yields the single linear second-order equation $x'' + 4x = 0$ with characteristic equation $r^2 + 4 = 0$ and general solution

$$x(t) = A \cos 2t + B \sin 2t.$$

Then the original first equation $y = -x'/2$ gives

$$y(t) = -B \cos 2t + A \sin 2t.$$

Finally, the condition $x(0) = 1$ implies that $A = 1$, and then the condition $y(0) = 0$ gives $B = 0$. Hence the desired particular solution is given by

$$x(t) = \cos 2t, \qquad y(t) = \sin 2t.$$

14. The computation $x'' = 10y' = -100x$ yields the single linear second-order equation $x'' + 100x = 0$ with characteristic equation $r^2 + 100 = 0$ and general solution

$$x(t) = A \cos 10t + B \sin 10t.$$

Then the original first equation $y = x'/10$ gives

$$y(t) = B \cos 10t - A \sin 10t.$$

Finally, the condition $x(0) = 3$ implies that $A = 3$, and then the condition $y(0) = 4$ gives $B = 4$. Hence the desired particular solution is given by

$$x(t) = 3 \cos 10t + 4 \sin 10t,$$

$$y(t) = 4 \cos 10t - 3 \sin 10t.$$

15. The computation $x'' = y'/2 = -4x$ yields the single linear second-order equation $x'' + 4x = 0$ with characteristic equation $r^2 + 4 = 0$ and general solution

$$x(t) = A \cos 2t + B \sin 2t.$$

Then the original first equation $y = 2x'$ gives

$$y(t) = 4B \cos 2t - 4A \sin 2t.$$

16. The computation $x'' = 8y' = -16x$ yields the single linear second-order equation $x'' + 16x = 0$ with characteristic equation $r^2 + 16 = 0$ and general solution

$$x(t) = A \cos 4t + B \sin 4t.$$

Then the original first equation $y = x'/8$ gives

$$y(t) = (B/2)\cos 4t - (A/2)\sin 4t.$$

17. The computation $x'' = y' = 6x - y = 6x - x'$ yields the single linear second-order equation $x'' + x' - 6x = 0$ with characteristic equation $r^2 + r - 6 = 0$ and characteristic roots $r = -3$ and 2, so the general solution

$$x(t) = A e^{-3t} + B e^{2t}.$$

Then the original first equation $y = x'$ gives

$$y(t) = -3A e^{-3t} + 2B e^{2t}.$$

Finally, the initial conditions

$$x(0) = A + B = 1, \quad y(0) = -3A + 2B = 2$$

imply that $A = 0$ and $B = 1$, so the desired particular solution is given by

$$x(t) = e^{2t}, \qquad y(t) = 2 e^{2t}.$$

18. The computation $x'' = -y' = -10x + 7y = -10x - 7x'$ yields the single linear second-order equation $x'' + 7x' + 10x = 0$ with characteristic equation $r^2 + 7r + 10 = 0$, characteristic roots $r = -2$ and -5, and general solution

$$x(t) = A e^{-2t} + B e^{-5t}.$$

Then the original first equation $y = -x'$ gives

$$y(t) = 2A e^{-2t} + 5B e^{-5t}.$$

Finally, the initial conditions

$$x(0) = A + B = 2, \quad y(0) = 2A + 5B = -7$$

imply that $A = 17/3$, $B = -11/3$, so the desired particular solution is given by

$$x(t) = (17 e^{-2t} - 11 e^{-5t})/3, \qquad y(t) = (34e^{-2t} + 55e^{-5t})/3.$$

19. The computation $x'' = -y' = -13x - 4y = -13x + 4x'$ yields the single linear second-order equation $x'' - 4x' + 13x = 0$ with characteristic equation $r^2 - 4r + 13 = 0$ and characteristic roots $r = 2 \pm 3i$, hence the general solution is

$$x(t) = e^{2t}(A \cos 3t + B \sin 3t).$$

The initial condition $x(0) = 0$ then gives $A = 0$, so $x(t) = B e^{2t}\sin 3t$. Then the original first equation $y = -x'$ gives

$$y(t) = -e^{2t}(3B \cos 3t + 2B \sin 3t).$$

Finally, the initial condition $y(0) = 3$ gives $B = -1$, so the desired particular solution is given by

$$x(t) = -e^{2t} \sin 3t, \qquad y(t) = e^{2t}(3 \cos 3t + 2 \sin 3t).$$

20. The computation $x'' = y' = -9x + 6y = -9x + 6x'$ yields the single linear second-order equation $x'' - 6x' + 9x = 0$ with characteristic equation $r^2 - 6r + 9 = 0$ and repeated characteristic root $r = 3, 3,$ so its general solution is given by

$$x(t) = (A + Bt)e^{3t}.$$

Then the original first equation $y = x'$ gives

$$y(t) = (3A + B + 3Bt)e^{3t}.$$

21. **(a)** Substituting the general solution found in Problem 11 we get

$$x^2 + y^2 = (A \cos t + B \sin t)^2 + (B \cos t - A \sin t)^2$$
$$= (A^2 + B^2)(\cos^2 t + \sin^2 t) = A^2 + B^2$$
$$x^2 + y^2 = C^2,$$

the equation of a circle of radius $C = (A^2 + B^2)^{1/2}$.

(b) Substituting the general solution found in Problem 12 we get

$$x^2 - y^2 = (Ae^t + Be^{-t})^2 - (Ae^t - Be^{-t})^2 = 4AB,$$

the equation of a hyperbola.

23. When we solve Equations (20) and (21) in the text for e^{-t} and e^{2t} we get

$$2x - y = 3Ae^{-t} \qquad \text{and} \qquad x + y = 3Be^{2t}.$$

Hence

$$(2x - y)^2(x + y) = (3Ae^{-t})^2(3Be^{2t}) = 27A^2B = C.$$

Clearly $y = 2x$ or $y = -x$ if $C = 0,$ and expansion gives the equation $4x^3 - 3xy^2 + y^3 = C.$

27. $2(I_1' - I_2') + 50I_1 = 100 \sin 60t$

$2(I_2' - I_1') + 25I_2 = 0$

28. First we apply Kirchhoff's law to each loop in Figure 4.1.14 in the text, denoting by Q the charge on the capacitor, and get the equations

$$50I_1 + 1000Q = 100, \qquad 25I_2 - 1000Q = 0.$$

Then we differentiate each equation and substitute $Q' = I_1 - I_2$ to get the system

$$I_1' = -20(I_1 - I_2), \qquad I_2' = 40(I_1 - I_2).$$

30. If we write (x', y') for the velocity vector and

$$v = [(x')^2 + (y')^2]^{1/2}$$

for the speed, then $(x'/v, y'/v)$ is a unit vector pointing in the direction of the velocity vector, and so the components of the air resistance force F_r are given by

$$F_r = -kv^2(x'/v, y'/v) = (-kvx', -kvy').$$

SECTION 4.2

THE METHOD OF ELIMINATION

1. $x = a_1 e^{-t} + a_2 e^{2t}, \qquad y = a_2 e^{2t}$

2. From the first differential equation we get $y = (x - x')/2$, so $y' = (x' - x'')/2$. Substitution of these expressions for y and y' into the second differential equation yields the second-order equation

$$x'' + 2x' + x = 0$$

with general solution

$$x = (c_1 + c_2 t)e^{-t}.$$

Substitution in $y = (x - x')/2$ now yields

$$y = (c_1 - c_2/2 + c_2 t)e^{-t}.$$

3. $x = 4(e^{3t} - e^{-2t})/5, \quad y = 2(6e^{3t} - e^{-2t})/5$

4. Elimination of y and y' yields the second-order equation $x'' - 4x = 0$ with general solution

$$x = c_1 e^{2t} + c_2 e^{-2t}.$$

Substitution in $y = 3x - x'$ gives

$$y = c_1 e^{2t} + 5c_2 e^{-2t}.$$

The initial conditions yield the equations

$$c_1 + c_2 = 1, \qquad c_1 + 5c_2 = -1$$

with solution $c_1 = 3/2$, $c_2 = -1/2$. Hence the desired particular solution is

$$x = (3e^{2t} - e^{-2t})/2, \qquad y = (3e^{2t} - 5e^{-2t})/2.$$

5. $x = e^{-t}(a_1 \cos 2t + a_2 \sin 2t)$

$y = -(1/2)e^{-t}[(a_1 + a_2)\cos 2t + (a_2 - a_1)\sin 2t]$

6. General solution:

$$x = e^{-2t}(c_1 \cos 3t + c_2 \sin 3t)$$

$$y = (1/3)e^{-2t}[(-c_1 + c_2)\cos 3t - (c_1 + c_2)\sin 3t]$$

Particular solution:

$$x = e^{-2t}(3 \cos 3t + 9 \sin 3t)$$

$$y = e^{-2t}(2 \cos 3t - 4 \sin 3t)$$

7. $x = a_1 e^{2t} + a_2 e^{3t} - t/3 + 1/18$

$y = -2a_1 e^{2t} - a_2 e^{3t} - 2t/3 - 5/9$

8. $x = c_1 e^{t} + c_2 e^{3t} + e^{2t}, \qquad y = -c_1 e^{t} + c_2 e^{3t}$

9. $x = 3a_1 e^{t} + a_2 e^{-t} - (1/5)[7 \cos 2t + 4 \sin 2t]$

$y = a_1 e^{t} + a_2 e^{-t} - (1/5)[2 \cos 2t + 4 \sin 2t]$

10. First we solve the given equations for

$$x' = 2x + y, \qquad y' = x + 2y.$$

The general solution is

$$x = c_1 e^{t} + c_2 e^{3t}, \qquad y = -c_1 e^{t} + c_2 e^{3t}.$$

The desired particular solution is

$$x = e^t, \qquad\qquad y = -e^t.$$

11. $x = a_1\cos 3t + a_2\sin 3t - (11/20)e^t - (1/4)e^{-t}$

$y = (1/3)[(a_1 - a_2)\cos 3t + (a_1 + a_2)\sin 3t] + (1/10)e^t$

12. The first equation yields $y = (x'' - 6x)/2$, so $y'' = (x^{(4)} - 6x'')/2$. Substitution in the second equation yields

$$x^{(4)} - 13x'' + 36x = 0.$$

The general solution is

$$x = c_1e^{2t} + c_2e^{-2t} + \qquad c_3e^{3t} + \qquad c_4e^{-3t},$$
$$y = -c_1e^{2t} - c_2e^{-2t} + (3/2)c_3e^{3t} + (3/2)c_4e^{-3t}.$$

13. $x = a_1\cos 2t + a_2\sin 2t + \quad b_1\cos 3t + b_2\sin 3t$

$y = (a_1\cos 2t + a_2\sin 2t)/2 - 2(b_1\cos 3t + b_2\sin 3t)$

14. $x = c_1\cos 2t + c_2\sin 2t + (1/3)\sin t$

$y = c_1\cos 2t + c_2\sin 2t + c_3\cos 2t\sqrt 2 + c_4\sin 2t\sqrt 2 + (4/21)\sin t$

15. $x = a_1\cos t + a_2\sin t + b_1\cos 2t + b_2\sin 2t$

$y = a_2\cos t - a_1\sin t + b_2\cos 2t - b_1\sin 2t$

16. In operational form our system is

$$(D^2 - 4)x + \quad 13Dy = 6\sin t$$
$$-2Dx + (D^2 - 9)y = 0$$

When we operate on the first equation with $D^2 - 9$, on the second with $13D$, and subtract, the result is

$$(D^4 + 13D^2 + 36)x = -60\sin t.$$

The general solution of this fourth-order equation is

$$x = a_1\cos 2t + a_2\sin 2t + a_3\cos 3t + a_4\sin 3t - (5/2)\sin t.$$

We find similarly that

$$y = b_1\cos 2t + b_2\sin 2t + b_3\cos 3t + b_4\sin 3t + (1/2)\cos t.$$

When we substitute these expressions into either of the original differential equations we find that

$$b_1 = -4a_2/13, \quad b_2 = 4a_1/13, \quad b_3 = -a_4/3, \quad b_4 = a_3/3.$$

Hence
$$y = (-4a_2\cos 2t + 4a_1\sin 2t)/13 + (-a_4\cos 3t + a_3\sin 3t)/3 + (1/2)\cos t.$$

17. $x = a_1\cos t + a_2\sin t + b_1e^{2t} + b_2e^{-2t}$

$y = 3a_2\cos t - 3a_1\sin t + b_1e^{2t} - b_2e^{-2t}$

18. From the first and third equations we see that $x' + z' = 0$, so $z = -x$. Hence the first equation reduces to $x' = 2y$, and substitution in the second equation yields $y'' + y' - 12y$, so it follows that
$$y = c_1e^{3t} + c_2e^{-4t}.$$

Since $x = (y + y')/6$, it follows that

$$x = (4c_1e^{3t} - 3c_2e^{-4t})/6,$$

$$z = (-4c_1e^{3t} + 3c_2e^{-4t})/6.$$

19. $x = a_1 + a_2e^{4t} + a_3e^{8t}$

$y = 2a_1 \qquad - 2a_3e^{8t}$

$z = 2a_1 - 2a_2e^{4t} + 2a_3e^{8t}$

20. The operational determinant of the given system is

$$L = D^3 - 3D - 2 = (D + 1)^2(D - 2),$$

and we find that
$$Lx = Ly = Lz = 0.$$
Hence
$$x = a_1e^{2t} + a_2e^{-t} + a_3te^{-t},$$

$$y = b_1e^{2t} + b_2e^{-t} + b_3te^{-t},$$

$$z = c_1e^{2t} + c_2e^{-t} + c_3te^{-t}.$$

When we substitute these expressions in the three differential equations and compare coefficients of e^{2t}, we find that $a_1 = b_1 = c_1$. When we compare coefficients of te^{-t} we find that $a_3 + b_3 + c_3 = 0$. Comparison of coefficients of e^{-t} yields

$$a_2 + b_2 + c_2 = a_3 - 1 = b_3 = c_3.$$

It follows that $a_3 = 2/3$ and $b_3 = c_3 = -1/3$. If a_2 and b_2 are chosen arbitrarily, then

$c_2 = -a_2 - b_2 - 1/3$. Hence the general solution is

$$x = a_1 e^{2t} + a_2 e^{-t} + (2/3)te^{-t},$$

$$y = a_1 e^{2t} + b_2 e^{-t} - (1/3)te^{-t},$$

$$z = a_1 e^{2t} - (a_2 + b_2 + 1/3)e^{-t} - (1/3)te^{-t}.$$

23. Subtraction of the two equations yields $x + y = e^{-2t} - e^{-3t}$. We then verify readily that any two differentiable functions $x(t)$ and $y(t)$ satisfying this condition will constitute a solution of the given system, which thus has infinitely many solutions.

24. Subtraction of one equation from the other yields $x + y = t^2 - t$. But then

$$(D + 2)x + (D + 2)y = D(x + y) + 2(x + y)$$

$$= (2t - 1) + 2(t^2 - t) = 2t^2 - 1 \neq t.$$

Thus the given system has no solution.

25. Infinitely many solutions, because any solution of the second equation also satisfies the first equation (because it is $D + 2$ times the second one).

26. Subtraction of the second equation from the first one gives $x = e^{-t}$. Then substitution in the second equation yields $D^2 y = 0$, so $y = b_1 t + b_2$. Thus there are *two* arbitrary constants.

27. Subtraction of the second equation from the first one gives $x + y = e^{-t}$. Then substitution in the second equation yields

$$x = D^2(x + y) = e^{-t},$$

so $y = 0$. Thus there are *no* arbitrary constants.

28. Differentiation of the difference of the two given equations yields

$$(D^2 + D)x + D^2 y = -2e^{-t},$$

which contradicts the first equation. Hence the system has *no* solution.

29. Addition of the two given equations yields $D^2 x = e^{-t}$, so $x(t) = a_1 t + a_2$. Then the second equation gives $D^2 y = a_1 t + a_2$, so

$$y(t) = (1/6)a_1 t^3 + (1/2)a_2 t^2 + a_3 t + a_4.$$

Thus there are *four* arbitrary constants.

30. $x(t) = a_1\exp(r_1t) + a_2\exp(r_2t)$

$y(t) = (6a_1 + 20r_1a_1)\exp(r_1t) + (6a_2 + 20r_2a_2)\exp(r_2t)$

where $r_1 = (-9 + \sqrt{33})/40$, $r_2 = (-9 - \sqrt{33})/40$, $a_1 + a_2 = 50$, $r_1a_1 + r_2a_2 = -10$.

31. $I_1(t) = 2 + e^{-5t}[-2\cos(10t/\sqrt{6}) + 4\sqrt{6}\sin(10t/\sqrt{6})]$

$I_2(t) = (20/\sqrt{6})e^{-5t}\sin(10t/\sqrt{6})$

32. The solution of the system

$$2(I_1' - I_2') + 50\,I_1 = 100\sin 60t$$

$$2(I_2' - I_1') + 25\,I_2 = 0$$

with $I_1(0) = I_2(0) = 0$ is

$$I_1 = (\ 120e^{-25t/3} - 120\cos 60t + 1778\sin 60t)/1321$$

$$I_2 = (-240e^{-25t/3} + 240\cos 60t + 1728\sin 60t)/1321$$

(Yes, one coefficient of $\sin 60t$ is 1778 and the other is 1728.)

33. See the solution to Problem 30 in Section 4.1. The solution of the system

$$I_1' = -20(I_1 - I_2), \qquad I_2' = 40(I_1 - I_2)$$

with $I_1(0) = 2$ and $I_2(0) = 0$ is given by

$$I_1(t) = 2(2 + e^{-60t})/3, \qquad I_2(t) = 4(1 - e^{-60t})/3.$$

34. $3x_1/100 = 1 + e^{-3t/20}[2\cos(t\sqrt{3}/20)]$

$3x_2/100 = 1 + e^{-3t/20}[-\cos(t\sqrt{3}/20) + \sqrt{3}\sin(t\sqrt{3}/20)]$

$3x_3/100 = 1 + e^{-3t/20}[-\cos(t\sqrt{3}/20) - \sqrt{3}\sin(t\sqrt{3}/20)]$

35. The two given equations yield

$$mx^{(3)} = qBy'' = -q^2B^2x'/m,$$

so $x^{(3)} + \omega^2 x' = 0$. The general solution is

$$x(t) = A\cos \omega t + B\sin \omega t + C.$$

Now $x'(0) = 0$ implies $B = 0$, and then $x(0) = r_0$ gives $A + C = r_0$. Next,

$$\omega y' = x'' = -A\omega^2 \cos \omega t,$$

so $y'(0) = -\omega r_0$ implies $A = r_0$, hence $C = 0$. It now follows readily that the trajectory is the circle

$$x(t) = r_0 \cos \omega t, \qquad y(t) = -r_0 \sin \omega t.$$

36. With $\omega = qB/m$ our differential equations are

$$x'' = \omega y' + qE/m, \qquad y'' = -\omega x'.$$

Elimination gives

$$x^{(4)} + \omega^2 x'' = y^{(4)} + \omega^2 y'' = 0,$$

so

$$x = a_1 + b_1 t + c_1 \cos \omega t + d_1 \sin \omega t,$$
$$y = a_2 + b_2 t + c_2 \cos \omega t + d_2 \sin \omega t.$$

The initial conditions $x(0) = x'(0) = 0 = y(0) = y'(0)$ yield

$$c_1 = -a_1, \quad b_1 = -\omega d_1, \quad c_2 = -a_2, \quad b_2 = -\omega d_2.$$

Then substitution in $y'' = -\omega x'$ yields

$$d_1 = b_1 = a_2 = c_2 = 0 \quad \text{and} \quad d_2 = a_1.$$

Finally, substitution in $x'' = \omega y' + qE/m$ yields $a = a_1 = E/\omega B$, so the solution is

$$x = a(1 - \cos \omega t), \quad y = -a(\omega t - \sin \omega t).$$

37. **(a)**
$$x = a_1 \cos 5t + a_2 \sin 5t + b_1 \cos 5t\sqrt{3} + b_2 \sin 5t\sqrt{3},$$
$$y = 2a_1 \cos 5t + 2a_2 \sin 5t - 2b_1 \cos 5t\sqrt{3} - 2b_2 \sin 5t\sqrt{3}$$

(b) In the natural mode with frequency $\omega_1 = 5$ the masses move in the same direction, while in the natural mode with frequency $\omega_2 = 5\sqrt{3}$ they move in opposite directions. In each case the amplitude of the motion of m_2 is twice that of m_1.

39.
$$x = a_1 \cos t + a_2 \sin t + b_1 \cos 2t + b_2 \sin 2t$$
$$y = 2a_1 \cos t + 2a_2 \sin t - b_1 \cos 2t - b_2 \sin 2t$$

In the natural mode with frequency $\omega_1 = 1$ the masses move in the same direction, with the amplitude of motion of the second mass twice that of the first mass. In the natural mode with frequency $\omega_2 = 2$ they move in opposite directions with the same amplitude of motion.

40. $x = a_1 \cos 5t + a_2 \sin 5t + b_1 \cos 10t + b_2 \sin 10t$

   $y = 2a_1 \cos 5t + 2a_2 \sin 5t - b_1 \cos 10t - b_2 \sin 10t$

In the natural mode with frequency $\omega_1 = 5$ the masses move in the same direction, with the amplitude of motion of the second mass twice that of the first mass. In the natural mode with frequency $\omega_2 = 10$ they move in opposite directions with the same amplitude of motion.

41. $x(t) = a_1 \cos t + a_2 \sin t + b_1 \cos 3t + b_2 \sin 3t$

   $y(t) = a_1 \cos t + a_2 \sin t - b_1 \cos 3t - b_2 \sin 3t$

42. $x = (a_1 \cos t + a_2 \sin t) + (b_1 \cos 2t + b_2 \sin 2t)$

   $y = (a_1 \cos t + a_2 \sin t) - (b_1 \cos 2t + b_2 \sin 2t)/2$

In the natural mode with frequency $\omega_1 = 1$ the two masses move in the same direction with equal amplitudes of oscillation. In the natural mode with frequency $\omega_2 = 2$ the two masses move in opposite directions with the amplitude of m_2 being half that of m_1.

43. $x = a_1 \cos t + a_2 \sin t + b_1 \cos t\sqrt{5} + b_2 \sin t\sqrt{5}$

   $y = a_1 \cos t + a_2 \sin t - b_1 \cos t\sqrt{5} - b_2 \sin t\sqrt{5}$

44. $x = (a_1 \cos t\sqrt{2} + a_2 \sin t\sqrt{2}) + (b_1 \cos 2t + b_2 \sin 2t)$

   $y = (a_1 \cos t\sqrt{2} + a_2 \sin t\sqrt{2}) - (b_1 \cos 2t + b_2 \sin 2t)$

In the natural mode with frequency $\omega_1 = \sqrt{2}$ the two masses move in the same direction; in the natural mode with frequency $\omega_2 = 2$ they move in opposite directions. In each natural mode their amplitudes of oscillation are equal.

45. $x = a_1 \cos t\sqrt{2} + a_2 \sin t\sqrt{2} + b_1 \cos t\sqrt{8} + b_2 \sin t\sqrt{8}$

   $y = a_1 \cos t\sqrt{2} + a_2 \sin t\sqrt{2} - (b_1 \cos t\sqrt{8} + b_2 \sin t\sqrt{8})/2$

46. $x = a_1 \cos 2t + a_2 \sin 2t + b_1 \cos 4t + b_2 \sin 4t$

   $y = a_1 \cos 2t + a_2 \sin 2t - b_1 \cos 4t - b_2 \sin 4t$

In the natural mode with frequency $\omega_1 = 2$ the masses move in the same direction with equal amplitudes of motion. In the natural mode with frequency $\omega_2 = 4$ they move in opposite directions with the same amplitude of motion.

47.   **(b)**   The operational determinant is

$$(D^2 + 2)[(D^2 + 2)^2 - 1] + [-(D^2 + 2)] = (D^2 + 2)[(D^2 + 2)^2 - 2],$$

and the characteristic equation

$$(r^2 + 2)[(r^2 + 2)^2 - 2] = 0$$

has roots $\pm i\sqrt{2}$ and $\pm i\sqrt{2 \pm \sqrt{2}}$.

SECTION 4.3

NUMERICAL METHODS FOR SYSTEMS

In Problems 1–8 we give the approximate and actual values $x(0.2)$ and $y(0.2)$ of the solution at $t = 0.2$.

1.
Euler values:	$x(0.2) \approx 0.8800,$	$y(0.2) \approx 2.5000$
Improved Euler:	$x(0.2) \approx 0.9600,$	$y(0.2) \approx 2.6000$
Runge-Kutta:	$x(0.2) \approx 1.0027,$	$y(0.2) \approx 2.6401$
Actual values:	$x(0.2) \approx 1.0034,$	$y(0.2) \approx 2.6408$

2.
Euler values:	$x(0.2) \approx 0.8100,$	$y(0.2) \approx -0.8100$
Improved Euler:	$x(0.2) \approx 0.8200,$	$y(0.2) \approx -0.8200$
Runge-Kutta:	$x(0.2) \approx 0.8187,$	$y(0.2) \approx -0.8187$
Actual values:	$x(0.2) \approx 0.8187,$	$y(0.2) \approx -0.8187$

3.
Euler values:	$x(0.2) \approx 2.8100,$	$y(0.2) \approx 2.3100$
Improved Euler:	$x(0.2) \approx 3.2200,$	$y(0.2) \approx 2.6200$
Runge-Kutta:	$x(0.2) \approx 3.6481,$	$y(0.2) \approx 2.9407$
Actual values:	$x(0.2) \approx 3.6775,$	$y(0.2) \approx 2.9628$

4.
Euler values:	$x(0.2) \approx 3.3100,$	$y(0.2) \approx -1.6200$
Improved Euler:	$x(0.2) \approx 3.8200,$	$y(0.2) \approx -2.0400$
Runge-Kutta:	$x(0.2) \approx 4.2274,$	$y(0.2) \approx -2.4060$
Actual values:	$x(0.2) \approx 4.2427,$	$y(0.2) \approx -2.4205$

5.
Euler values:	$x(0.2) \approx -0.5200,$	$y(0.2) \approx 2.9200$
Improved Euler:	$x(0.2) \approx -0.5400,$	$y(0.2) \approx 2.4400$
Runge-Kutta:	$x(0.2) \approx -0.5712,$	$y(0.2) \approx 2.4485$
Actual values:	$x(0.2) \approx -0.5793,$	$y(0.2) \approx 2.4488$

6.
Euler values:	$x(0.2) \approx -1.7600,$	$y(0.2) \approx 4.6800$
Improved Euler:	$x(0.2) \approx -1.9200,$	$y(0.2) \approx 4.5600$
Runge-Kutta:	$x(0.2) \approx -1.9029,$	$y(0.2) \approx 4.4995$
Actual values:	$x(0.2) \approx -1.9025,$	$y(0.2) \approx 4.4999$

7. Euler values: $x(0.2) \approx 3.1200$, $y(0.2) \approx 1.6800$
     Improved Euler: $x(0.2) \approx 3.2400$, $y(0.2) \approx 1.7600$
     Runge-Kutta: $x(0.2) \approx 3.2816$, $y(0.2) \approx 1.7899$
     Actual values: $x(0.2) \approx 3.2820$, $y(0.2) \approx 1.7902$

8. Euler values: $x(0.2) \approx 2.1600$, $y(0.2) \approx -0.6300$
     Improved Euler: $x(0.2) \approx 2.5200$, $y(0.2) \approx -0.4600$
     Runge-Kutta: $x(0.2) \approx 2.5320$, $y(0.2) \approx -0.3867$
     Actual values: $x(0.2) \approx 2.5270$, $y(0.2) \approx -0.3889$

In Problems 9–11 we give the Runge-Kutta approximate values with step sizes $h = 0.1$ and $h = 0.05$, and also the actual values.

9. With $h = 0.1$: $x(1) \approx 3.99261$, $y(1) \approx 6.21770$
     With $h = 0.05$: $x(1) \approx 3.99234$, $y(1) \approx 6.21768$
     Actual values: $x(1) \approx 3.99232$, $y(1) \approx 6.21768$

10. With $h = 0.1$: $x(1) \approx 1.31498$, $y(1) \approx 1.02537$
     With $h = 0.05$: $x(1) \approx 1.31501$, $y(1) \approx 1.02538$
     Actual values: $x(1) \approx 1.31501$, $y(1) \approx 1.02538$

11. With $h = 0.1$: $x(1) \approx -0.05832$, $y(1) \approx 0.56664$
     With $h = 0.05$: $x(1) \approx -0.05832$, $y(1) \approx 0.56665$
     Actual values: $x(1) \approx -0.05832$, $y(1) \approx 0.56665$

12. We first convert the given initial value problem to the two-dimensional problem

$$x' = y, \qquad\qquad x(0) = 0,$$
$$y' = -x + \sin t, \qquad y(0) = 0.$$

Then with both step sizes h = 0.1 and h = 0.05 we get the actual value $x(1) \approx 0.15058$ accurate to 5 decimal places.

13. With $y = x'$ we want to solve numerically the initial value problem

$$x' = y, \qquad\qquad x(0) = 0$$
$$y' = -32 - 0.04y, \qquad y(0) = 288.$$

When we run Program RK2DIM with step size $h = 0.1$ we find that the change of sign in the velocity v occurs as follows:

t	x	v
7.6	1050.2	+2.8
7.7	1050.3	−0.4

Thus the bolt attains a maximum height of about 1050 feet in about 7.7 seconds.

14. Now we want to solve numerically the initial value problem

$$x' = y, \qquad\qquad x(0) = 0,$$
$$y' = -32 - 0.0002y^2, \qquad y(0) = 288.$$

Running Program RK2DIM with step size $h = 0.1$, we find that the bolt attains a maximum height of about 1044 ft in about 7.8 sec. Note that these values are comparable to those found in Problem 13.

15. With $y = x'$, and with x in miles and t in seconds, we want to solve numerically the initial value problem

$$x' = y$$
$$y' = -95485.5/(x^2 + 7920x + 15681600)$$
$$x(0) = 0, \qquad\qquad y(0) = 1.$$

We find (running RK2DIM with $h = 1$) that the projectile reaches a maximum height of about 83.83 miles in about $168 \text{ sec} = 2 \text{ min } 48 \text{ sec}$.

16. We first defined the MATLAB function

```
function  xp  =  fnball(t,x)
%  Defines the baseball system
%       x1'  =  x'  =  x3,   x3'  =   -cvx'
%       x2'  =  y'  =  x4,   x4'  =   -cvy'- g
%  with air resistance coefficient c.

g    =  32;
c    =  0.0025;
xp   =  x;
v    =  sqrt(x(3).^2) + x(4).^2);
xp(1)  =    x(3);
xp(2)  =    x(4);
xp(3)  =    -c*v*x(3);
xp(4)  =    -c*v*x(4) - g;
```

Then, using the n-dimensional program **rkn** with step size 0.1 and initial data corresponding to the indicated initial inclination angles, we got the following results:

Angle	Time	Range
40	5.0	352.9
45	5.4	347.2
50	5.8	334.2

We have listed the time to the nearest tenth of a second, but have interpolated to find the range in feet.

17. The data in Problem 16 indicate that the range increases when the initial angle is decreased below $45°$. The further data

Angle	Range
41.0	352.1
40.5	352.6
40.0	352.9
39.5	352.8
39.0	352.7
35.0	350.8

indicate that a maximum range of about 353 ft is attained with $\alpha \approx 40°$.

18. We "shoot" for the proper inclination angle by running program **rkn** (with $h = 0.1$) as follows:

Angle	Range
60	287.1
58	298.5
57.5	301.1

Thus we get a range of 300 ft with an initial angle just under $57.5°$.

19. First we run program **rkn** (with $h = 0.1$) with $v_0 = 250$ ft/sec and obtain the following results:

t	x	y
5.0	457.43	103.90
6.0	503.73	36.36

Interpolation gives $x = 494.4$ when $y = 50$. Then a run with $v_0 = 255$ ft/sec gives the following results:

t	x	y
5.5	486.75	77.46
6.0	508.86	41.62

Finally a run with $v_0 = 253$ ft/sec gives these results:

t	x	y
5.5	484.77	75.44
6.0	506.82	39.53

Now $x \approx 500$ ft when $y = 50$ ft. Thus Babe Ruth's home run ball had an initial velocity of 253 ft/sec.

20.   A run of program **rkn** with $h = 0.1$ and with the given data yields the following results:

t	x	y	v	α
5.5	989	539	162	+0.95
5.6	1005	539	161	−0.18
.	.	.	.	.
.	.	.	.	.
.	.	.	.	.
.	.	.	.	.
11.5	1868	16	214	−52
11.6	1881	−1	216	−53

The first two lines of data above indicate that the crossbow bolt attains a maximum height of about 1005 ft in about 5.6 sec. About 6 sec later (total time 11.6 sec) it hits the ground, having traveled about 1880 ft horizontally.

21.   A run with $h = 0.1$ indicates that the projectile has a range of about 21,400 ft ≈ 4.05 mi and a flight time of about 46 sec. It attains a maximum height of about 8970 ft in about 17.5 sec. At time $t \approx 23$ sec it has its minimum velocity of about 368 ft/sec. It hits the ground ($t \approx 46$ sec) at an angle of about $77°$ with a velocity of about 518 ft/sec.

CHAPTER 5

LINEAR SYSTEMS OF DIFFERENTIAL EQUATIONS

Along with Chapter 4, this chapter is designed to offer considerable flexibility in the treatment of linear systems, depending on the background in linear algebra that students are assumed to have. Sections 4.1 and 4.2 of the previous chapter can stand alone as a brief introduction to linear systems without the use of linear algebra and matrices. But this chapter employs the notation and terminology of elementary linear algebra. For ready reference and review, Section 5.1 includes a complete and self-contained account of the needed background of determinants, matrices, and vectors. The additional linear theory that is needed in subsequent sections is introduced along the way.

SECTION 5.1

MATRICES AND LINEAR SYSTEMS

The first half-dozen pages of this section are devoted to a review of matrix notation and terminology. With students who've had some prior exposure to matrices and determinants, this review material can be skimmed rapidly. In this event serious study of the section can begin with the subsections on matrix-valued functions and first-order linear systems. About all that's actually needed for this purpose is some acquaintance with determinants, with matrix multiplication and inverse matrices, and with the fact that a square matrix is invertible if and only if its determinant is nonzero.

1.   **(a)** $\begin{bmatrix} 13 & -18 \\ 23 & 17 \end{bmatrix}$ **(b)** $\begin{bmatrix} 0 & -1 \\ 2 & 19 \end{bmatrix}$

     (c) $\begin{bmatrix} -9 & -11 \\ 47 & -9 \end{bmatrix}$ **(d)** $\begin{bmatrix} -10 & -37 \\ 14 & -8 \end{bmatrix}$

2. $(\mathbf{AB})\mathbf{C} = \mathbf{A}(\mathbf{BC}) = \begin{bmatrix} -33 & -7 \\ -27 & 103 \end{bmatrix}$

     $\mathbf{A}(\mathbf{B}+\mathbf{C}) = \mathbf{AB}+\mathbf{AC} = \begin{bmatrix} -18 & -4 \\ 68 & -8 \end{bmatrix}$

3. $\mathbf{AB} = \begin{bmatrix} -1 & 8 \\ 46 & -1 \end{bmatrix};$ $\qquad\qquad$ $\mathbf{BA} = \begin{bmatrix} 11 & -12 & 14 \\ -14 & 0 & 7 \\ 0 & 8 & -13 \end{bmatrix}$

4. $\mathbf{Ay} = \begin{bmatrix} 2t^2 - \cos t \\ 3t^2 - 4\sin t + 5\cos t \end{bmatrix};$ $\qquad$ $\mathbf{Bx} = \begin{bmatrix} 2t + 3e^{-t} \\ -14t \\ 6t - 2e^{-t} \end{bmatrix}$

The products **Ax** and **By** are not defined, because in neither case is the number of columns of the first factor equal to the number of rows of the second factor.

5. **(a)** $\begin{bmatrix} 21 & 2 & 1 \\ 4 & 44 & 9 \\ -27 & 34 & 45 \end{bmatrix}$ $\qquad$ **(b)** $\begin{bmatrix} 9 & 21 & -13 \\ -5 & -8 & 24 \\ -25 & -19 & 26 \end{bmatrix}$

$\qquad$ **(c)** $\begin{bmatrix} 0 & -6 & 1 \\ 10 & 31 & -15 \\ 16 & 58 & -23 \end{bmatrix}$ $\qquad$ **(d)** $\begin{bmatrix} -10 & -8 & 5 \\ 18 & 12 & -10 \\ 11 & 22 & 6 \end{bmatrix}$

$\qquad$ **(e)** $\begin{bmatrix} 3-t & 2 & -1 \\ 0 & 4-t & 3 \\ -5 & 2 & 7-t \end{bmatrix}$

6. **(a)** $\mathbf{A_1 B} = \mathbf{A_2 B} = \begin{bmatrix} 5 & 10 \\ -4 & -8 \end{bmatrix}$

7. $\det(\mathbf{A}) = \det(\mathbf{B}) = 0$

8. $\det(\mathbf{AB}) = \det(\mathbf{BA}) = 144$

9. $(\mathbf{AB})' = \begin{bmatrix} 1 - 8t + 18t^2 & 1 + 2t - 12t^2 + 32t^3 \\ 3 + 3t^2 - 4t^3 & 8t + 3t^2 + 4t^3 \end{bmatrix}$

10. $(\mathbf{AB})' = \mathbf{A'B} + \mathbf{AB'} = \begin{bmatrix} 3e^t + 2e^{-t} - 2te^{-t} + 9t^2 \\ 3 \\ 24 + 2e^{-t} + 12t^3 \end{bmatrix}$

11. $\mathbf{x} = \begin{bmatrix} x \\ y \end{bmatrix},$ $\qquad$ $\mathbf{P}(t) = \begin{bmatrix} 0 & -3 \\ 3 & 0 \end{bmatrix},$ $\qquad$ $\mathbf{f}(t) = \begin{bmatrix} 0 \\ 0 \end{bmatrix}$

12. $\mathbf{x} = \begin{bmatrix} x \\ y \end{bmatrix}$, $\mathbf{P}(t) = \begin{bmatrix} 3 & -2 \\ 2 & 1 \end{bmatrix}$, $\mathbf{f}(t) = \begin{bmatrix} 0 \\ 0 \end{bmatrix}$

13. $\mathbf{x} = \begin{bmatrix} x \\ y \end{bmatrix}$, $\mathbf{P}(t) = \begin{bmatrix} 2 & 4 \\ 5 & -1 \end{bmatrix}$, $\mathbf{f}(t) = \begin{bmatrix} 3e^t \\ -t^2 \end{bmatrix}$

14. $\mathbf{x} = \begin{bmatrix} x \\ y \end{bmatrix}$, $\mathbf{P}(t) = \begin{bmatrix} t & -e^t \\ e^{-t} & t^2 \end{bmatrix}$, $\mathbf{f}(t) = \begin{bmatrix} \cos t \\ -\sin t \end{bmatrix}$

15. $\mathbf{x} = \begin{bmatrix} x \\ y \\ z \end{bmatrix}$, $\mathbf{P}(t) = \begin{bmatrix} 0 & 1 & 1 \\ 1 & 0 & 1 \\ 1 & 1 & 0 \end{bmatrix}$, $\mathbf{f}(t) = \begin{bmatrix} 0 \\ 0 \\ 0 \end{bmatrix}$

16. $\mathbf{x} = \begin{bmatrix} x \\ y \\ z \end{bmatrix}$, $\mathbf{P}(t) = \begin{bmatrix} 2 & -3 & 0 \\ 1 & 1 & 2 \\ 0 & 5 & -7 \end{bmatrix}$, $\mathbf{f}(t) = \begin{bmatrix} 0 \\ 0 \\ 0 \end{bmatrix}$

17. $\mathbf{x} = \begin{bmatrix} x \\ y \\ z \end{bmatrix}$, $\mathbf{P}(t) = \begin{bmatrix} 3 & -4 & 1 \\ 1 & 0 & -3 \\ 0 & 6 & -7 \end{bmatrix}$, $\mathbf{f}(t) = \begin{bmatrix} t \\ t^2 \\ t^3 \end{bmatrix}$

18. $\mathbf{x} = \begin{bmatrix} x \\ y \\ z \end{bmatrix}$, $\mathbf{P}(t) = \begin{bmatrix} t & -1 & e^t \\ 2 & t^2 & -1 \\ e^{-t} & 3t & t^3 \end{bmatrix}$, $\mathbf{f}(t) = \begin{bmatrix} 0 \\ 0 \\ 0 \end{bmatrix}$

19. $\mathbf{x} = \begin{bmatrix} x_1 \\ x_2 \\ x_3 \\ x_4 \end{bmatrix}$, $\mathbf{P}(t) = \begin{bmatrix} 0 & 1 & 0 & 0 \\ 0 & 0 & 2 & 0 \\ 0 & 0 & 0 & 3 \\ 4 & 0 & 0 & 0 \end{bmatrix}$, $\mathbf{f}(t) = \begin{bmatrix} 0 \\ 0 \\ 0 \\ 0 \end{bmatrix}$

20. $\mathbf{x} = \begin{bmatrix} x_1 \\ x_2 \\ x_3 \\ x_4 \end{bmatrix}$, $\mathbf{P}(t) = \begin{bmatrix} 0 & 1 & 1 & 0 \\ 0 & 0 & 1 & 1 \\ 1 & 0 & 0 & 1 \\ 1 & 1 & 0 & 0 \end{bmatrix}$, $\mathbf{f}(t) = \begin{bmatrix} 0 \\ t \\ t^2 \\ t^3 \end{bmatrix}$

21. $W(t) = e^{3t}$, $\mathbf{x}(t) = \begin{bmatrix} 2c_1e^t + c_2e^{2t} \\ -3c_1e^t - c_2e^{2t} \end{bmatrix}$

22. $\mathbf{x}(t) = c_1 \begin{bmatrix} 1 \\ 3 \end{bmatrix} e^{3t} + c_2 \begin{bmatrix} 2 \\ 1 \end{bmatrix} e^{-2t}$

23. $W(t) = 4,$ $\qquad \mathbf{x}(t) = \begin{bmatrix} c_1 e^{2t} + c_2 e^{-2t} \\ c_1 e^{2t} + 5c_2 e^{-2t} \end{bmatrix}$

24. $\mathbf{x}(t) = c_1 \begin{bmatrix} 1 \\ -1 \end{bmatrix} e^{3t} + c_2 \begin{bmatrix} 2 \\ -1 \end{bmatrix} e^{2t}$

25. $W(t) = 7e^{-3t},$ $\qquad \mathbf{x}(t) = \begin{bmatrix} 3c_1 e^{2t} + c_2 e^{-5t} \\ 2c_1 e^{2t} + 3c_2 e^{-5t} \end{bmatrix}$

26. $\mathbf{x}(t) = c_1 \begin{bmatrix} 2 \\ 2 \\ 1 \end{bmatrix} e^{t} + c_2 \begin{bmatrix} -2 \\ 0 \\ 1 \end{bmatrix} e^{3t} + c_3 \begin{bmatrix} 2 \\ -2 \\ 1 \end{bmatrix} e^{5t}$

27. $W(t) = 3,$ $\qquad \mathbf{x}(t) = \begin{bmatrix} c_1 e^{2t} + c_2 e^{-t} \\ c_1 e^{2t} + c_3 e^{-t} \\ c_1 e^{2t} - (c_2 + c_3)e^{-t} \end{bmatrix}$

28. $\mathbf{x}(t) = c_1 \begin{bmatrix} 1 \\ 6 \\ -13 \end{bmatrix} + c_2 \begin{bmatrix} 2 \\ 3 \\ -2 \end{bmatrix} e^{3t} + c_3 \begin{bmatrix} -1 \\ 2 \\ 1 \end{bmatrix} e^{-4t}$

29. $W(t) = e^{2t},$ $\qquad \mathbf{x}(t) = \begin{bmatrix} 3c_1 e^{-2t} + c_2 e^{t} + c_3 e^{3t} \\ -2c_1 e^{-2t} - c_2 e^{t} - c_3 e^{3t} \\ 2c_1 e^{-2t} + c_2 e^{t} \end{bmatrix}$

30. $W(t) = 1,$ $\qquad \mathbf{x}(t) = \begin{bmatrix} c_1 e^{-t} + c_4 e^{t} \\ c_3 e^{t} \\ c_2 e^{-t} + 3c_4 e^{t} \\ c_1 e^{-t} - 2c_3 e^{t} \end{bmatrix}$

31. $x = 2x_1 - x_2$ $\qquad\qquad$ **32.** $x = 7x_1 - 2x_2$

33. $x = 3x_1 + 4x_2$ $\qquad\qquad$ **34.** $x = 3x_1 - 2x_2$

35. $x = x_1 + 2x_2 + x_3$ $\qquad\qquad$ **36.** $x = 7x_1 + 3x_2 + 5x_3$

37. $\quad \mathbf{x} = 3x_1 - 3x_2 - 5x_3$ $\qquad\qquad$ **38.** $\quad \mathbf{x} = -2x_1 + 15x_2 - 4x_3$

39. $\quad \mathbf{x} = 3x_1 + 7x_2 + x_3 - 2x_4$ $\qquad$ **40.** $\quad \mathbf{x} = 13x_1 + 41x_2 + 3x_3 - 12x_4$

41. $\quad$ **(a)** $\quad \mathbf{x_2} = t\mathbf{x_1}$, so neither is a constant multiple of the other.

$\qquad\quad$ **(b)** $\quad W(\mathbf{x_1}, \mathbf{x_2}) = 0$, whereas Theorem 2 would imply that $W \neq 0$ if $\mathbf{x_1}$ and $\mathbf{x_2}$ were independent solutions of a system of the indicated form.

42. $\quad$ If $x_{12}(t) = c\, x_{11}(t)$ and $x_{22}(t) = c\, x_{21}(t)$ then

$$W(t) = x_{11}(t)x_{22}(t) - x_{12}(t)x_{21}(t) = c\, x_{11}(t)x_{21}(t) - c x_{11}(t)x_{21}(t) = 0.$$

SECTION 5.2

THE EIGENVALUE METHOD FOR HOMOGENEOUS LINEAR SYSTEMS

In each of Problems 1–16 we give the eigenvalues λ_1 and λ_2 of the coefficient matrix of the given system, their associated eigenvectors $\mathbf{v_1}$ and $\mathbf{v_2}$, and the resulting scalar components $x_1(t)$ and $x_2(t)$ of a general solution of the system.

1. $\quad$ Eigenvalues $\quad \lambda_1 = -1$ and $\lambda_2 = 3$

$\qquad$ Eigenvectors $\quad \mathbf{v_1} = [1 \quad -1]^T$ and $\mathbf{v_2} = [1 \quad 1]^T$

$\qquad x_1 = \quad c_1 e^{-t} + c_2 e^{3t}$

$\qquad x_2 = -c_1 e^{-t} + c_2 e^{3t}$

2. $\quad$ Eigenvalues $\quad \lambda_1 = -1$ and $\lambda_2 = 4$

$\qquad$ Eigenvectors $\quad \mathbf{v_1} = [1 \quad -1]^T$ and $\mathbf{v_2} = [3 \quad 2]^T$

$\qquad x_1 = \quad c_1 e^{-t} + 3c_2 e^{4t}$

$\qquad x_2 = -c_1 e^{-t} + 2c_2 e^{4t}$

3. $\quad$ Eigenvalues $\quad \lambda_1 = -1$ and $\lambda_2 = 6$

$\qquad$ Eigenvectors $\quad \mathbf{v_1} = [1 \quad -1]^T$ and $\mathbf{v_2} = [4 \quad 3]^T$

$\qquad x_1 = \quad c_1 e^{-t} + 4c_2 e^{6t}$

$\qquad x_2 = -c_1 e^{-t} + 3c_2 e^{6t}$

The equations

$$x_1(0) = c_1 + 4c_2 = 1$$
$$x_2(0) = -c_1 + 3c_2 = 1$$

yield $c_1 = -1/7$ and $c_2 = 2/7$, so the desired particular solution is given by

$$x_1 = (-e^{-t} + 8e^{6t})/7$$
$$x_2 = (\ e^{-t} + 6e^{6t})/7.$$

4.   Eigenvalues $\lambda_1 = -2$ and $\lambda_2 = 5$

Eigenvectors $\mathbf{v}_1 = [1 \ -6]^T$ and $\mathbf{v}_2 = [1 \quad 1]^T$

$$x_1 = \quad c_1e^{-2t} + c_2e^{5t}$$
$$x_2 = -6c_1e^{-2t} + c_2e^{5t}$$

5.   Eigenvalues $\lambda_1 = -1$ and $\lambda_2 = 5$

Eigenvectors $\mathbf{v}_1 = [1 \quad 1]^T$ and $\mathbf{v}_2 = [7 \quad 1]^T$

$$x_1 = c_1e^{-t} + 7c_2e^{5t}$$
$$x_2 = c_1e^{-t} + \quad c_2e^{5t}$$

6.   Eigenvalues $\lambda_1 = 3$ and $\lambda_2 = 4$

Eigenvectors $\mathbf{v}_1 = [5 \ -6]^T$ and $\mathbf{v}_2 = [1 \ -1]^T$

$$x_1 = \quad 5c_1e^{3t} + c_2e^{4t}$$
$$x_2 = -6c_1e^{3t} - c_2e^{4t}$$

The initial conditions yield $c_1 = -1$ and $c_2 = 6$, so

$$x_1 = -5e^{3t} + 6e^{4t}, \qquad x_2 = 6e^{3t} - 6e^{4t}.$$

7.   Eigenvalues $\lambda_1 = 1$ and $\lambda_2 = -9$

Eigenvectors $\mathbf{v}_1 = [1 \quad 1]^T$ and $\mathbf{v}_2 = [2 \ -3]^T$

$$x_1 = c_1e^{t} + 2c_2e^{-9t}$$
$$x_2 = c_1e^{t} - 3c_2e^{-9t}$$

8.   Characteristic equation $\lambda^2 + 4 = 0$

Eigenvalue $\lambda = 2i$, eigenvector $\mathbf{v} = [5 \quad 1-2i]^T$

$$x_1 = 5c_1\cos 2t + 5c_2\sin 2t$$
$$x_2 = c_1(\cos 2t + 2\sin 2t) + c_2(\sin 2t - 2\cos 2t)$$
$$= (c_1 - 2c_2)\cos 2t + (2c_1 + c_2)\sin 2t$$

9.   Characteristic equation $\lambda^2 + 16 = 0$

Eigenvalue $\lambda = 4i$, eigenvector $\mathbf{v} = [5 \quad 2-4i]^T$

The real and imaginary parts of

$$\mathbf{x} = [5 \quad 2-4i]^T (\cos 4t + i\sin 4t)$$

yield the general solution

$$x_1 = 5c_1\cos 4t + 5c_2\sin 4t$$
$$x_2 = c_1(2\cos 4t + 4\sin 4t) + c_2(2\sin 4t - 4\cos 4t).$$

The initial conditions $x_1(0) = 2$ and $x_2(0) = 3$ give $c_1 = 2/5$ and $c_2 = -11/20$, so the desired particular solution is

$$x_1 = 2\cos 4t - (11/4)\sin 4t$$
$$x_2 = 3\cos 4t + (1/2)\sin 4t.$$

10.   Characteristic equation $\lambda^2 + 9 = 0$

Eigenvalue $\lambda = 3i$, eigenvector $\mathbf{v} = [-2 \quad 3+2i]^T$

$$x_1 = -2c_1\cos 3t - 2c_2\sin 3t$$
$$x_2 = c_1(3\cos 3t - 3\sin 3t) + c_2(3\cos 3t + 3\sin 3t)$$
$$= (3c_1 + 3c_2)\cos 3t + (3c_2 - 3c_1)\sin 3t$$

11.   Characteristic equation $(\lambda - 1)^2 + 4 = 0$

Eigenvalue $\lambda = 1 - 2i$, eigenvector $\mathbf{v} = [1 \quad i]^T$

The real and imaginary parts of

$$\mathbf{x} = [1 \quad i]^T e^t(\cos 2t - i\sin 2t)$$
$$= e^t [\cos 2t \quad \sin 2t]^T + ie^t [-\sin 2t \quad \cos 2t]^T$$

yield the general solution

$$x_1 = e^t(c_1 \cos 2t - c_2 \sin 2t)$$
$$x_2 = e^t(c_1 \sin 2t + c_2 \cos 2t).$$

The particular solution with $x_1(0) = 0$ and $x_2(0) = 4$ is obtained with $c_1 = 0$ and $c_2 = 4$, so

$$x_1 = -4e^t \sin 2t, \qquad\qquad x_2 = 4e^t \cos 2t.$$

12. Characteristic equation $\lambda^2 - 4\lambda + 8 = 0$

Eigenvalue $\lambda = 2 + 2i$, eigenvector $\mathbf{v} = [-5 \quad 1+2i]^T$

$$x_1 = e^{2t}(-5c_1 \cos 2t - 5c_2 \sin 2t)$$
$$x_2 = e^{2t}[c_1(\cos 2t - 2\sin 2t) + c_2(2\cos 2t + \sin 2t)]$$
$$= e^{2t}[(c_1 + 2c_2)\cos 2t + (-2c_1 + c_2)\sin 2t]$$

13. Characteristic equation $\lambda^2 - 4\lambda + 13 = 0$

Eigenvalue $\lambda = 2 - 3i$, eigenvector $\mathbf{v} = [3 \quad 1+i]^T$

The real and imaginary parts of

$$\mathbf{x} = e^{2t}[3 \quad 1+i]^T(\cos 3t - i\sin 3t)$$

yield the general solution

$$x_1 = 3e^{2t}(c_1 \cos 3t - c_2 \sin 3t)$$
$$x_2 = e^{2t}[(c_1 + c_2)\cos 3t + (c_1 - c_2)\sin 3t].$$

14. Characteristic equation $(3 - \lambda)^2 + 16 = 0$

Eigenvalue $\lambda = 3 + 4i$, eigenvector $\mathbf{v} = [1 \quad -i]^T$

$$x_1 = e^{3t}(c_1 \cos 4t + c_2 \sin 4t)$$
$$x_2 = e^{3t}(c_1 \sin 4t - c_2 \cos 4t)$$

15. Characteristic equation $\lambda^2 - 10\lambda + 41 = 0$

Eigenvalue $\lambda = 5 - 4i$, eigenvector $\mathbf{v} = [5 \quad 2+4i]^T$

$$\mathbf{x}(t) = 5e^{5t}[5 \quad 2+4i]^T(\cos 4t - i\sin 4t)$$

$$x_1 = 5e^{5t}(c_1 \cos 4t - c_2 \sin 4t)$$
$$x_2 = e^{5t}[(2c_1 + 4c_2)\cos 4t + (4c_1 - 2c_2)\sin 4t]$$

16.   Characteristic equation $\lambda^2 + 110\lambda + 1000 = 0$

Eigenvalues $\lambda_1 = -10$ and $\lambda_2 = -100$

Eigenvectors $v_1 = [1 \quad 2]^T$ and $v_2 = [2 \quad -5]^T$

$$x_1 = c_1 e^{-10t} + 2c_2 e^{-100t}$$

$$x_2 = 2c_1 e^{-10t} - 5c_2 e^{-100t}$$

17.   Eigenvalues $\lambda_1 = 9$, $\lambda_2 = 6$, $\lambda_3 = 0$

Eigenvectors $v_1 = [1 \quad 1 \quad 1]^T$, $v_2 = [1 \quad -2 \quad 1]^T$, $v_3 = [1 \quad 0 \quad -1]^T$

$$x_1 = c_1 e^{9t} + c_2 e^{6t} + c_3$$

$$x_2 = c_1 e^{9t} - 2c_2 e^{6t}$$

$$x_3 = c_1 e^{9t} + c_2 e^{6t} - c_3$$

18.   Eigenvalues $\lambda_1 = 9$, $\lambda_2 = 6$, $\lambda_3 = 0$

Eigenvectors $v_1 = [1 \quad 2 \quad 2]^T$, $v_2 = [0 \quad 1 \quad -1]^T$, $v_3 = [4 \quad -1 \quad -1]^T$

$$x_1 = c_1 e^{9t} \qquad\qquad + 4c_3$$

$$x_2 = 2c_1 e^{9t} + c_2 e^{6t} - c_3$$

$$x_3 = 2c_1 e^{9t} - c_2 e^{6t} - c_3$$

19.   Eigenvalues $\lambda_1 = 6$, $\lambda_2 = 3$, $\lambda_3 = 3$

Eigenvectors $v_1 = [1 \quad 1 \quad 1]^T$, $v_2 = [1 \quad -2 \quad 1]^T$, $v_3 = [1 \quad 0 \quad -1]^T$

$$x_1 = c_1 e^{6t} + c_2 e^{3t} + c_3 e^{3t}$$

$$x_2 = c_1 e^{6t} - 2c_2 e^{3t}$$

$$x_3 = c_1 e^{6t} + c_2 e^{3t} - c_3 e^{3t}$$

20.   Eigenvalues $\lambda_1 = 9$, $\lambda_2 = 6$, $\lambda_3 = 2$

Eigenvectors $v_1 = [1 \quad 1 \quad 1]^T$, $v_2 = [1 \quad -2 \quad 1]^T$, $v_3 = [1 \quad 0 \quad -1]^T$

$$x_1 = c_1 e^{9t} + c_2 e^{6t} + c_3 e^{2t}$$

$$x_2 = c_1 e^{9t} - 2c_2 e^{6t}$$

$$x_3 = c_1 e^{9t} + c_2 e^{6t} - c_3 e^{2t}$$

21.   Eigenvalues $\lambda_1 = 0$, $\lambda_2 = 1$, $\lambda_3 = -1$

Eigenvectors $\mathbf{v}_1 = [6 \quad 2 \quad 5]^T$, $\mathbf{v}_2 = [3 \quad 1 \quad 2]^T$, $\mathbf{v}_3 = [2 \quad 1 \quad 2]^T$

$x_1 = 6c_1 + 3c_2e^t + 2c_3e^{-t}$

$x_2 = 2c_1 + c_2e^t + c_3e^{-t}$

$x_3 = 5c_1 + 2c_2e^t + 2c_3e^{-t}$

22. Characteristic equation $(3 - \lambda)(\lambda^2 + \lambda - 2) = 0$

Distinct eigenvalues $\lambda_1 = -2$, $\lambda_2 = 1$, $\lambda_3 = 3$

Eigenvectors $\mathbf{v}_1 = [0 \quad 1 \quad -1]^T$, $\mathbf{v}_2 = [1 \quad -1 \quad 0]^T$, $\mathbf{v}_3 = [1 \quad -1 \quad 1]^T$

$x_1 = \qquad c_2e^t + c_3e^{3t}$

$x_2 = c_1e^{-2t} - c_2e^t - c_3e^{3t}$

$x_3 = -c_1e^{-2t} \qquad + c_3e^{3t}$

23. Eigenvalues $\lambda_1 = 2$, $\lambda_2 = -2$, $\lambda_3 = 3$

Eigenvectors $\mathbf{v}_1 = [1 \quad -1 \quad 0]^T$, $\mathbf{v}_2 = [0 \quad 1 \quad -1]^T$, $\mathbf{v}_3 = [1 \quad -1 \quad 1]^T$

$x_1 = c_1e^{2t} \qquad + c_3e^{3t}$

$x_2 = -c_1e^{2t} + c_2e^{-2t} - c_3e^{3t}$

$x_3 = \qquad - c_2e^{-2t} + c_3e^{3t}$

24. Characteristic equation $4(1 - \lambda)(\lambda^2 + 4) = 0$

Eigenvalues $\lambda = 1$ and $\lambda = \pm 2i$

Eigenvector $[1 \quad -1 \quad 0]^T$ associated with $\lambda = 1$

To find an eigenvector $\mathbf{v} = [a \quad b \quad c]^T$ associated with $\lambda = 2i$ we must find a nontrivial solution of the equations

$$(2 - 2i)a + \qquad b - \qquad c = 0$$
$$-4a + (-3 - 2i)b - \qquad c = 0$$
$$4a + \qquad 4b + (2 - 2i)c = 0.$$

Subtraction of the first two equations yields

$$(6 - 2i)a + (4 + 2i)b = 0,$$

so we take $a = 2 + i$ and $b = -3 + i$. Then the first equation gives $c = 3 - i$. Thus $\mathbf{v} = [2+i \quad -3+i \quad 3-i]^T$. Finally

$$(2 + i)e^{2it} = (2 \cos 2t - \sin 2t) + i (\cos 2t + 2 \sin 2t)$$

$$(3 - i)e^{2it} = (3 \cos 2t + \sin 2t) + i (3 \sin 2t - \cos 2t),$$

so the solution is

$$x_1 = c_1 e^t + c_2(2 \cos 2t - \sin 2t) + c_3(\cos 2t + 2 \sin 2t)$$

$$x_2 = -c_1 e^t - c_2(3 \cos 2t + \sin 2t) + c_3(\cos 2t - 3 \sin 2t)$$

$$x_3 = c_2(3 \cos 2t + \sin 2t) + c_3(3 \sin 2t - \cos 2t).$$

25. Eigenvalues $\lambda = 0, \ 2 \pm 3i$

$$x_1 = c_1 + e^{2t} [(-c_2 + c_3)\cos 3t + (c_2 + c_3)\sin 3t]$$

$$x_2 = -c_1 + 2e^{2t}(c_2\cos 3t - c_3\sin 3t)$$

$$x_3 = 2e^{2t}(-c_2\cos 3t + c_3\sin 3t)$$

26. Characteristic equation $(3 - \lambda)[(\lambda + 1)^2 + 1] = 0$

Eigenvalues $\lambda = 3$ and $\lambda = -1 \pm i$

Eigenvector $\mathbf{v}_0 = [4 \quad 9 \quad 0]$ associated with $\lambda_0 = 3$.

To find an eigenvector $\mathbf{v} = [a \quad b \quad c]^T$ associated with the complex eigenvalue $\lambda = -1 + i$ we must find a nontrivial solution of the equations

$$(4 - i)a \quad + \quad c = 0$$

$$9a - ib + 2c = 0$$

$$-9a + 4b - ic = 0.$$

The choice $a = 1$ in the first equation gives $c = -4 + i$. Then the third equation yields $b = 2 - i$. Thus the complex eigenvector associated with $\lambda = -1 + i$ is

$$\mathbf{v} = [1 \quad 2-i \quad -4+i]^T.$$

Finding the real and imaginary parts $\mathbf{x}_1(t)$ and $\mathbf{x}_2(t)$ of

$$\mathbf{x}(t) = \mathbf{v}e^{(-1+i)t} = \mathbf{v}e^{-t}(\cos t + i \sin t)$$

and assembling the general solution $c_0\mathbf{x}_0 + c_1\mathbf{x}_1 + c_2\mathbf{x}_2$, we get the scalar equations

$$x_1(t) = 4c_0e^{3t} + e^{-t} [c_1\cos t + c_2\sin t]$$

$$x_2(t) = 9c_0e^{3t} + e^{-t} [(2c_1 - c_2)\cos t + (c_1 + 2c_2)\sin t]$$

$$x_3(t) = e^{-t} [(-4c_1 + c_2)\cos t + (-c_1 - 4c_2)\sin t].$$

Finally, the given initial conditions yield the values $c_0 = 1$, $c_1 = -4$, $c_2 = 1$, so the desired particular solution is

$$x_1(t) = 4e^{3t} - e^{-t}(4 \cos t - \sin t)$$
$$x_2(t) = 9e^{3t} - e^{-t}(9 \cos t + 2 \sin t)$$
$$x_3(t) = 17e^{-t}\cos t.$$

27. The matrix

$$A = \begin{bmatrix} -0.2 & 0 \\ 0.2 & -0.4 \end{bmatrix}$$

has eigenvalues $\lambda_1 = -0.2$ and $\lambda_2 = -0.4$, with eigenvectors $v_1 = [1 \quad 1]^T$ and $v_2 = [0 \quad 1]^T$ that yield the scalar solution equations

$$x_1(t) = 15e^{-0.2t}, \qquad x_2(t) = 15e^{-0.2t} - 15e^{-0.4t}.$$

The maximum value of $x_2(t)$, when $x_2'(t) = 0$, is 3.75 lb.

28. The matrix

$$A = \begin{bmatrix} -0.4 & 0 \\ 0.4 & -0.25 \end{bmatrix}$$

has eigenvalues $\lambda_1 = -0.4$ and $\lambda_2 = -0.25$, with eigenvectors $v_1 = [3 \quad -8]^T$ and $v_2 = [0 \quad 1]^T$ that yield the scalar solution equations

$$x_1(t) = 15e^{-0.4t}, \qquad x_2(t) = -40e^{-0.4t} + 40e^{-0.25t}.$$

The maximum value of $x_2(t)$, when $x_2'(t) = 0$, is 6.85 lb.

29. The matrix

$$A = \begin{bmatrix} -0.2 & 0.4 \\ 0.2 & -0.4 \end{bmatrix}$$

has eigenvalues $\lambda_1 = 0$ and $\lambda_2 = -0.6$, with eigenvectors $v_1 = [2 \quad 1]^T$ and $v_2 = [1 \quad -1]^T$ that yield the scalar solution equations

$$x_1(t) = 10 + 5e^{-0.6t}, \quad x_2(t) = 5 - 5e^{-0.6t}.$$

30. The matrix

$$A = \begin{bmatrix} -0.4 & 0.25 \\ 0.4 & -0.25 \end{bmatrix}$$

has eigenvalues $\lambda_1 = 0$ and $\lambda_2 = -0.65$, with eigenvectors $\mathbf{v}_1 = [5 \quad 8]^T$ and $\mathbf{v}_2 = [1 \quad -1]^T$ that yield the scalar solution equations

$$x_1(t) = (75 + 120e^{-0.65t})/13$$

$$x_2(t) = (120 - 120e^{-0.65t})/13.$$

31. The matrix

$$\mathbf{A} = \begin{bmatrix} -1 & 0 & 0 \\ 1 & -2 & 0 \\ 0 & 2 & -3 \end{bmatrix}$$

has eigenvalues $\lambda_1 = -1$, $\lambda_2 = -2$, and $\lambda_3 = -3$, with associated eigenvectors $\mathbf{v}_1 = [1 \quad 1 \quad 1]^T$, $\mathbf{v}_2 = [0 \quad 1 \quad 2]^T$, and $\mathbf{v}_3 = [0 \quad 0 \quad 1]^T$. The desired particular solution is given by

$$x_1(t) = 27e^{-t}$$

$$x_2(t) = 27e^{-t} - 27e^{-2t}$$

$$x_3(t) = 27e^{-t} - 54e^{-2t} + 27e^{-3t}.$$

The maximum amount of salt ever in tank 3 is $x_3(\ln 3) = 4$ pounds.

32. The matrix

$$\mathbf{A} = \begin{bmatrix} -3 & 0 & 0 \\ 3 & -2 & 0 \\ 0 & 2 & -1 \end{bmatrix}$$

has eigenvalues $\lambda_1 = -3$, $\lambda_2 = -2$, and $\lambda_3 = -1$, with associated eigenvectors $\mathbf{v}_1 = [1 \quad -3 \quad 3]^T$, $\mathbf{v}_2 = [0 \quad -1 \quad 2]^T$, and $\mathbf{v}_3 = [0 \quad 0 \quad 1]^T$. The desired particular solution is given by

$$x_1(t) = 45e^{-3t}$$

$$x_2(t) = -135e^{-3t} + 135e^{-2t}$$

$$x_3(t) = -135e^{-t} - 270e^{-2t} + 135e^{-t}.$$

The maximum amount of salt ever in tank 3 is $x_3(\ln 3) = 20$ pounds.

33. The matrix

$$\mathbf{A} = \begin{bmatrix} -4 & 0 & 0 \\ 4 & -6 & 0 \\ 0 & 6 & -2 \end{bmatrix}$$

has eigenvalues $\lambda_1 = -4$, $\lambda_2 = -6$, and $\lambda_3 = -2$, with associated eigenvectors $\mathbf{v}_1 = [-1 \quad -2 \quad 6]^T$, $\mathbf{v}_2 = [0 \quad -2 \quad 3]^T$, and $\mathbf{v}_3 = [0 \quad 0 \quad 1]^T$. The desired particular solution is given by

$$x_1(t) = 45e^{-4t}$$
$$x_2(t) = 90e^{-4t} - 90e^{-6t}$$
$$x_3(t) = -270e^{-4t} + 135e^{-6t} + 135e^{-2t}.$$

The maximum amount of salt ever in tank 3 is $x_3(\tfrac{1}{2}\ln 3) = 20$ pounds.

34.   The matrix

$$\mathbf{A} = \begin{bmatrix} -3 & 0 & 0 \\ 3 & -5 & 0 \\ 0 & 5 & -1 \end{bmatrix}$$

has eigenvalues $\lambda_1 = -3$, $\lambda_2 = -5$, and $\lambda_3 = -1$, with associated eigenvectors $\mathbf{v}_1 = [-4 \;\; -6 \;\; 15]^T$, $\mathbf{v}_2 = [0 \;\; -4 \;\; 5]^T$, and $\mathbf{v}_3 = [0 \;\; 0 \;\; 1]^T$. The desired particular solution is given by

$$x_1(t) = 40e^{-3t}$$
$$x_2(t) = 60e^{-3t} - 60e^{-5t}$$
$$x_3(t) = -150e^{-3t} + 75e^{-5t} + 75e^{-t}.$$

The maximum amount of salt ever in tank 3 is $x_3(\tfrac{1}{2}\ln 5) \approx 21.4663$ pounds.

35.   The matrix

$$\mathbf{A} = \begin{bmatrix} -6 & 0 & 3 \\ 6 & -20 & 0 \\ 0 & 20 & -3 \end{bmatrix}$$

has eigenvalues $\lambda_1 = 0$, $\lambda_2 = -18$, and $\lambda_3 = -11$, with associated eigenvectors $\mathbf{v}_1 = [10 \;\; 3 \;\; 20]^T$, $\mathbf{v}_2 = [-1 \;\; -3 \;\; 4]^T$, and $\mathbf{v}_3 = [-3 \;\; -2 \;\; 5]^T$. The desired particular solution is given by

$$x_1(t) = 10 - \tfrac{1}{7}\left(55e^{-18t} - 216e^{-11t}\right)$$
$$x_2(t) = 3 - \tfrac{1}{7}\left(165e^{-18t} - 144e^{-11t}\right)$$
$$x_3(t) = 20 + \tfrac{1}{7}\left(220e^{-18t} - 360e^{-11t}\right).$$

Thus the limiting amounts of salt in tanks 1, 2, and 3 are 10 lb, 3 lb, and 20 lb.

36.   The matrix

$$A = \begin{bmatrix} -\frac{1}{2} & 0 & \frac{1}{2} \\ \frac{1}{2} & -\frac{1}{5} & 0 \\ 0 & \frac{1}{5} & -\frac{1}{2} \end{bmatrix}$$

has eigenvalues $\lambda_1 = 0$, $\lambda_2 = -3(2+i)/10$, and $\lambda_3 = -3(2-i)/10$, with associated eigenvectors $\mathbf{v_1} = [1 \quad 5/2 \quad 1]^T$, $\mathbf{v_2} = [-(1-3i)/2 \quad -(1+3i)/2 \quad 1]^T$, and $\mathbf{v_3} = [-(1+3i)/2 \quad -(1-3i)/2 \quad 1]^T$. The desired particular solution is given by

$$x_1(t) = 4 + e^{-3t/5}[14\cos(3t/10) - 2\sin(3t/10)]$$
$$x_2(t) = 10 - e^{-3t/5}[10\cos(3t/10) - 10\sin(3t/10)]$$
$$x_3(t) = 4 - e^{-3t/5}[4\cos(3t/10) + 8\sin(3t/10)].$$

Thus the limiting amounts of salt in tanks 1, 2, and 3 are 4 lb, 10 lb, and 4 lb.

37. The matrix

$$A = \begin{bmatrix} -1 & 0 & 2 \\ 1 & -3 & 0 \\ 0 & 3 & -2 \end{bmatrix}$$

has eigenvalues $\lambda_1 = 0$, $\lambda_2 = -3 - i\sqrt{2}$, and $\lambda_3 = -3 + i\sqrt{2}$, with associated eigenvectors $\mathbf{v_1} = [6 \quad 2 \quad 3]^T$, $\mathbf{v_2} = \left[(-2+i\sqrt{2})/3 \quad (-1-i\sqrt{2})/3 \quad 1\right]^T$, and $\mathbf{v_3} = \left[(-2-i\sqrt{2})/3 \quad (-1+i\sqrt{2})/3 \quad 1\right]^T$. The desired particular solution is given by

$$x_1(t) = 30 + e^{-3t}\left[25\cos(t\sqrt{2}) + 10\sqrt{2}\sin(t\sqrt{2})\right]$$
$$x_2(t) = 10 - e^{-3t}\left[10\cos(t\sqrt{2}) - \frac{25}{2}\sqrt{2}\sin(t\sqrt{2})\right]$$
$$x_3(t) = 15 - e^{-3t}\left[15\cos(t\sqrt{2}) + \frac{45}{2}\sqrt{2}\sin(t\sqrt{2})\right].$$

Thus the limiting amounts of salt in tanks 1, 2, and 3 are 30 lb, 10 lb, and 15 lb.

38. Characteristic equation: $(\lambda - 1)(\lambda - 2)(\lambda - 3)(\lambda - 4) = 0$

Eigenvalues and associated eigenvectors:

$$\begin{aligned}
\lambda = 1, \qquad & \mathbf{v} = [1 \quad -2 \quad 3 \quad -4]^T \\
\lambda = 2, \qquad & \mathbf{v} = [0 \quad 1 \quad -3 \quad 6]^T \\
\lambda = 3, \qquad & \mathbf{v} = [0 \quad 0 \quad 1 \quad -4]^T \\
\lambda = 4, \qquad & \mathbf{v} = [0 \quad 0 \quad 0 \quad 1]^T
\end{aligned}$$

Scalar solution equations:

$$x_1(t) = c_1 e^t$$

$$x_2(t) = -2c_1 e^t + c_2 e^{2t}$$

$$x_3(t) = 3c_1 e^t - 3c_2 e^{2t} - c_3 e^{3t}$$

$$x_4(t) = -4c_1 e^t + 6c_2 e^{2t} - 4c_3 e^{3t} + c_4 e^{4t}$$

39. Characteristic equation: $(\lambda^2 - 1)(\lambda^2 - 4) = 0$

Eigenvalues and associated eigenvectors:

$$\lambda = 1, \qquad \mathbf{v} = [3 \quad -2 \quad 4 \quad 1]^T$$
$$\lambda = -1, \qquad \mathbf{v} = [0 \quad 0 \quad 1 \quad 0]^T$$
$$\lambda = 2, \qquad \mathbf{v} = [0 \quad 1 \quad 0 \quad 0]^T$$
$$\lambda = -2, \qquad \mathbf{v} = [1 \quad -1 \quad 0 \quad 0]^T$$

Scalar solution equations:

$$x_1(t) = 3c_1 e^t \qquad\qquad + c_4 e^{-2t}$$

$$x_2(t) = -2c_1 e^t \qquad + c_3 e^{2t} - c_4 e^{-2t}$$

$$x_3(t) = 4c_1 e^t + c_2 e^{-t}$$

$$x_4(t) = c_1 e^t$$

40. Characteristic equation: $(\lambda^2 - 4)(\lambda^2 - 25) = 0$

Eigenvalues and associated eigenvectors:

$$\lambda = 2, \qquad \mathbf{v} = [1 \quad -3 \quad 0 \quad 0]^T$$
$$\lambda = -2, \qquad \mathbf{v} = [0 \quad 3 \quad 0 \quad -1]^T$$
$$\lambda = 5, \qquad \mathbf{v} = [0 \quad 0 \quad 1 \quad -3]^T$$
$$\lambda = -5, \qquad \mathbf{v} = [0 \quad 1 \quad 0 \quad 0]^T$$

Scalar solution equations:

$$x_1(t) = c_1 e^{2t}$$

$$x_2(t) = -3c_1 e^{2t} + 3c_2 e^{-2t} \qquad\qquad - c_4 e^{-5t}$$

$$x_3(t) = \qquad\qquad\qquad c_3 e^{5t}$$

$$x_4(t) = \qquad - c_2 e^{-2t} - 3c_3 e^{5t}$$

41. The eigenvectors associated with the respective eigenvalues $\lambda_1 = -3$, $\lambda_2 = -6$, $\lambda_3 = 10$, and $\lambda_4 = 15$ are

$$\mathbf{v_1} = [\ 1 \quad 0 \quad 0 \quad -1]^T$$
$$\mathbf{v_2} = [\ 0 \quad 1 \quad -1 \quad 0]^T$$
$$\mathbf{v_3} = [-2 \quad 1 \quad 1 \quad -2]^T$$
$$\mathbf{v_4} = [\ 1 \quad 2 \quad 2 \quad 1]^T.$$

Hence the general solution is

$$x_1 = c_1 e^{-3t} \qquad\qquad - 2c_3 e^{10t} + c_4 e^{15t}$$

$$x_2 = \qquad\qquad c_2 e^{-6t} + c_3 e^{10t} + 2c_4 e^{15t}$$

$$x_3 = \qquad\quad - c_2 e^{-6t} + c_3 e^{10t} + 2c_4 e^{15t}$$

$$x_4 = -c_1 e^{-3t} \qquad\qquad - 2c_3 e^{10t} + c_4 e^{15t}.$$

The given initial conditions are satisfied by choosing $c_1 = c_2 = 0$, $c_3 = -1$, and $c_4 = 1$, so the desired particular solution is given by

$$x_1 = 2e^{10t} + e^{15t} = x_4$$
$$x_2 = -e^{10t} + 2e^{15t} = x_3.$$

SECTION 5.3

SECOND ORDER SYSTEMS
AND MECHANICAL APPLICATIONS

This section uses the eigenvalue method to exhibit realistic applications of linear systems. If a computer system like Maple, Mathematica, MATLAB, or even a TI-85/86/89/92 calculator is available, then a system of more than three railway cars, or a multistory building with four or more floors (as in the project), can be investigated. However, the problems in the text are intended for manual solution.

Problems 1-6 involve the system

$$m_1 x_1'' = -(k_1 + k_2)x_1 + k_2 x_2$$
$$m_2 x_2'' = k_2 x_1 - (k_2 + k_3)x_2$$

with various values of m_1, m_2 and k_1, k_2, k_3.

1. $x_1 = a_1 + a_2 t + b_1 \cos 2t + b_2 \sin 2t$

    $x_2 = a_1 + a_2 t - b_1 \cos 2t - b_2 \sin 2t$

    The natural frequencies are $\omega_1 = 0$ and $\omega_2 = 2$. In the degenerate natural mode with "frequency" $\omega_1 = 0$ the two masses move by translation without oscillating. At frequency $\omega_2 = 2$ they oscillate in opposite directions with equal amplitudes.

2. $\quad x_1 = a_1 \cos t + a_2 \sin t + b_1 \cos 3t + b_2 \sin 3t$

$\quad\quad x_2 = a_1 \cos t + a_2 \sin t - b_1 \cos 3t - b_2 \sin 3t$

The natural frequencies are $\omega_1 = 1$ and $\omega_2 = 3$. In the natural mode with frequency ω_1, the two masses m_1 and m_2 move in the same direction with equal amplitudes of oscillation. At frequency ω_2 they move in opposite directions with equal amplitudes.

3. $\quad x_1 = a_1 \cos t + a_2 \sin t - 2b_1 \cos 2t - 2b_2 \sin 2t$

$\quad\quad x_2 = a_1 \cos t + a_2 \sin t + b_1 \cos 2t + b_2 \sin 2t$

The natural frequencies are $\omega_1 = 1$ and $\omega_2 = 2$. In the natural mode with frequency ω_1, the two masses m_1 and m_2 move in the same direction with equal amplitudes of oscillation. In the natural mode with frequency ω_2 they move in opposite directions with the amplitude of oscillation of m_1 twice that of m_2.

4. $\quad x_1 = a_1 \cos t + a_2 \sin t + b_1 \cos t\sqrt{5} + b_2 \sin t\sqrt{5}$

$\quad\quad x_2 = a_1 \cos t + a_2 \sin t - b_1 \cos t\sqrt{5} - b_2 \sin t\sqrt{5}$

The natural modes of oscillation are the same as in Problem 2, except with $\omega_1 = 1$ and $\omega_2 = \sqrt{5}$.

5. $\quad x_1 = a_1 \cos t\sqrt{2} + a_2 \sin t\sqrt{2} + b_1 \cos 2t + b_2 \sin 2t$

$\quad\quad x_2 = a_1 \cos t\sqrt{2} + a_2 \sin t\sqrt{2} - b_1 \cos 2t - b_2 \sin 2t$

The natural modes of oscillation are the same as in Problem 2, except with $\omega_1 = \sqrt{2}$ and $\omega_2 = 2$.

6. $\quad x_1 = a_1 \cos t\sqrt{2} + a_2 \sin t\sqrt{2} + b_1 \cos 2t\sqrt{2} + b_2 \sin 2t\sqrt{2}$

$\quad\quad x_2 = a_1 \cos t\sqrt{2} + a_2 \sin t\sqrt{2} - (b_1/2)\cos 2t\sqrt{2} - (b_2/2)\sin 2t\sqrt{2}$

At natural frequency $\omega_1 = \sqrt{2}$ the two masses move in the same direction with equal amplitudes of oscillation. At natural frequency $\omega_2 = 2\sqrt{2}$ they move in opposite directions with the amplitude of m_2 being half that of m_1.

7. $\quad x_1 = a_1 \cos 2t + a_2 \sin 2t - b_1 \cos 4t - b_2 \sin 4t$

$\quad\quad x_2 = a_1 \cos 2t + a_2 \sin 2t - b_1 \cos 4t - b_2 \sin 4t$

At natural frequency $\omega_1 = 2$ the two masses move in the same direction with equal amplitudes of oscillation. At natural frequency $\omega_2 = 2\sqrt{2}$ they move in opposite directions with equal amplitudes of oscillation.

8. $x_1(t) = 10\cos t + 15\cos 3t - 25\cos 5t$

$x_2(t) = 10\cos t - 15\cos 3t + 5\cos 5t$

We have a superposition of three oscillations, in which the two masses move

- in the same direction with frequency $\omega_1 = 1$ and equal amplitudes;
- in opposite directions with frequency $\omega_2 = 3$ and equal amplitudes;
- in opposite directions with frequency $\omega_3 = 5$ and with the amplitude of motion of m_1 being 5 times that of m_2.

9. $x_1(t) = 5\cos t - 8\cos 3t + 3\cos 5t$

$x_2(t) = 5\cos t + 4\cos 3t - 9\cos 5t$

We have a superposition of three oscillations, in which the two masses move

- in the same direction with frequency $\omega_1 = 1$ and equal amplitudes;
- in opposite directions with frequency $\omega_2 = 3$ and with the amplitude of motion of m_1 being twice that of m_2;
- in opposite directions with frequency $\omega_3 = 5$ and with the amplitude of motion of m_2 being 3 times that of m_1.

10. $x_1(t) = 14\cos t - 15\cos 2t + \cos 4t$

$x_2(t) = 16\cos t - 15\cos 3t - \cos 4t$

We have a superposition of three oscillations, in which the two masses move

- in the same direction with frequency $\omega_1 = 1$ and with the amplitude of motion of m_1 being 8/7 times that of m_2;
- in the same direction with frequency $\omega_2 = 2$ and equal amplitudes;
- in opposite directions with frequency $\omega_3 = 4$ and equal amplitudes.

11. **(a)** In mode 1 the two masses oscillate in the same direction with frequency $\omega_1 = 6$ and with the amplitude of motion of m_1 being twice that of m_2. In mode 2 the two masses oscillate in opposite directions with frequency $\omega_2 = 8$ and with the amplitude of motion of m_2 being 3 times that of m_1.

(b) The motion of the masses satisfying the given initial conditions is described by

$$x(t) = 2\sin 6t + 19\cos 7t$$
$$y(t) = \sin 6t + 3\cos 7t$$

Thus the expected oscillation with frequency $\omega_2 = 8$ is missing, and we have a superposition of (only two) oscillations, in which the two masses move

- in the same direction with frequency $\omega_1 = 6$ and with the amplitude of motion of m_1 being twice that of m_2;
- in the same direction with frequency $\omega_3 = 7$ and with the amplitude of motion of m_1 being 19/7 times that of m_2.

12. The characteristic polynomial of $\mathbf{A}$ is

$$\lambda^3 + 6\lambda^2 + 10\lambda + 4 = (\lambda + 2)(\lambda^2 + 4\lambda + 2)$$

Natural frequency $\omega_1 = \sqrt{(2 - \sqrt{2})}$ with amplitude ratios $1 : \sqrt{2} : 1$
Natural frequency $\omega_2 = \sqrt{2}$ with amplitude ratios $1 : 0 : -1$
Natural frequency $\omega_3 = \sqrt{(2 + \sqrt{2})}$ with amplitude ratios $1 : -\sqrt{2} : 1$

13. The characteristic polynomial of $\mathbf{A}$ is

$$\lambda^3 + 12\lambda^2 + 40\lambda + 32 = (\lambda + 4)(\lambda^2 + 8\lambda + 8)$$

Natural frequency $\omega_1 = \sqrt{(4 - 2\sqrt{2})}$ with amplitude ratios $1 : \sqrt{2} : 1$
Natural frequency $\omega_2 = 2$ with amplitude ratios $1 : 0 : -1$
Natural frequency $\omega_3 = \sqrt{(4 + 2\sqrt{2})}$ with amplitude ratios $1 : -\sqrt{2} : 1$

14. The equations of motion of the given system are

$$x_1'' = -50x_1 + 10(x_2 - x_1) + 5\cos 10t$$

$$m_2 x_2'' = -10(x_2 - x_1).$$

When we substitute $x_1 = A\cos 10t$, $x_2 = B\cos 10t$ and cancel $\cos 10t$ throughout we get the equations

$$-40A - 10B = 5$$

$$-10A + (10 - 100m_2)B = 0.$$

If $m_2 = 0.1$ (slug) then it follows that $A = 0$, so the mass m_1 remains at rest.

15. First we need the general solution of the homogeneous system $\mathbf{x}'' = \mathbf{A}\mathbf{x}$ with

$$\mathbf{A} = \begin{bmatrix} -50 & 25/2 \\ 50 & -50 \end{bmatrix}$$

The eigenvalues of $\mathbf{A}$ are $\lambda_1 = -25$ and $\lambda_2 = -75$, so the natural frequencies of the system are $\omega_1 = 5$ and $\omega_2 = 5\sqrt{3}$. The associated eigenvectors are $\mathbf{v}_1 = \begin{bmatrix} 1 & 2 \end{bmatrix}^T$ and $\mathbf{v}_2 = \begin{bmatrix} 1 & -2 \end{bmatrix}^T$, so the complementary solution $\mathbf{x}_c(t)$ is given by

$$x_1(t) = c_1 \cos 5t + c_2 \sin 5t + c_3 \cos 5\sqrt{3}t + c_4 \sin 5\sqrt{3}t$$

$$x_2(t) = 2c_1 \cos 5t + 2c_2 \sin 5t - 2c_3 \cos 5\sqrt{3}t - 2c_4 \sin 5\sqrt{3}t.$$

When we substitute the trial solution $x_p(t) = [a \quad b]^T \cos 10t$ in the nonhomogeneous system, we find that $a = 4/3$ and $b = -16/3$, so a particular solution $x_p(t)$ is described by

$$x_1(t) = (4/3)\cos 10t, \qquad x_2(t) = -(16/3)\cos 10t.$$

Finally, when we impose the zero initial conditions on the solution $x(t) = x_c(t) + x_p(t)$ we find that $c_1 = 2/3$, $c_2 = 0$, $c_3 = -2$, and $c_4 = 0$. Thus the solution we seek is described by

$$x_1(t) = (2/3)\cos 5t - 2\cos 5\sqrt{3}t + (4/3)\cos 10t$$

$$x_2(t) = (4/3)\cos 5t + 4\cos 5\sqrt{3}t + (16/3)\cos 10t.$$

We have a superposition of two oscillations with the natural frequencies $\omega_1 = 5$ and $\omega_2 = 5\sqrt{3}$ and a forced oscillation with frequency $\omega = 10$. In each of the two natural oscillations the amplitude of motion of m_2 is twice that of m_1, while in the forced oscillation the amplitude of motion of m_2 is four times that of m_1.

16. The characteristic equation of A is

$$(-c_1 - \lambda)(-c_2 - \lambda) - c_1 c_2 = \lambda^2 + (c_1 + c_2)\lambda = 0,$$

whence the given eigenvalues and eigenvectors follow readily.

17. With $c_1 = c_2 = 2$, it follows from Problem 16 that the natural frequencies and associated eigenvectors are $\omega_1 = 0$, $v_1 = [1 \quad 1]^T$ and $\omega_2 = 2$, $v_2 = [1 \quad -1]^T$. Hence Theorem 1 gives the general solution

$$x_1(t) = a_1 + b_1 t + a_2 \cos 2t + b_2 \sin 2t$$

$$x_2(t) = a_1 + b_1 t - a_2 \cos 2t - b_2 \sin 2t.$$

The initial conditions $x_1'(0) = v_0$, $x_1(0) = x_2(0) = x_2'(0) = 0$ yield $a_1 = a_2 = 0$ and $b_1 = v_0/2$, $b_2 = v_0/4$, so

$$x_1(t) = (v_0/4)(2t + \sin 2t)$$

$$x_2(t) = (v_0/4)(2t - \sin 2t)$$

while $x_2 - x_1 = (v_0/4)(-2\sin 2t) < 0$, that is, until $t = \pi/2$. Finally, $x_1'(\pi/2) = 0$ and $x_2'(\pi/2) = v_0$.

18. With $c_1 = 6$ and $c_2 = 3$, it follows from Problem 16 that the natural frequencies and associated eigenvectors are $\omega_1 = 0$, $\mathbf{v}_1 = \begin{bmatrix} 1 & 1 \end{bmatrix}^T$ and $\omega_2 = 3$, $\mathbf{v}_2 = \begin{bmatrix} 2 & -1 \end{bmatrix}^T$. Hence Theorem 1 gives the general solution

$$x_1(t) = a_1 + b_1 t + 2a_2 \cos 3t + 2b_2 \sin 3t$$

$$x_2(t) = a_1 + b_1 t - a_2 \cos 3t - b_2 \sin 3t.$$

The initial conditions $x_1'(0) = v_0$, $x_1(0) = x_2(0) = x_2'(0) = 0$ yield $a_1 = a_2 = 0$ and $b_1 = v_0/3$, $b_2 = v_0/9$, so

$$x_1(t) = (v_0/9)(3t + 2 \sin 3t)$$

$$x_2(t) = (v_0/9)(3t - \sin 3t)$$

while $x_2 - x_1 = (v_0/9)(-3 \sin 3t) < 0$; that is, until $t = \pi/3$. Finally, $x_1'(\pi/3) = -v_0/3$ and $x_2'(\pi/3) = 2v_0/3$.

19.   With $c_1 = 1$ and $c_2 = 3$, it follows from Problem 16 that the natural frequencies and associated eigenvectors are $\omega_1 = 0$, $\mathbf{v}_1 = \begin{bmatrix} 1 & 1 \end{bmatrix}^T$ and $\omega_2 = 2$, $\mathbf{v}_2 = \begin{bmatrix} 1 & -3 \end{bmatrix}^T$. Hence Theorem 1 gives the general solution

$$x_1(t) = a_1 + b_1 t + a_2 \cos 2t + b_2 \sin 2t$$

$$x_2(t) = a_1 + b_1 t - 3a_2 \cos 2t - 3b_2 \sin 2t.$$

The initial conditions $x_1'(0) = v_0$, $x_1(0) = x_2(0) = x_2'(0) = 0$ yield $a_1 = a_2 = 0$ and $b_1 = 3v_0/4$, $b_2 = v_0/8$, so

$$x_1(t) = (v_0/8)(6t + \sin 2t)$$

$$x_2(t) = (v_0/8)(6t - 3 \sin 2t)$$

while $x_2 - x_1 = (v_0/8)(-4 \sin 2t) < 0$; that is, until $t = \pi/2$. Finally, $x_1'(\pi/2) = v_0/2$ and $x_2'(\pi/2) = 3v_0/2$.

20.   With $c_1 = c_3 = 4$ and $c_2 = 16$ the characteristic equation of the matrix

$$\mathbf{A} = \begin{bmatrix} -4 & 4 & 0 \\ 16 & -32 & 16 \\ 0 & 4 & -4 \end{bmatrix}$$

is

$$\lambda^3 + 40\lambda^2 + 144\lambda = \lambda(\lambda + 4)(\lambda + 36) = 0.$$

The resulting eigenvalues, natural frequencies, and associated eigenvectors are

$$\lambda_1 = 0, \qquad \omega_1 = 0, \qquad \mathbf{v}_1 = \begin{bmatrix} 1 & 1 & 1 \end{bmatrix}^T$$

$$\lambda_2 = -4, \qquad \omega_2 = 2, \qquad \mathbf{v}_2 = \begin{bmatrix} 1 & 0 & -1 \end{bmatrix}^T$$
$$\lambda_3 = -36, \qquad \omega_3 = 6, \qquad \mathbf{v}_3 = \begin{bmatrix} 1 & -8 & 1 \end{bmatrix}^T.$$

Theorem 1 then gives the general solution

$$x_1(t) = a_1 + b_1 t + a_2 \cos 2t + b_2 \sin 2t + a_3 \cos 6t + b_3 \sin 6t$$
$$x_2(t) = a_1 + b_1 t \qquad\qquad\qquad\qquad\quad - 8a_3 \cos 6t - 8b_3 \sin 6t$$
$$x_3(t) = a_1 + b_1 t - a_2 \cos 2t - b_2 \sin 2t + a_3 \cos 6t + b_3 \sin 6t.$$

The initial conditons yield $a_1 = a_2 = a_3 = 0$ and $b_1 = 4v_0/9$, $b_2 = v_0/4$, $b_3 = v_0/108$, so

$$x_1(t) = (v_0/108)(48t + 27 \sin 2t + \sin 6t)$$
$$x_2(t) = (v_0/108)(48t \qquad\qquad - 8 \sin 6t)$$
$$x_3(t) = (v_0/108)(48t - 27 \sin 2t + \sin 6t)$$

while

$$x_2 - x_1 = -18(\sin 2t)(3 - 2 \sin^3 2t) < 0,$$
$$x_3 - x_2 = -9(4 \sin^3 2t) < 0;$$

that is, until $t = \pi/2$. Finally

$$x_1'(\pi/2) = -v_0/9, \quad x_2'(\pi/2) = 8v_0/9, \quad x_3'(\pi/2) = 8v_0/9.$$

21. **(a)** The matrix

$$\mathbf{A} = \begin{bmatrix} -160/3 & 320/3 \\ 8 & -116 \end{bmatrix}$$

has eigenvalues $\lambda_1 \approx -41.8285$ and $\lambda_2 \approx -127.5049$, so the natural frequencies are

$$\omega_1 \approx 6.4675 \text{ rad/sec} \approx 1.0293 \text{ Hz}$$
$$\omega_2 \approx 11.2918 \text{ rad/sec} \approx 1.7971 \text{ Hz}.$$

(b) Resonance occurs at the two critical speeds

$$v_1 = 20\omega_1/\pi \approx 41 \text{ ft/sec} \approx 28 \text{ mi/h}$$
$$v_2 = 20\omega_2/\pi \approx 72 \text{ ft/sec} \approx 49 \text{ mi/h}.$$

22. With $k_1 = k_2 = k$ and $L_1 = L_2 = L/2$ the equations in (42) reduce to

$$mx'' = -2kx \quad \text{and} \quad I\theta'' = -kL^2\theta/2.$$

The first equation yields $\omega_1 = \sqrt{(2k/m)}$ and the second one yields $\omega_2 = \sqrt{(kL^2/2I)}$.

In Problems 23-25 we substitute the given physical parameters into the equations in (42):

$$mx'' = -(k_1 + k_2)x + (k_1L_1 - k_2L_2)\theta$$

$$I\theta'' = (k_1L_1 - k_2L_2)x - (k_1L_1^2 + k_2L_2^2)\theta$$

As in Problem 21, a critical frequency of ω rad/sec yields a critical velocity of $v = 20\omega/\pi$ ft/sec.

23. $100x'' + 4000x = 0$, $800\theta'' + 100000\theta = 0$
    Up-and-down: $\omega_1 = \sqrt{40}$, $v_1 \approx 40.26$ ft/sec ≈ 27 mph
    Angular: $\omega_2 = \sqrt{125}$, $v_2 \approx 71.18$ ft/sec ≈ 49 mph

24. $100x'' + 4000x - 4000\theta = 0$
    $1000\theta'' + 4000x + 104000\theta = 0$
    $\omega_1 \approx 6.1311$, $v_1 \approx 39.03$ ft/sec ≈ 27 mph
    $\omega_2 \approx 10.3155$, $v_2 \approx 65.67$ ft/sec ≈ 45 mph

25. $100x'' + 3000x + 5000\theta = 0$
    $800\theta'' + 5000x + 75000\theta = 0$
    $\omega_1 \approx 5.0424$, $v_1 \approx 32.10$ ft/sec ≈ 22 mph
    $\omega_2 \approx 9.9158$, $v_2 \approx 63.13$ ft/sec ≈ 43 mph

SECTION 5.4

MULTIPLE EIGENVALUE SOLUTIONS

In each of Problems 1-6 we give the characteristic equation with repeated eigenvalue λ, the single eigenvector $\mathbf{v}$ and a generalized eigenvector $\mathbf{w}$ such that $(A - \lambda I)\mathbf{w} = \mathbf{v}$, and the scalar component functions $x_1(t)$, $x_2(t)$ of the general solution

$$\mathbf{x}(t) = c_1\mathbf{v}e^{\lambda t} + c_2(\mathbf{v}t + \mathbf{w})e^{\lambda t}$$

of the given system $\mathbf{x}' = A\mathbf{x}$.

1. Characteristic equation $\lambda^2 + 6\lambda + 9 = 0$
    Repeated eigenvalue $\lambda = -3$
    Eigenvector $\mathbf{v} = [1 \quad -1]^T$
    Generalized eigenvector $\mathbf{w} = [1 \quad 0]^T$

    $x_1(t) = (c_1 + c_2 + c_2t)e^{-3t}$

    $x_2(t) = (-c_1 \quad - c_2t)e^{-3t}$.

2. 　 Characteristic equation 　　 $\lambda^2 - 4\lambda + 4 = 0$
　　 Repeated eigenvalue 　　　 $\lambda = 2$
　　 Eigenvector 　　　　　　 $\mathbf{v} = [1 \quad 1]^T$.
　　 Generalized eigenvector 　 $\mathbf{w} = [1 \quad 0]^T$

$$x_1(t) = (c_1 + c_2 + c_2 t)e^{2t}$$

$$x_2(t) = (c_1 + \quad c_2 t)e^{2t}.$$

3. 　 Characteristic equation 　　 $\lambda^2 - 6\lambda + 9 = 0$
　　 Repeated eigenvalue 　　　 $\lambda = 3$
　　 Single eigenvector 　　　　 $\mathbf{v} = [-2 \quad 2]^T$.
　　 Generalized eigenvector 　 $\mathbf{w} = [1 \quad 0]^T$

$$x_1(t) = (-2c_1 + c_2 - 2c_2 t)e^{3t}$$

$$x_2(t) = (2c_1 + \quad 2c_2 t)e^{3t}.$$

4. 　 Characteristic equation 　　 $\lambda^2 - 8\lambda + 16 = 0$
　　 Repeated eigenvalue 　　　 $\lambda = 4$
　　 Single eigenvector 　　　　 $\mathbf{v} = [-1 \quad 1]^T$
　　 Generalized eigenvector 　 $\mathbf{w} = [1 \quad 0]^T$

$$x_1(t) = (-c_1 + c_2 - c_2 t)e^{4t}$$

$$x_2(t) = (c_1 + \quad c_2 t)e^{4t}.$$

5. 　 Characteristic equation 　　 $\lambda^2 - 10\lambda + 25 = 0$
　　 Repeated eigenvalue 　　　 $\lambda = 5$
　　 Single eigenvector 　　　　 $\mathbf{v} = [2 \quad -4]^T$
　　 Generalized eigenvector 　 $\mathbf{w} = [1 \quad 0]^T$

$$x_1(t) = (2c_1 + c_2 + 2c_2 t)e^{5t}$$

$$x_2(t) = (-4c_1 \quad - 4c_2 t)e^{5t}.$$

6. 　 Characteristic equation 　　 $\lambda^2 - 10\lambda + 25 = 0$
　　 Repeated eigenvalue 　　　 $\lambda = 5$
　　 Single eigenvector 　　　　 $\mathbf{v} = [-4 \quad -4]^T$
　　 Generalized eigenvector 　 $\mathbf{w} = [1 \quad 0]^T$

$$x_1(t) = (-4c_1 + c_2 - 4c_2 t)e^{5t}$$

$$x_2(t) = (4c_1 \quad + 4c_2 t)e^{5t}.$$

In each of Problems 7–10 the characteristic polynomial is easily calculated by expansion along the row or column of $\mathbf{A}$ that contains two zeros. The matrix $\mathbf{A}$ has a double eigenvalue, but nevertheless has 3 linearly independent eigenvectors. We give also the scalar components $x_1(t)$, $x_2(t)$, $x_3(t)$ of the general solution of the system.

7. Characteristic equation $\qquad (\lambda - 2)^2(\lambda - 9) = 0$

Eigenvalues $\qquad\qquad\qquad \lambda = 2, 2, 9$

Eigenvectors $\qquad\qquad\quad [1 \quad 1 \quad 0]^T, [1 \quad 0 \quad 1]^T, [0 \quad 1 \quad 0]^T$

$$x_1(t) = c_1 e^{2t} + c_2 e^{2t}$$

$$x_2(t) = c_1 e^{2t} \qquad\quad + c_3 e^{9t}$$

$$x_3(t) = \qquad\quad c_2 e^{2t}$$

8. Characteristic equation $\qquad (\lambda - 7)(\lambda - 13)^2 = 0$

Eigenvalues $\qquad\qquad\qquad \lambda = 7, 13, 13$

Eignevectors $\qquad\qquad\quad [2 \ \ -3 \ \ 1]^T, [1 \ \ -1 \ \ 0]^T, [0 \qquad 1]^T$

$$x_1(t) = \quad 2c_1 e^{7t} + c_2 e^{13t}$$

$$x_2(t) = -3c_1 e^{7t} - c_2 e^{13t}$$

$$x_3(t) = \quad c_1 e^{7t} \qquad\quad + c_3 e^{13t}$$

9. Characteristic equation $\qquad (\lambda - 5)^2(\lambda - 9) = 0$

Eigenvalues $\qquad\qquad\qquad \lambda = 5, 5, 9$

Eigenvectors $\qquad\qquad\quad [1 \quad 2 \quad 0]^T, [7 \quad 0 \quad 2]^T, [3 \quad 0 \quad 1]^T$

$$x_1(t) = c_1 e^{5t} + 7c_2 e^{5t} + 3c_3 e^{9t}$$

$$x_2(t) = 2c_1 e^{5t}$$

$$x_3(t) = \qquad\quad 2c_2 e^{5t} + c_3 e^{9t}$$

10. Characteristic equation $\qquad (\lambda - 3)^2(\lambda - 7) = 0$

Eigenvalues $\qquad\qquad\qquad \lambda = 3, 3, 7$

Eigenvectors $\qquad\qquad\quad [5 \quad 2 \quad 0]^T, [3 \quad 0 \ \ -1]^T, [2 \quad 1 \quad 0]^T$

$$x_1(t) = 5c_1 e^{3t} + 3c_2 e^{3t} + 2c_3 e^{7t}$$

$$x_2(t) = 2c_1 e^{3t} \qquad\quad + \ c_3 e^{7t}$$

$$x_3(t) = \qquad\quad - c_2 e^{3t}$$

In each of Problems 11–14, $\lambda = -1$ is a triple eigenvalue of defect 2, and we give a length 2 chain $\{v_1, v_2, v_3\}$ of generalized eigenvectors. The general solution then is given by

$$\mathbf{x}(t) = e^{-t}[c_1 \mathbf{v}_1 + c_2(\mathbf{v}_1 t + \mathbf{v}_2) + c_3(\mathbf{v}_1 t^2/2 + \mathbf{v}_2 t + \mathbf{v}_3)].$$

We give the scalar components $x_1(t), x_2(t), x_3(t)$ of $\mathbf{x}(t)$.

11. $\mathbf{v}_1 = [0 \ \ 1 \ \ 0]^T, \ \mathbf{v}_2 = [-2 \ \ -1 \ \ 1]^T, \ \mathbf{v}_3 = [1 \ \ 0 \ \ 0]^T$

$$x_1(t) = e^{-t}(-2c_2 + c_3 - 2c_3 t)$$

$$x_2(t) = e^{-t}(c_1 - c_2 + c_2 t - c_3 t + c_3 t^2/2)$$

$$x_3(t) = e^{-t}(c_2 + c_3 t)$$

12. $\mathbf{v}_1 = [1 \ 1 \ 0]^T, \ \mathbf{v}_2 = [0 \ 0 \ 1]^T, \ \mathbf{v}_3 = [1 \ 1 \ 0]^T$

$$x_1(t) = e^{-t}(c_1 + c_3 + c_2 t + c_3 t^2/2)$$

$$x_2(t) = e^{-t}(c_1 + c_2 t + c_3 t^2/2)$$

$$x_3(t) = e^{-t}(c_2 + c_3 t)$$

13. $\mathbf{v}_1 = [1 \ 0 \ 0]^T, \ \mathbf{v}_2 = [0 \ 2 \ 1]^T, \ \mathbf{v}_3 = [0 \ 1 \ 0]^T$

$$x_1(t) = e^{-t}(c_1 + c_2 t + c_3 t^2/2)$$

$$x_2(t) = e^{-t}(2c_2 + c_3 + 2c_3 t)$$

$$x_3(t) = e^{-t}(c_2 + c_3 t)$$

14. $\mathbf{v}_1 = [5 \ -25 \ -5]^T, \ \mathbf{v}_2 = [1 \ -5 \ 4]^T, \ \mathbf{v}_3 = [1 \ 0 \ 0]^T$

$$x_1(t) = e^{-t}(5c_1 + c_2 + c_3 + 5c_2 t + c_3 t + 5c_3 t^2/2)$$

$$x_2(t) = e^{-t}(-25c_1 - 5c_2 - 25c_2 t - 5c_3 t - 25c_3 t^2/2)$$

$$x_3(t) = e^{-t}(-5c_1 + 4c_2 - 5c_2 t + 4c_3 t - 5c_3 t^2/2)$$

In each of Problems 15–18, $\lambda = 1$ is a triple eigenvalue of defect 1. We give two eigenvectors $\mathbf{u}_1$ and $\mathbf{u}_2$, and a length 2 chain $\{\mathbf{v}_1, \mathbf{v}_2\}$ of generalized eigenvectors. The general solution is then given by

$$\mathbf{x}(t) = e^t[c_1\mathbf{u}_1 + c_2\mathbf{u}_2 + c_3(\mathbf{v}_1 t + \mathbf{v}_2)]$$

We give the scalar components $x_1(t), x_2(t), x_3(t)$ of $\mathbf{x}(t)$.

15. $\mathbf{u}_1 = [3 \ -1 \ 0]^T \qquad \mathbf{u}_2 = [0 \ 0 \ 1]^T$

$\qquad \mathbf{v}_1 = [-3 \ 1 \ 1]^T \qquad \mathbf{v}_2 = [1 \ 0 \ 0]^T$

$$x_1(t) = e^t(3c_1 - 3c_2 + c_3 - 3c_3 t)$$

$$x_2(t) = e^t(-c_1 + c_2 + c_3 t)$$

$$x_3(t) = e^t(c_2 + c_3 t)$$

16. $\mathbf{u}_1 = [3 \ -2 \ 0]^T \qquad \mathbf{u}_2 = [3 \ 0 \ -2]^T$

$\qquad \mathbf{v}_1 = [0 \ -2 \ 2]^T \qquad \mathbf{v}_2 = [1 \ 0 \ 0]^T$

$$x_1(t) = e^t(3c_1 + c_3)$$

$$x_2(t) = e^t(-2c_1 - 2c_2 - 2c_3t)$$

$$x_3(t) = e^t(2c_2 + 2c_3t)$$

17. $\mathbf{u}_1 = [2 \quad 0 \quad -9]^T \qquad \mathbf{u}_2 = [1 \quad -3 \quad 0]^T$

   $\mathbf{v}_1 = [0 \quad 6 \quad -9]^T \qquad \mathbf{v}_2 = [0 \quad 1 \quad 0]^T$

   $x_1(t) = e^t(2c_1)$

   $x_2(t) = e^t(6c_2 + c_3 + 6c_3t)$

   $x_3(t) = e^t(-9c_1 - 9c_2 - 9c_3t)$

18. $\mathbf{u}_1 = [-1 \quad 0 \quad 1]^T \qquad \mathbf{u}_2 = [-2 \quad 1 \quad 0]^T$

   $\mathbf{v}_1 = [0 \quad 1 \quad -2]^T \qquad \mathbf{v}_2 = [1 \quad 0 \quad 0]^T$

   $x_1(t) = e^t(-c_1 + c_3)$

   $x_2(t) = e^t(c_2 + c_2t)$

   $x_3(t) = e^t(c_1 - 2c_2 - 2c_2t)$

19. Characteristic equation $\qquad \lambda^4 - 2\lambda^2 + 1 = 0$
   Double eigenvalue $\lambda = -1$ with eigenvectors

$$\mathbf{v}_1 = [1 \quad 0 \quad 0 \quad 1]^T \text{ and } \mathbf{v}_2 = [0 \quad 0 \quad 1 \quad 0]^T.$$

   Double eigenvalue $\lambda = +1$ with eigenvectors

$$\mathbf{v}_3 = [0 \quad 1 \quad 0 \quad -2]^T \text{ and } \mathbf{v}_4 = [1 \quad 0 \quad 3 \quad 0]^T.$$

   General solution

$$\mathbf{x}(t) = e^{-t}(c_1\mathbf{v}_1 + c_2\mathbf{v}_2) + e^t(c_3\mathbf{v}_3 + c_4\mathbf{v}_4)$$

   Scalar components

$$x_1(t) = c_1e^{-t} + c_4e^t$$

$$x_2(t) = c_3e^t$$

$$x_3(t) = c_2e^{-t} + 3c_4e^t$$

$$x_4(t) = c_1e^{-t} - 2c_3e^t$$

20. Characteristic equation $\qquad (\lambda - 2)^4 = 0$
   Eigenvalue $\lambda = 2$ with multiplicity 4 and defect 3.
   Length 4 chain $\{\mathbf{v}_1, \mathbf{v}_2, \mathbf{v}_3, \mathbf{v}_4\}$ with

$$\mathbf{v}_1 = [1 \ 0 \ 0 \ 0]^T \qquad\qquad \mathbf{v}_2 = [0 \ 1 \ 0 \ 0]^T$$
$$\mathbf{v}_3 = [1 \ 0 \ 1 \ 0]^T \qquad\qquad \mathbf{v}_4 = [0 \ 0 \ 0 \ 1]^T$$

General solution

$$\mathbf{x}(t) = e^{-t}\,[c_1\mathbf{v}_1 + c_2(\mathbf{v}_1 t + \mathbf{v}_2) + c_3(\mathbf{v}_1 t^2/2 + \mathbf{v}_2 t + \mathbf{v}_3)$$
$$+ \, c_4(\mathbf{v}_1 t^3/6 + \mathbf{v}_2 t^2/2 + \mathbf{v}_3 t + \mathbf{v}_4)]$$

Scalar components

$$x_1(t) = e^{2t}(c_1 + c_3 + c_2 t + c_4 t + c_3 t^2/2 + c_4 t^3/6)$$
$$x_2(t) = e^{2t}(c_2 + c_3 t + c_4 t^2/2)$$
$$x_3(t) = e^{2t}(c_3 + c_4 t)$$
$$x_4(t) = e^{2t}(c_4)$$

21. Characteristic equation $\qquad (\lambda - 1)^4 = 0$
Eigenvalue $\lambda = 1$ with multiplicity 4 and defect 2.
Chains $\{\mathbf{v}_1, \ \mathbf{v}_2, \ \mathbf{v}_3\}$ and $\{\mathbf{v}_4\}$ with

$$\mathbf{v}_1 = [0 \ 0 \ 0 \ 1]^T \qquad\qquad \mathbf{v}_2 = [-2 \ 1 \ 1 \ 0]^T$$
$$\mathbf{v}_3 = [1 \ 0 \ 0 \ 0]^T \qquad\qquad \mathbf{v}_4 = [0 \ \ 0 \ 1 \ 0]^T$$

General solution

$$\mathbf{x}(t) = e^{t}\,[c_1\mathbf{v}_1 + c_2(\mathbf{v}_1 t + \mathbf{v}_2) + c_3(\mathbf{v}_1 t^2/2 + \mathbf{v}_2 t + \mathbf{v}_3) + c_4\mathbf{v}_4]$$

Scalar components

$$x_1(t) = e^{t}(-2c_2 + c_3 - 2c_3 t)$$
$$x_2(t) = e^{t}(c_2 + c_3 t)$$
$$x_3(t) = e^{t}(c_2 + c_4 + c_3 t)$$
$$x_4(t) = e^{t}(c_1 + c_2 t + c_3 t^2/2)$$

22. Same eigenvalue and chain structure as in Problem 21, but with generalized eigenvectors

$$\mathbf{v}_1 = [1 \ 0 \ 0 \ -2]^T \qquad\qquad \mathbf{v}_2 = [3 \ -2 \ 1 \ -6]^T$$
$$\mathbf{v}_3 = [0 \ 1 \ 0 \ \ 0]^T \qquad\qquad \mathbf{v}_4 = [1 \ \ 0 \ 0 \ \ 0]^T$$

Scalar components

$$x_1(t) = e^{t}(c_1 + 3c_2 + c_4 + c_2 t + 3c_3 t + c_3 t^2/2)$$
$$x_2(t) = e^{t}(-2c_2 + c_3 - 2c_3 t)$$

$$x_3(t) = e^t(c_2 + c_3 t)$$

$$x_4(t) = e^t(-2c_1 - 6c_2 - 2c_2 t - 6c_3 t - c_3 t^2)$$

In Problems 23–32 we give the generalized eigenvector chain(s) associated with each eigenvalue.

23. $\lambda = -1$: $\{v_1\}$ with $v_1 = [1 \ -1 \ 2]^T$
   $\lambda = 3$: $\{v_2\}$ with $v_2 = [4 \ \ 0 \ 9]^T$ and
        $\{v_3\}$ with $v_3 = [0 \ \ 2 \ 1]^T$

Scalar components

$$x_1(t) = \ \ c_1 e^{-t} + 4c_2 e^{3t}$$

$$x_2(t) = -c_1 e^{-t} \qquad + 2c_3 e^{3t}$$

$$x_3(t) = 2c_1 e^{-t} + 9c_2 e^{3t} + \ c_3 e^{3t}$$

24. $\lambda = -2$: $\{v_1\}$ with $v_1 = [5 \ \ 3 \ -3]^T$

   $\lambda = 3$: $\{v_2\}$ with $v_2 = [4 \ \ 0 \ -1]^T$ and
        $\{v_3\}$ with $v_3 = [2 \ -1 \ \ 0]^T$

Scalar components

$$x_1(t) = \ \ 5c_1 e^{-2t} + 4c_2 e^{3t} + 2c_3 e^{3t}$$

$$x_2(t) = \ \ 3c_1 e^{-2t} \qquad - \ c_3 e^{3t}$$

$$x_3(t) = -3c_1 e^{-2t} - c_2 e^{3t}$$

25. $\{v_1, v_2, v_3\}$ with

$$v_1 = [-1 \ \ 0 \ -1]^T, \quad v_2 = [-4 \ -1 \ 0]^T, \quad v_3 = [1 \ \ 0 \ \ 0]^T$$

General solution

$$\mathbf{x}(t) = c_1 v_1 e^{2t} + c_2(v_1 t + v_2)e^{2t} + c_3(v_1 t^2/2 + v_2 t + v_3)e^{2t}$$

26. $\{v_1, v_2, v_3\}$ with

$$v_1 = [0 \ \ 2 \ \ 2]^T, \quad v_2 = [2 \ \ 1 \ -3]^T, \quad v_3 = [1 \ \ 0 \ \ 0]^T$$

General solution

$$\mathbf{x}(t) = e^{3t}[c_1 v_1 + c_2(v_1 t + v_2) + c_3(v_1 t^2/2 + v_2 t + v_3)]$$

27. $\{v_1, v_2\}$ and $\{v_3\}$ with

$$\mathbf{v}_1 = [-5 \ \ 3 \ \ 8]^T, \quad \mathbf{v}_2 = [1 \ \ 0 \ \ 0]^T \quad \text{and} \quad \mathbf{v}_3 = [1 \ \ 1 \ \ 0]^T.$$

General solution

$$\mathbf{x}(t) = e^{2t}[c_1\mathbf{v}_1 + c_2(\mathbf{v}_1 t + \mathbf{v}_2) + c_3\mathbf{v}_3]$$

28. $\{\mathbf{v}_1, \mathbf{v}_2, \mathbf{v}_3\}$ with

$$\mathbf{v}_1 = [119 \ -289 \ \ 0]^T, \quad \mathbf{v}_2 = [-17 \ \ 34 \ \ 17]^T, \quad \mathbf{v}_3 = [1 \ \ 0 \ \ 0]^T$$

General solution

$$\mathbf{x}(t) = e^{2t}[c_1\mathbf{v}_1 + c_2(\mathbf{v}_1 t + \mathbf{v}_2) + c_3(\mathbf{v}_1 t^2/2 + \mathbf{v}_2 t + \mathbf{v}_3)]$$

29. $\lambda = -1$: $\{\mathbf{v}_1, \mathbf{v}_2\}$ with $\mathbf{v}_1 = [1 \ -3 \ -1 \ -2]^T$ and $\mathbf{v}_2 = [0 \ \ 1 \ \ 0 \ \ 0]^T$,

$\lambda = \ \ 2$: $\{\mathbf{u}_1, \mathbf{u}_2\}$ with $\mathbf{u}_1 = [0 \ -1 \ \ 1 \ \ 0]^T$ and $\mathbf{u}_2 = [0 \ \ 0 \ \ 2 \ \ 1]^T$

General solution

$$\mathbf{x}(t) = e^{-t}[c_1\mathbf{v}_1 + c_2(\mathbf{v}_1 t + \mathbf{v}_2)] + e^{2t}[c_3\mathbf{u}_1 + c_4(\mathbf{u}_1 t + \mathbf{u}_2)]$$

30. $\lambda = -1$: $\{\mathbf{v}_1, \mathbf{v}_2\}$ with $\mathbf{v}_1 = [0 \ \ 1 \ -1 \ -3]^T$ and $\mathbf{v}_2 = [0 \ \ 0 \ \ 1 \ \ 2]^T$,

$\lambda = \ \ 2$: $\{\mathbf{u}_1, \mathbf{u}_2\}$ with $\mathbf{u}_1 = [-1 \ 0 \ \ 0 \ \ 0]^T$ and $\mathbf{u}_2 = [0 \ \ 0 \ \ 3 \ \ 5]^T$

General solution

$$\mathbf{x}(t) = e^{-t}[c_1\mathbf{v}_1 + c_2(\mathbf{v}_1 t + \mathbf{v}_2)] + e^{2t}[c_3\mathbf{u}_1 + c_4(\mathbf{u}_1 t + \mathbf{u}_2)]$$

31. $\{\mathbf{v}_1, \mathbf{v}_2, \mathbf{v}_3\}$ and $\{\mathbf{v}_4\}$ with

$$\mathbf{v}_1 = [42 \ \ 7 \ -21 \ -42]^T, \quad \mathbf{v}_2 = [34 \ \ 22 \ -10 \ -27]^T,$$

$$\mathbf{v}_3 = [1 \ \ 0 \ \ 0 \ \ 0]^T \quad \text{and} \quad \mathbf{v}_4 = [0 \ \ 1 \ \ 3 \ \ 0]$$

General solution

$$\mathbf{x}(t) = e^{t}[c_1\mathbf{v}_1 + c_2(\mathbf{v}_1 t + \mathbf{v}_2) + c_3(\mathbf{v}_1 t^2/2 + \mathbf{v}_2 t + \mathbf{v}_3) + c_4\mathbf{v}_4]$$

32. $\lambda = 2$: eigenvectors $\mathbf{v}_1 = [8 \ \ 0 \ -3 \ \ 1 \ \ 0]^T$ and $\mathbf{v}_2 = [1 \ 0 \ \ 0 \ \ 0 \ \ 3]^T$

$\lambda = 3$: eigenvectors $\mathbf{v}_3 = [3 \ -2 \ -1 \ \ 0 \ \ 0]^T$, $\mathbf{v}_4 = [2 \ -2 \ \ 0 \ -3 \ \ 0]^T$,

$$\mathbf{v}_5 = [1 \ -1 \ \ 0 \ \ 0 \ \ 3]^T$$

General solution

$$\mathbf{x}(t) = e^{2t}(c_1\mathbf{v}_1 + c_2\mathbf{v}_2) + e^{3t}(c_3\mathbf{v}_3 + c_4\mathbf{v}_4 + c_5\mathbf{v}_5)$$

33. The chain $\{\mathbf{v}_1, \mathbf{v}_2\}$ was found using the matrices

$$\mathbf{A} - \lambda\mathbf{I} = \begin{bmatrix} 4i & -4 & 1 & 0 \\ 4 & 4i & 0 & 1 \\ 0 & 0 & 4i & -4 \\ 0 & 0 & 4 & 4i \end{bmatrix} \rightarrow \begin{bmatrix} 1 & i & 0 & 0 \\ 0 & 0 & 1 & 0 \\ 0 & 0 & 0 & 1 \\ 0 & 0 & 0 & 0 \end{bmatrix}$$

and

$$(\mathbf{A} - \lambda\mathbf{I})^2 = \begin{bmatrix} -32 & -32i & 8i & -8 \\ 32i & -32 & 8 & 8i \\ 0 & 0 & -32 & -32i \\ 0 & 0 & 32i & -32 \end{bmatrix} \rightarrow \begin{bmatrix} 1 & i & 0 & 0 \\ 0 & 0 & 1 & i \\ 0 & 0 & 0 & 0 \\ 0 & 0 & 0 & 0 \end{bmatrix}$$

where $\rightarrow$ signifies reduction to row-echelon form. The resulting real-valued solution vectors are

$$\mathbf{x}_1(t) = e^{3t}\begin{bmatrix} \cos 4t & \sin 4t & 0 & 0 \end{bmatrix}^T$$
$$\mathbf{x}_2(t) = e^{3t}\begin{bmatrix} -\sin 4t & \cos 4t & 0 & 0 \end{bmatrix}^T$$
$$\mathbf{x}_3(t) = e^{3t}\begin{bmatrix} t\cos 4t & t\sin 4t & \cos 4t & \sin 4t \end{bmatrix}^T$$
$$\mathbf{x}_4(t) = e^{3t}\begin{bmatrix} -t\sin 4t & t\cos 4t & -\sin 4t & \cos 4t \end{bmatrix}^T.$$

34. The chain $\{\mathbf{v}_1, \mathbf{v}_2\}$ was found using the matrices

$$\mathbf{A} - \lambda\mathbf{I} = \begin{bmatrix} 3i & 0 & -8 & -3 \\ -18 & -3-3i & 0 & 0 \\ -9 & -3 & -27-3i & -9 \\ 33 & 10 & 90 & 30-3i \end{bmatrix} \rightarrow \begin{bmatrix} 1 & 0 & 0 & 0 \\ 0 & 1 & 0 & 3+3i \\ 0 & 0 & 1 & 0 \\ 0 & 0 & 0 & 0 \end{bmatrix}$$

and

$$(\mathbf{A} - \lambda\mathbf{I})^2 = \begin{bmatrix} -36 & -6 & -54+48i & -18+18i \\ 54+108i & 18i & 144 & 54 \\ 54i & 18i & -18+162i & 54i \\ -198i & -60i & 6-540i & -18-180i \end{bmatrix} \rightarrow \begin{bmatrix} 1 & 0 & -3i & -i \\ 0 & 1 & 9+10i & 3+3i \\ 0 & 0 & 0 & 0 \\ 0 & 0 & 0 & 0 \end{bmatrix}$$

where $\rightarrow$ signifies reduction to row-echelon form. The resulting real-valued solution vectors are

$$\mathbf{x}_1(t) = e^{2t}\begin{bmatrix} \sin 3t & 3\cos 3t - 3\sin 3t & 0 & \sin 3t \end{bmatrix}^T$$
$$\mathbf{x}_2(t) = e^{2t}\begin{bmatrix} -\cos 3t & 3\sin 3t + 3\cos 3t & 0 & -\cos 3t \end{bmatrix}^T$$

$\mathbf{x}_3(t) = e^{2t} [3\cos 3t + t\sin 3t \quad (3t-10)\cos 3t - (3t+9)\sin 3t \quad \sin 3t \quad t\sin 3t \ ]^T$

$\mathbf{x}_4(t) = e^{2t} [-t\cos 3t + 3\sin 3t \quad (3t+9)\cos 3t + (3t-10)\sin 3t \quad -\cos 3t \quad -t\cos 3t]^T.$

35.   The coefficient matrix

$$\mathbf{A} = \begin{bmatrix} 0 & 0 & 1 & 0 \\ 0 & 0 & 0 & 1 \\ -1 & 1 & -2 & 1 \\ 1 & -1 & 1 & -2 \end{bmatrix}$$

has eigenvalues

$\lambda = 0$ with eigenvector $\quad \mathbf{v}_1 = [1 \quad 1 \quad 0 \quad 0]^T$

$\lambda = -1$ with eigenvectors $\quad \mathbf{v}_2 = [1 \quad 0 \ -1 \quad 0]^T$ and $\mathbf{v}_3 = [0 \quad 1 \quad 0 \ -1]^T$,

$\lambda = -2$ with eigenvector $\quad \mathbf{v}_4 = [1 \ -1 \ -2 \quad 2]^T.$

When we impose the given initial conditions on the general solution

$$\mathbf{x}(t) = c_1\mathbf{v}_1 + c_2\mathbf{v}_2 e^{-t} + c_3\mathbf{v}_3 e^{-t} + c_4\mathbf{v}_4 e^{-2t}$$

We find that $c_1 = v_0$, $c_2 = c_3 = -v_0$, $c_4 = 0$. Hence the position functions of the two masses are given by

$$x_1(t) = x_2(t) = v_0(1 - e^{-t})$$

Each mass travels a distance v_0 before stopping.

36.   The coefficient matrix is the same as in Problem 35 except that $a_{44} = -1$. Now the matrix $\mathbf{A}$ has the eigenvalue $\lambda = 0$ with eigenvector $\mathbf{v}_0 = [1 \quad 1 \quad 0 \quad 0]^T$, and the triple eigenvalue $\lambda = -1$ with associated length 2 chain $\{\mathbf{v}_1, \mathbf{v}_2, \mathbf{v}_3\}$ consisting of the generalized eigenvectors

$$\mathbf{v}_1 = [0 \quad 1 \quad 0 \ -1]^T$$
$$\mathbf{v}_2 = [1 \quad 0 \ -1 \quad 1]^T$$
$$\mathbf{v}_3 = [1 \quad 0 \quad 0 \quad 0]^T.$$

When we impose the given initial conditions on the general solution

$$\mathbf{x}(t) = c_0\mathbf{v}_0 + e^{-t} [c_1\mathbf{v}_1 + c_2(\mathbf{v}_1 t + \mathbf{v}_2) + c_3(\mathbf{v}_1 t^2/2 + \mathbf{v}_2 t + \mathbf{v}_3)]$$

We find that $c_0 = 2v_0$, $c_1 = -2v_0$, $c_2 = c_3 = -v_0$. Hence the position functions of the two masses are given by

$$x_1(t) = v_0(2 - 2e^{-t} - te^{-t}),$$

$$x_2(t) = v_0(2 - 2e^{-t} - te^{-t} - t^2 e^{-t}/2).$$

Each travels a distance $2v_0$ before stopping.

SECTION 5.5

MATRIX EXPONENTIALS AND LINEAR SYSTEMS

In Problems 1–8 we use the formula

$$\mathbf{x}(t) = \Phi(t)\Phi(0)^{-1}\mathbf{x}_0,$$

where $\Phi(t)$ is a fundamental matrix for the homogeneous system $\mathbf{x}' = \mathbf{A}\mathbf{x}$, to find the solution vector $\mathbf{x}(t)$ that satisfies the initial condition $\mathbf{x}(0) = \mathbf{x}_0$. Formulas (11) and (12) in the text provide inverses of 2-by-2 and 3-by-3 matrices.

1. $\Phi(t) = \begin{bmatrix} e^t & e^{3t} \\ -e^t & e^{3t} \end{bmatrix}$, $\quad \mathbf{x}(t) = \dfrac{1}{2}\begin{bmatrix} 5e^t + e^{3t} \\ -5e^t + e^{3t} \end{bmatrix}$

2. $\mathbf{x}(t) = \begin{bmatrix} 1 & e^{4t} \\ 2 & -2e^{4t} \end{bmatrix}\begin{bmatrix} 1 & 1 \\ 2 & -2 \end{bmatrix}^{-1}\begin{bmatrix} 2 \\ -1 \end{bmatrix} = \begin{bmatrix} 1 & e^{4t} \\ 2 & -2e^{4t} \end{bmatrix}\begin{bmatrix} \frac{1}{2} & \frac{1}{4} \\ \frac{1}{2} & -\frac{1}{4} \end{bmatrix}\begin{bmatrix} 2 \\ -1 \end{bmatrix} = \begin{bmatrix} \frac{1}{4}(3 + 5e^{4t}) \\ \frac{1}{4}(6 - 10e^{4t}) \end{bmatrix}$

3. $\Phi(t) = \begin{bmatrix} 5\cos 4t & -5\sin 4t \\ 2\cos 4t + 4\sin 4t & 4\cos 4t - 2\sin 4t \end{bmatrix}$, $\quad \mathbf{x}(t) = \dfrac{1}{4}\begin{bmatrix} -5\sin 4t \\ 4\cos 4t - 2\sin 4t \end{bmatrix}$

4. $\mathbf{x}(t) = e^{2t}\begin{bmatrix} 1 & 2+t \\ 1 & 1+t \end{bmatrix}\begin{bmatrix} 1 & 2 \\ 1 & 1 \end{bmatrix}^{-1}\begin{bmatrix} 1 \\ 0 \end{bmatrix} = e^{2t}\begin{bmatrix} 1 & 2+t \\ 1 & 1+t \end{bmatrix}\begin{bmatrix} -1 & 2 \\ 1 & -1 \end{bmatrix}^{-1}\begin{bmatrix} 1 \\ 0 \end{bmatrix} = e^{2t}\begin{bmatrix} 1+t \\ t \end{bmatrix}$

5. $\Phi(t) = \begin{bmatrix} 2\cos 3t & -2\sin 3t \\ -3\cos 3t + 3\sin 3t & 3\cos 3t + 3\sin 3t \end{bmatrix}$, $\quad \mathbf{x}(t) = \dfrac{1}{3}\begin{bmatrix} 3\cos 3t - \sin 3t \\ -3\cos 3t + 6\sin 3t \end{bmatrix}$

6. $\Phi(t) = e^{5t}\begin{bmatrix} 5\cos 4t & 5\sin 4t \\ 2\cos 4t + 4\sin 4t & 2\sin 4t - 4\cos 4t \end{bmatrix}$

$\Phi(0) = \begin{bmatrix} 5 & 0 \\ 2 & -4 \end{bmatrix}$, $\quad \Phi(0)^{-1} = \begin{bmatrix} \frac{1}{5} & 0 \\ \frac{1}{10} & -\frac{1}{4} \end{bmatrix}$

$\mathbf{x}(t) = \Phi(t)\Phi(0)^{-1}\begin{bmatrix} 2 \\ 0 \end{bmatrix} = \Phi(t)\begin{bmatrix} \frac{2}{5} \\ \frac{1}{5} \end{bmatrix} = e^{5t}\begin{bmatrix} 2\cos 4t + \sin 4t \\ 2\sin 4t \end{bmatrix}$

7. $\Phi(t) = \begin{bmatrix} 6 & 3e^t & 2e^{-t} \\ 2 & e^t & e^{-t} \\ 5 & 2e^t & 2e^{-t} \end{bmatrix}, \qquad \mathbf{x}(t) = \begin{bmatrix} -12+12e^t+2e^{-t} \\ -4+4e^t+e^{-t} \\ -10+8e^t+2e^{-t} \end{bmatrix}$

8. $\Phi(t) = \begin{bmatrix} e^{3t} & e^t & 0 \\ -e^{3t} & -e^t & e^{-t} \\ e^{3t} & 0 & -e^{-t} \end{bmatrix}, \quad \Phi(0) = \begin{bmatrix} 1 & 1 & 0 \\ -1 & -1 & 1 \\ 1 & 0 & -1 \end{bmatrix}, \quad \Phi(0)^{-1} = \begin{bmatrix} 1 & 1 & 1 \\ 0 & -1 & -1 \\ 1 & 1 & 0 \end{bmatrix}$

$\mathbf{x}(t) = \Phi(t)\Phi(0)^{-1}\begin{bmatrix} 1 \\ 0 \\ -1 \end{bmatrix} = \Phi(t)\begin{bmatrix} 0 \\ 1 \\ 1 \end{bmatrix} = \begin{bmatrix} e^t \\ e^{-t}-e^t \\ -e^{-t} \end{bmatrix}$

In each of Problems 9–20 we give the fundamental matrix $\Phi(t) = \begin{bmatrix} \mathbf{x}_1(t) & \mathbf{x}_2(t) \end{bmatrix}$ and the matrix exponential $e^{\mathbf{A}t} = \Phi(t)\,\Phi(0)^{-1}$.

9. $\Phi(t) = \begin{bmatrix} 2e^{3t} & e^t \\ e^{3t} & e^t \end{bmatrix}, \qquad e^{\mathbf{A}t} = \begin{bmatrix} 2e^{3t}-e^t & -2e^{3t}+2e^t \\ e^{3t}-e^t & -e^{3t}+2e^t \end{bmatrix}$

10. $\Phi(t) = \begin{bmatrix} 3e^{2t} & 1 \\ 2e^{2t} & 1 \end{bmatrix}, \qquad e^{\mathbf{A}t} = \begin{bmatrix} 3e^{2t}-2 & -3e^{2t}+3 \\ 2e^{2t}-2 & -2e^{2t}+3 \end{bmatrix}$

11. $\Phi(t) = \begin{bmatrix} 3e^{3t} & e^{2t} \\ 2e^{3t} & e^{2t} \end{bmatrix}, \qquad e^{\mathbf{A}t} = \begin{bmatrix} 3e^{3t}-2e^{2t} & -3e^{3t}+3e^{2t} \\ 2e^{3t}-2e^{2t} & -2e^{3t}+3e^{2t} \end{bmatrix}$

12. $\Phi(t) = \begin{bmatrix} 4e^{2t} & e^t \\ 3e^{2t} & e^t \end{bmatrix}, \qquad e^{\mathbf{A}t} = \begin{bmatrix} 4e^{2t}-3e^t & -4e^{2t}+4e^t \\ 3e^{2t}-3e^t & -3e^{2t}+4e^t \end{bmatrix}$

13. $\Phi(t) = \begin{bmatrix} 4e^{3t} & e^t \\ 3e^{3t} & e^t \end{bmatrix}, \qquad e^{\mathbf{A}t} = \begin{bmatrix} 4e^{3t}-3e^t & -4e^{3t}+4e^t \\ 3e^{3t}-3e^t & -3e^{3t}+4e^t \end{bmatrix}$

14. $\Phi(t) = \begin{bmatrix} 3e^{2t} & 2e^t \\ 4e^{2t} & 3e^t \end{bmatrix}, \qquad e^{\mathbf{A}t} = \begin{bmatrix} 9e^{2t}-8e^t & -6e^{2t}+6e^t \\ 12e^{2t}-12e^t & -8e^{2t}+9e^t \end{bmatrix}$

15. $\Phi(t) = \begin{bmatrix} 5e^{2t} & 2e^t \\ 2e^{2t} & e^t \end{bmatrix}, \qquad e^{\mathbf{A}t} = \begin{bmatrix} 5e^{2t}-4e^t & -10e^{2t}+10e^t \\ 2e^{2t}-2e^t & -4e^{2t}+5e^t \end{bmatrix}$

16. $\Phi(t) = \begin{bmatrix} 5e^{2t} & 3e^{t} \\ 3e^{2t} & 2e^{t} \end{bmatrix}$, $\qquad e^{\mathbf{A}t} = \begin{bmatrix} 10e^{2t} - 9e^{t} & -15e^{2t} + 15e^{t} \\ 6e^{2t} - 6e^{t} & -9e^{2t} + 10e^{t} \end{bmatrix}$

17. $\Phi(t) = \begin{bmatrix} e^{4t} & e^{2t} \\ e^{4t} & -e^{2t} \end{bmatrix}$, $\qquad e^{\mathbf{A}t} = \frac{1}{2}\begin{bmatrix} e^{4t} + e^{2t} & e^{4t} - e^{2t} \\ e^{4t} - e^{2t} & e^{4t} + e^{2t} \end{bmatrix}$

18. $\Phi(t) = \begin{bmatrix} e^{6t} & e^{2t} \\ e^{6t} & -e^{2t} \end{bmatrix}$, $\qquad e^{\mathbf{A}t} = \frac{1}{2}\begin{bmatrix} e^{6t} + e^{2t} & e^{6t} - e^{2t} \\ e^{6t} - e^{2t} & e^{6t} + e^{2t} \end{bmatrix}$

19. $\Phi(t) = \begin{bmatrix} 2e^{10t} & -e^{5t} \\ e^{10t} & 2e^{5t} \end{bmatrix}$, $\qquad e^{\mathbf{A}t} = \frac{1}{5}\begin{bmatrix} 4e^{10t} + e^{5t} & 2e^{10t} - 2e^{5t} \\ 2e^{10t} - 2e^{5t} & e^{10t} + 4e^{5t} \end{bmatrix}$

20. $\Phi(t) = \begin{bmatrix} 2e^{15t} & -e^{5t} \\ e^{15t} & 2e^{5t} \end{bmatrix}$, $\qquad e^{\mathbf{A}t} = \frac{1}{5}\begin{bmatrix} 4e^{15t} + e^{5t} & 2e^{15t} - 2e^{5t} \\ 2e^{15t} - 2e^{5t} & e^{15t} + 4e^{5t} \end{bmatrix}$

21. $\mathbf{A}^2 = \mathbf{0}$ so $e^{\mathbf{A}t} = \mathbf{I} + \mathbf{A}t = \begin{bmatrix} 1+t & -t \\ t & 1-t \end{bmatrix}$

22. $\mathbf{A}^2 = \mathbf{0}$ so $e^{\mathbf{A}t} = \mathbf{I} + \mathbf{A}t = \begin{bmatrix} 1+6t & 4t \\ -9t & 1-6t \end{bmatrix}$

23. $\mathbf{A}^3 = \mathbf{0}$ so $e^{\mathbf{A}t} = \mathbf{I} + \mathbf{A}t + \frac{1}{2}\mathbf{A}^2t^2 = \begin{bmatrix} 1+t & -t & -t-t^2 \\ t & 1-t & t-t^2 \\ 0 & 0 & 1 \end{bmatrix}$

24. $\mathbf{A}^3 = \mathbf{0}$ so $e^{\mathbf{A}t} = \mathbf{I} + \mathbf{A}t + \frac{1}{2}\mathbf{A}^2t^2 = \begin{bmatrix} 1+3t & 0 & -3t \\ 5t+18t^2 & 1 & 7t-18t^2 \\ 3t & 0 & 1-3t \end{bmatrix}$

25. $\mathbf{A} = 2\mathbf{I} + \mathbf{D}$ where $\mathbf{D}^2 = \mathbf{0}$, so $e^{\mathbf{A}t} = e^{2\mathbf{I}t}e^{\mathbf{D}t} = (e^{2t}\mathbf{I})(\mathbf{I} + \mathbf{D}t)$. Hence

$$e^{\mathbf{A}t} = \begin{bmatrix} e^{2t} & 5t\,e^{2t} \\ 0 & e^{2t} \end{bmatrix}, \qquad \mathbf{x}(t) = e^{\mathbf{A}t}\begin{bmatrix} 4 \\ 7 \end{bmatrix} = e^{2t}\begin{bmatrix} 4+35t \\ 7 \end{bmatrix}$$

26. $\mathbf{A} = 7\mathbf{I} + \mathbf{D}$ where $\mathbf{D}^2 = \mathbf{0}$, so $e^{\mathbf{A}t} = e^{7\mathbf{I}t}e^{\mathbf{D}t} = (e^{7t}\mathbf{I})(\mathbf{I} + \mathbf{D}t)$. Hence

$$e^{\mathbf{A}t} = \begin{bmatrix} e^{7t} & 0 \\ 11t\,e^{7t} & e^{7t} \end{bmatrix}, \qquad \mathbf{x}(t) = e^{\mathbf{A}t}\begin{bmatrix} 5 \\ -10 \end{bmatrix} = e^{7t}\begin{bmatrix} 5 \\ -10+55t \end{bmatrix}$$

27. $\mathbf{A} = \mathbf{I}+\mathbf{D}$ where $\mathbf{D}^3 = \mathbf{0}$, so $e^{\mathbf{A}t} = e^{\mathbf{I}t}e^{\mathbf{D}t} = (e^t\mathbf{I})(\mathbf{I}+\mathbf{D}t+\frac{1}{2}\mathbf{D}^2t^2)$. Hence

$$e^{\mathbf{A}t} = \begin{bmatrix} e^t & 2te^t & (3t+2t^2)e^t \\ 0 & e^t & 2te^t \\ 0 & 0 & e^t \end{bmatrix}, \quad \mathbf{x}(t) = e^{\mathbf{A}t}\begin{bmatrix} 4 \\ 5 \\ 6 \end{bmatrix} = e^t\begin{bmatrix} 4+28t+12t^2 \\ 5+12t \\ 6 \end{bmatrix}$$

28. $\mathbf{A} = 5\mathbf{I}+\mathbf{D}$ where $\mathbf{D}^3 = \mathbf{0}$, so $e^{\mathbf{A}t} = e^{5\mathbf{I}t}e^{\mathbf{D}t} = (e^{5t}\mathbf{I})(\mathbf{I}+\mathbf{D}t+\frac{1}{2}\mathbf{D}^2t^2)$. Hence

$$e^{\mathbf{A}t} = \begin{bmatrix} e^{5t} & 0 & 0 \\ 10te^{5t} & e^{5t} & 0 \\ (20t+150t^2)e^{5t} & 30te^{5t} & e^{5t} \end{bmatrix}, \quad \mathbf{x}(t) = e^{\mathbf{A}t}\begin{bmatrix} 40 \\ 50 \\ 60 \end{bmatrix} = e^{5t}\begin{bmatrix} 40 \\ 50+400t \\ 60+2300t+6000t^2 \end{bmatrix}$$

29. $\mathbf{A} = \mathbf{I}+\mathbf{D}$ where $\mathbf{D}^4 = \mathbf{0}$, so $e^{\mathbf{A}t} = e^{\mathbf{I}t}e^{\mathbf{D}t} = (e^t\mathbf{I})(\mathbf{I}+\mathbf{D}t+\frac{1}{2}\mathbf{D}^2t^2+\frac{1}{6}\mathbf{D}^3t^3)$. Hence

$$e^{\mathbf{A}t} = e^t\begin{bmatrix} 1 & 2t & 3t+6t^2 & 4t+6t^2+4t^3 \\ 0 & 1 & 6t & 3t+6t^2 \\ 0 & 0 & 1 & 2t \\ 0 & 0 & 0 & 1 \end{bmatrix}, \quad \mathbf{x}(t) = e^{\mathbf{A}t}\begin{bmatrix} 1 \\ 1 \\ 1 \\ 1 \end{bmatrix} = e^t\begin{bmatrix} 1+9t+12t^2+4t^3 \\ 1+9t+6t^2 \\ 1+2t \\ 1 \end{bmatrix}$$

30. $\mathbf{A} = 3\mathbf{I}+\mathbf{D}$ where $\mathbf{D}^4 = \mathbf{0}$, so $e^{\mathbf{A}t} = e^{3\mathbf{I}t}e^{\mathbf{D}t} = (e^{3t}\mathbf{I})(\mathbf{I}+\mathbf{D}t+\frac{1}{2}\mathbf{D}^2t^2+\frac{1}{6}\mathbf{D}^3t^3)$.
Hence

$$e^{\mathbf{A}t} = e^{3t}\begin{bmatrix} 1 & 0 & 0 & 0 \\ 6t & 1 & 0 & 0 \\ 9t+18t^2 & 6t & 1 & 0 \\ 12t+54t^2+36t^3 & 9t+18t^2 & 6t & 1 \end{bmatrix}, \quad \mathbf{x}(t) = e^{\mathbf{A}t}\begin{bmatrix} 1 \\ 1 \\ 1 \\ 1 \end{bmatrix} = e^{3t}\begin{bmatrix} 1 \\ 1+6t \\ 1+15t+18t^2 \\ 1+27t+72t^2+36t^3 \end{bmatrix}$$

33. $e^{\mathbf{A}t} = \mathbf{I}\cosh t + \mathbf{A}\sinh t = \begin{bmatrix} \cosh t & \sinh t \\ \sinh t & \cosh t \end{bmatrix}$, so the general solution of $\mathbf{x}' = \mathbf{A}\mathbf{x}$ is

$$\mathbf{x}(t) = e^{\mathbf{A}t}\mathbf{c} = \begin{bmatrix} c_1\cosh t + c_2\sinh t \\ c_1\sinh t + c_2\cosh t \end{bmatrix}.$$

34. Direct calculation gives $\mathbf{A}^2 = -4\mathbf{I}$, and it follows that $\mathbf{A}^3 = -4\mathbf{A}$ and $\mathbf{A}^4 = 16\mathbf{I}$.
Therefore

$$e^{At} = I + At - \frac{4It^2}{2!} - \frac{4At^3}{3!} + \frac{16It^4}{4!} + \frac{16At^5}{5!} + \cdots$$

$$= I\left[1 - \frac{(2t)^2}{2!} + \frac{(2t)^4}{4!} + \cdots\right] + \frac{1}{2}A\left[(2t) - \frac{(2t)^3}{3!} + \frac{(2t)^5}{5!} + \cdots\right]$$

$$e^{At} = I\cos 2t + \tfrac{1}{2}A\sin 2t$$

35. $e^{At} = \begin{bmatrix} e^{3t} & 4te^{3t} \\ 0 & e^{3t} \end{bmatrix}$

36. $e^{At} = \begin{bmatrix} e^t & 2te^t & (3t+4t^2)e^t \\ 0 & e^t & 4te^t \\ 0 & 0 & e^t \end{bmatrix}$

37. $e^{At} = \begin{bmatrix} e^{2t} & 3e^{2t} - 3e^t & 13e^{2t} - (13+9t)e^t \\ 0 & e^t & 3te^t \\ 0 & 0 & e^t \end{bmatrix}$

38. $e^{At} = \begin{bmatrix} e^{5t} & 4e^{10t} - 4e^{5t} & 16e^{10t} - (16+50t)e^{5t} \\ 0 & e^{10t} & 4e^{10t} - 4e^{5t} \\ 0 & 0 & e^{5t} \end{bmatrix}$

39. $e^{At} = \begin{bmatrix} e^t & 3te^t & 12e^{2t} - (12+9t)e^t & (51+18t)e^t - (51-36t)e^{2t} \\ 0 & e^t & 3e^{2t} - 3e^t & 6e^t - (6-9t)e^{2t} \\ 0 & 0 & e^{2t} & 3te^{2t} \\ 0 & 0 & 0 & e^{2t} \end{bmatrix}$

40. $e^{At} = \begin{bmatrix} e^{2t} & 4te^{2t} & (4t+18t^2)e^{2t} & 100e^{3t} - (100+96t+32t^2)e^{2t} \\ 0 & e^{2t} & 4te^{2t} & 20e^{3t} - (20+16t)e^{2t} \\ 0 & 0 & e^{2t} & 4e^{3t} - 4e^{2t} \\ 0 & 0 & 0 & e^{3t} \end{bmatrix}$

SECTION 5.6

NONHOMOGENEOUS LINEAR SYSTEMS

1. Substitution of the trial solution $x_p(t) = a$, $y_p(t) = b$ leads to the particular solution $x(t) = 7/3$, $y(t) = -8/3$.

2. The trial solution $x_p(t) = a_1 + b_1 t$, $y_p(t) = a_2 + b_2 t$ yields the particular solution

$$x(t) = \tfrac{1}{8}(1 + 12t), \quad y(t) = -\tfrac{1}{4}(5 + 4t).$$

3. $x(t) = (864 e^{-t} + 4 e^{6t} - 868 + 840 t - 504 t^2)/756$

$y(t) = (-864 e^{-t} + 3 e^{6t} + 861 - 882 t + 378 t^2)/756$

4. By the eigenvalue method we find first the complementary solution

$$x_c(t) = c_1 e^{5t} + c_2 e^{-2t}, \quad y_c(t) = c_1 e^{5t} - 6 c_2 e^{-2t}.$$

Then we try $x_p(t) = a e^t$, $y_p(t) = b e^t$ and find the particular solution $x_p(t) = -\tfrac{1}{12} e^t$, $y_p(t) = -\tfrac{3}{4} e^t$. Thus the general solution is

$$x(t) = c_1 e^{5t} + c_2 e^{-2t} - \tfrac{1}{12} e^t, \quad y(t) = c_1 e^{5t} - 6 c_2 e^{-2t} - \tfrac{3}{4} e^t.$$

Finally we apply the initial conditions $x(0) = y(0) = 1$ to determine c_1 and c_2. The result is

$$x(t) = \tfrac{1}{84}(99 e^{5t} - 8 e^{-2t} - 7 e^t), \quad y(t) = \tfrac{1}{84}(99 e^{5t} + 48 e^{-2t} - 63 e^t).$$

5. The e^{-t} term duplicates part of the complementary functions, so we try $x_p(t) = a_1 + b_1 e^{-t} + c_1 t e^{-t}$, $y_p(t) = a_2 + b_2 e^{-t} + c_2 t e^{-t}$. This leads to the particular solution

$$x(t) = \tfrac{1}{3}(-12 - e^{-t} - 7 t e^{-t}), \quad y(t) = \tfrac{1}{3}(-6 - 7 t e^{-t}).$$

6. Substitution of the trial solution $x_p(t) = b_1 e^t + c_1 t e^t$, $y_p(t) = b_2 e^t + c_2 t e^t$ leads to the particular solution

$$x(t) = -\tfrac{1}{256}(91 + 16t) e^t, \quad y(t) = -\tfrac{1}{32}(25 + 16t) e^t.$$

7. Substitution of the trial solution $x_p(t) = a_1 \sin t + b_1 \cos t$, $y_p(t) = a_2 \sin t + b_2 \cos t$ and imposition of the given initial conditions leads to the particular solution

$$x(t) = \tfrac{1}{410}(369 e^t + 166 e^{-9t} - 125 \cos t - 105 \sin t),$$
$$y(t) = \tfrac{1}{410}(369 e^t - 249 e^{-9t} - 120 \cos t - 150 \sin t).$$

8. Substitution of the trial solution $x_p(t) = a_1 \sin t + b_1 \cos t$, $y_p(t) = a_2 \sin t + b_2 \cos t$ leads to the particular solution

$$x(t) = \tfrac{1}{3}(17 \cos t + 2 \sin t), \quad y(t) = \tfrac{1}{3}(5 \cos t + 5 \sin t).$$

9. The $\cos 2t$ term duplicates the complementary function. Substitution of the trial solution

$$x_p(t) = a_1 \sin 2t + b_1 \cos 2t + c_1 t \sin 2t + d_1 t \cos 2t,$$
$$y_p(t) = a_2 \sin 2t + b_2 \cos 2t + c_2 t \sin 2t + d_2 t \cos 2t$$

leads to the particular solution

$$x(t) = \tfrac{1}{4}(\sin 2t + 2t \cos 2t + t \sin 2t), \quad y(t) = \tfrac{1}{4} t \sin 2t.$$

10. Substitution of the trial solution

$$x_p(t) = a_1 e^t \cos t + b_1 e^t \sin t, \quad y_p(t) = a_2 e^t \cos t + b_2 e^t \sin t$$

leads to the particular solution

$$x(t) = \tfrac{1}{13} e^t (4 \cos t - 6 \sin t), \quad y(t) = \tfrac{1}{13} e^t (3 \cos t + 2 \sin t).$$

11. The constant terms duplicate the complementary function. Substitution of the trial solution $x_p(t) = a_1 + b_1 t, \quad y_p(t) = a_2 + b_2 t$ followed by imposition of the given initial conditions leads to the solution

$$y(t) = \tfrac{1}{2}(1 - 4t + e^{4t}), \quad y(t) = \tfrac{1}{4}(-5 + 4t + e^{4t}).$$

12. Because $\lambda = 0$ is an eigenvalue of the associated homogeneous system, we must multiply the t-terms by t and include all lower degree terms in the trial solution. Thus we substitute the the trial solution

$$x_p(t) = a_1 + b_1 t + c_1 t^2, \quad y_p(t) = a_2 + b_2 t + c_2 t^2.$$

The resulting six equations in the coefficients are satisfied by $a_1 = b_1 = a_2 = b_2 = 0$, $c_1 = 1, \ c_2 = -1$. This gives the particular solution $x(t) = t^2, \ y(t) = -t^2$.

13. The e^t-terms duplicate the complementary function, so we substitute the trial solution

$$x_p(t) = (a_1 + b_1 t)e^t, \quad y_p(t) = (a_2 + b_2 t)e^t.$$

This leads to the solution $x(t) = \tfrac{1}{2}(1 + 5t)e^t, \ y(t) = -\tfrac{5}{2} t e^t.$

14. Because the associated homogeneous system has the eigenvalues $\lambda = 0$ and $\lambda = 4$ we substitute the trial solution

$$x_p(t) = a_1 + b_1 t + c_1 e^{4t} + d_1 t e^{4t}, \quad y_p(t) = a_2 + b_2 t + c_2 e^{4t} + d_2 t e^{4t}.$$

Upon solving the resulting eight equations in eight unknowns we obtain the particular solution

$$x(t) = \tfrac{1}{4}(-1 + 2t + t e^{4t}), \quad y(t) = \tfrac{1}{4}(-4t + e^{4t} + 2t e^{4t}).$$

15.　(a)　$x_1(t) = 200(1 - e^{-t/10}), \quad x_2(t) = 400(1 + e^{-t/10} - 2e^{-t/20})$

　　　(b)　$x_1(t) \to 200$ gal and $x_2(t) \to 400$ gal as $t \to \infty$.

　　　(c)　It takes about 6 min 56 sec for tank 1 to reach a salt concentration of 1 lb/gal, and about 24 min 34 sec for tank 2 to reach this concentration.

16.　(a)　$x_1(t) = 600(1 - e^{-t/20}), \quad x_2(t) = 300(1 + e^{-t/10} - 2e^{-t/20})$

　　　(b)　$x_1(t) \to 600$ gal and $x_2(t) \to 300$ gal as $t \to \infty$.

　　　(c)　It takes about 8 min 7 sec for tank 1 to reach a salt concentration of 1 lb/gal, and about 17 min 13 sec for tank 2 to reach this concentration.

In Problems 17-34 we apply the variation of parameters formula in Eq. (28) of Section 5.6. The answers shown below were actually calculated using the Mathematica code listed in the computing project for Section 5.6.

17.　$x_1(t) = 102 - 95e^{-t} - 7e^{5t}, \quad x_2(t) = 96 - 95e^{-t} - e^{5t}$

18.　$x_1(t) = 68 - 110t - 75e^{-t} + 7e^{5t}, \quad x_2(t) = 74 - 80t - 75e^{-t} + e^{5t}$

19.　$x_1(t) = -70 - 60t + 16e^{-3t} + 54e^{2t}, \quad x_2(t) = 5 - 60t - 32e^{-3t} + 27e^{2t}$

20.　$x_1(t) = 3e^{2t} + 60t e^{2t} - 3e^{-3t}, \quad x_2(t) = -6e^{2t} + 30t e^{2t} + 6e^{-3t}$

21.　$x_1(t) = -e^{-t} - 14e^{2t} + 15e^{3t}, \quad x_2(t) = -5e^{-t} - 10e^{2t} + 15e^{3t}$

22.　$x_1(t) = -10e^{-t} - 7t e^{-t} + 10e^{3t} - 5t e^{3t}, \quad x_2(t) = -15e^{-t} - 35t e^{-t} + 15e^{3t} - 5t e^{3t}$

23.　$x_1(t) = 3 + 11t + 8t^2, \quad x_2(t) = 5 + 17t + 24t^2$

24.　$x_1(t) = 2 + t + \ln t, \quad x_2(t) = 5 + 3t - \dfrac{1}{t} + 3\ln t$

25.　$x_1(t) = -1 + 8t + \cos t - 8\sin t, \quad x_2(t) = -2 + 4t + 2\cos t - 3\sin t$

26. $x_1(t) = 3\cos t - 32\sin t + 17t\cos t + 4t\sin t$
$x_2(t) = 5\cos t - 13\sin t + 6t\cos t + 5t\sin t$

27. $x_1(t) = 8t^3 + 6t^4, \quad x_2(t) = 3t^2 - 2t^3 + 3t^4$

28. $x_1(t) = -7 + 14t - 6t^2 + 4t^2\ln t, \quad x_2(t) = -7 + 9t - 3t^2 + \ln t - 2t\ln t + 2t^2\ln t$

29. $x_1(t) = t\cos t - \ln(\cos t)\sin t, \quad x_2(t) = t\sin t - \ln(\cos t)\cos t$

30. $x_1(t) = \frac{1}{2}t^2\cos 2t, \quad x_2(t) = \frac{1}{2}t^2\sin 2t$

31. $x_1(t) = (9t^2 + 4t^3)e^t, \quad x_2(t) = 6t^2 e^t, \quad x_3(t) = 6t e^t$

32. $x_1(t) = (44 + 18t)e^t + (-44 + 26t)e^{2t}, \quad x_2(t) = 6e^t + (-6 + 6t)e^{2t}, \quad x_3(t) = 2t e^{2t}$

33. $x_1(t) = 15t^2 + 60t^3 + 95t^4 + 12t^5, \quad x_2(t) = 15t^2 + 55t^3 + 15t^4,$
$x_3(t) = 15t^2 + 20t^3, \quad x_4(t) = 15t^2$

34. $x_1(t) = 4t^3 + (4 + 16t + 8t^2)e^{2t}, \quad x_2(t) = 3t^2 + (2 + 4t)e^{2t},$
$x_3(t) = (2 + 4t + 2t^2)e^{2t}, \quad x_4(t) = (1 + t)e^{2t}$

CHAPTER 6

NONLINEAR DIFFERENTIAL EQUATIONS
AND PHENOMENA

SECTION 6.1

STABILITY AND THE PHASE PLANE

1.   The only critical point is the saddle point $(0, 0)$ shown in Figure 6.1.13 in the text.

2.   The only critical point is the node $(1, 1)$ shown in Figure 6.1.15 in the text.

3.   The only critical point is the stable center $(-1, 1)$ shown in Figure 6.1.18 in the text.

4.   The only critical point is the spiral point $(1, -1)$ shown in Figure 6.1.12 in the text.

5.   The first equation gives $y = 1$ or $y = -1$ at a critical point. Then the second equation gives $x = -2$ or $x = 2$, respectively. Thus we find the spiral point $(-2, 1)$ and the saddle point $(2, 1)$ shown in Figure 6.1.11 in the text.

6.   The second equation gives $x = -2$ or $x = 2$ at a critical point. Then the first equation gives $y = 2/3$ or $y = -2/5$, respectively. Thus we find the spiral points $(-2, 2/3)$ and $(2, -2/5)$ shown in Figure 6.1.17.

7.   The second equation gives $x = -2$, $x = 0$, or $x = 2$ at a critical point. Then the first equation gives $y = -1$, $y = 0$, or $y = 1$, respectively. Thus we find the spiral point $(0, 0)$ and the saddle points $(-2, 1)$ and $(2, 1)$ shown in Figure 6.1.14 in the text.

8.   The second equation gives $y = -x^2$ at a critical point. Substitution of this in the first equation then gives $x - x^3 = 0$, so $x = -1$, $x = 0$, or $x = 1$. This gives the spiral point $(-1, -1)$, the saddle point $(0, 0)$, and the node $(1, -1)$ shown in Figure 6.1.16 in the text.

In each of Problems 9–12 we need only set $x' = x'' = 0$ and solve the resulting equation for x.

9. $x(t) = 0$, $x(t) = 2$, $x(t) = -2$

10. $x(t) = 0$

11. There are infinitely many equilibrium solutions: $x(t) = n\pi$ for any integer n.

12. $x(t) = 0$

13.   Solution: $x(t) = x_0 e^{-2t}, \quad y(t) = y_0 e^{-2t}$

The origin is a stable proper node like the one shown in Figure 6.1.4 in the text.

14.   Solution: $x(t) = x_0 e^{2t}, \quad y(t) = y_0 e^{-2t}$

The origin is an unstable saddle point like the one illustrated in Figure 6.1.6 in the text, except with all the arrows reversed.

15.   Solution: $x(t) = x_0 e^{-2t}, \quad y(t) = y_0 e^{-t}$

The origin is a stable improper node like the one shown in Figure 6.1.5 in the text, except that the trajectories consist of the x-axis and parabolas of the form $x = ky^2$.

16.   Solution: $x(t) = x_0 e^{t}, \quad y(t) = y_0 e^{3t}$

The origin is an unstable improper node. The trajectories consist of the y-axis and curves of the form $y = kx^3$, departing from the origin.

17.   Solution: $x(t) = A \cos t + B \sin t$
$y(t) = B \cos t - A \sin t$

The origin is a stable center. The trajectories are clockwise-oriented circles centered at the origin.

18.   Solution: $x(t) = A \cos 2t + B \sin 2t,$
$y(t) = -2B \cos 2t + 2A \sin 2t$

The origin is a stable center like the one illustrated in Figure 6.1.7, except that the arrows point in a counter-clockwise direction, and the vertical semiaxis of each ellipse is twice its horizontal semiaxis.

19.   Solution: $x(t) = A \cos 2t + B \sin 2t,$
$y(t) = B \cos 2t - A \sin 2t$

The origin is a stable center, and the trajectories are clockwise-oriented circles centered at (0, 0).

20.   Solution: $x(t) = e^{-2t}(A \cos t + D \sin t),$
$y(t) = e^{-2t}[(-2A + B)\cos t - (A + 2B)\sin t]$

The origin is an asymptotically stable spiral point with trajectories approaching (0,0) as in Figure 6.1.9 in the text.

23. Origin $(0, 0)$ and the circles $x^2 + y^2 = C > 0$.

24. Origin $(0, 0)$ and the hyperbolas $y^2 - x^2 = C$.

25. Origin $(0, 0)$ and the ellipses $x^2 + 4y^2 = C > 0$.

26. Origin $(0, 0)$ and the ovals of the form $x^4 + y^4 = C > 0$.

27. If $\phi(t) = x(t + \gamma)$ and $\psi(t) = y(t + \gamma)$ then

$$\phi'(t) = x'(t + \gamma) = y(t + \gamma) = \psi(t),$$

but

$$\psi(t) = y'(t + \gamma) = x(t + \gamma) \cdot (t + \gamma) = t\,\phi(t) + \gamma\,\phi(t) \neq t\,\phi(t).$$

28. If $\phi(t) = x(t + \gamma)$ and $\psi(t) = y(t + \gamma)$ then

$$\phi'(t) = x'(t + \gamma) = F(x(t + \gamma), \quad y(t + \gamma)) = F(\phi(t), \psi(t)),$$

and

$$\psi'(t) = G(\phi(t), \psi(t))$$

similarly. Therefore $\phi(t)$ and $\psi(t)$ satisfy the given differential equations.

SECTION 6.2

LINEAR AND ALMOST LINEAR SYSTEMS

In Problems 1–10 we first find the roots λ_1 and λ_2 of the characteristic equation of the given system. We can then read the type and stability of the critical point (0,0) from Theorem 1 and the table of Figure 6.2.9 in the text.

1. $\lambda_1 = -1, \quad \lambda_2 = -3$ so (0,0) is an asymptotically stable node.

2. $\lambda_1 = 2, \quad \lambda_2 = 3$ so (0,0) is an unstable improper node.

3. $\lambda_1 = -1, \quad \lambda_2 = 3$ so (0,0) is an unstable saddle point.

4. $\lambda_1 = -2, \quad \lambda_2 = 4$ so (0,0) is an unstable saddle point.

5. $\lambda_1 = \lambda_2 = -1$ so (0,0) is an asymptotically stable node.

6. $\lambda_1 = \lambda_2 = 2$ so (0,0) is an unstable node.

7. $\lambda_1, \lambda_2 = 1 \pm 2i$ so (0,0) is an unstable spiral point.

8. $\lambda_1, \lambda_2 = -2 \pm 3i$ so $(0,0)$ is an asymptotically stable spiral point.

9. $\lambda_1, \lambda_2 = \pm 2i$ so $(0,0)$ is a stable (but not asymptotically stable) center.

10. $\lambda_1, \lambda_2 = \pm 3i$ so $(0,0)$ is a stable (but not asymptotically stable) center.

11. The substitution $u = x - 2$, $v = y - 1$ transforms the given system to the system

$$u' = u - 2v, \qquad v' = 3u - 4v$$

with characteristic roots $\lambda_1 = -1$, $\lambda_2 = -2$. Hence $(2, 1)$ is an asymptotically stable node.

12. The substitution $u = x - 2$, $v = y + 3$ transforms the given system to the system

$$u' = u - 2v, \qquad v' = u + 4v$$

with characteristic roots $\lambda_1 = 2$, $\lambda_2 = 3$. Hence $(2, -3)$ is an unstable improper node.

13. The substitution $u = x - 2$, $v = y - 2$ transforms the given system to the system

$$u' = 2u - v, \qquad v' = 3u - 2v$$

with characteristic roots $\lambda_1 = 1$, $\lambda_2 = -1$. Hence $(2, 2)$ is an unstable saddle point.

14. The substitution $u = x - 3$, $v = y - 4$ transforms the given system to the system

$$u' = u + v, \qquad v' = 3u - v$$

with characteristic roots $\lambda_1 = -2$, $\lambda_2 = 2$. Hence $(3, 4)$ is an unstable saddle point.

15. The substitution $u = x - 1$, $v = y - 1$ transforms the given system to the system

$$u' = u - v, \qquad v' = 5u - 3v$$

with characteristic roots $\lambda_1, \lambda_2 = -1 \pm i$. Hence $(1, 1)$ is an asymptotically stable spiral point.

16. The substitution $u = x - 3$, $v = y - 2$ transforms the given system to the system

$$u' = u - 2v, \qquad v' = u + 3v$$

with characteristic roots $\lambda_1, \lambda_2 = 2 \pm i$. Hence $(3, 2)$ is an unstable spiral point.

17. The substitution $u = x - 5/2$, $v = y + 1/2$ transforms the given system to the system

$$u' = u - 5v, \qquad v' = u - v$$

with characteristic roots $\lambda_1, \lambda_2 = \pm 2\, i$. Hence $(5/2, -1/2)$ is a stable center.

18.   The substitution $u = x + 2$, $v = y + 1$ transforms the given system to the system

$$u' = 4u - 5v, \qquad v' = 5u - 4v$$

with characteristic roots $\lambda_1, \lambda_2 = \pm 3\, i$. Hence $(-2, -1)$ is a stable (but not asymptotically stable) center.

In Problems 19–28 we first find the characteristic roots λ_1 and λ_2 of the associated linear system, and then apply Theorem 2 to determine as much as we can about the type and stability of the critical point $(0,0)$ of the given almost linear system.

19. $\lambda_1 = -2$, $\lambda_2 = -3$ so $(0,0)$ is an asymptotically stable node.

20. $\lambda_1 = 1$, $\lambda_2 = 4$ so $(0,0)$ is an unstable improper node.

21. $\lambda_1 = -3$, $\lambda_2 = 2$ so $(0,0)$ is an unstable saddle point.

22. $\lambda_1, \lambda_2 = \pm 3\, i$ so $(0,0)$ is either a center or a spiral point, but its stability is not determined by Theorem 2.

23. $\lambda_1, \lambda_2 = -2 \pm 2\, i$ so $(0,0)$ is an asymptotically stable spiral point.

24. $\lambda_1, \lambda_2 = 1 \pm 3\, i$ so $(0,0)$ is an unstable spiral point.

25. $\lambda_1 = \lambda_2 = -1$ so $(0,0)$ is an asymptotically stable node or spiral point.

26. $\lambda_1 = \lambda_2 = 1$ so $(0,0)$ is an unstable critical point that is either a node or a spiral point.

27. $\lambda_1, \lambda_2 = \pm i$ so $(0,0)$ is either a center or a spiral point, but its stability is not determined by Theorem 2.

28. $\lambda_1, \lambda_2 = \pm 2\, i$ so $(0,0)$ is either a center or a spiral point, but its stability is not determined by Theorem 2.

29.   The critical points of the given system are $(0,0)$ and $(1, 1)$. At $(0,0)$ the characteristic roots are $\lambda_1 = -1, \lambda_2 = 1$ so $(0,0)$ is an unstable saddle point. The substitution $u = x - 1$, $v = y - 1$ transforms the given system to the almost linear system

$$u' = u - v, \qquad v' = 2u + v + u^2$$

whose linearization has characteristic roots $\lambda_1, \lambda_2 = \pm i$. Hence $(1, 1)$ is either a center or a spiral point, but its stability is indeterminate.

30. The critical points of the given system are $(1, 1)$ and $(-1, 1)$. The substitution $u = x - 1$, $v = y - 1$ transforms it to the almost linear system

$$u' = v, \qquad v' = 2u - v + u^2$$

whose linearized system has characteristic roots $\lambda_1 = -2$, $\lambda_2 = 1$. Hence $(1, 1)$ is an unstable saddle point of the given system. The substitution $u = x + 1$, $v = y - 1$ transforms it to the almost linear system

$$u' = v, \qquad v' = -2u + v + u^2$$

whose linearized system has characteristic roots $\lambda_1, \lambda_2 = (-1 \pm i\sqrt{7})/2$. Hence $(-1, 1)$ is an asymptotically stable spiral point of the given system.

31. The critical points of the given system are $(1, 1)$ and $(-1, -1)$. The substitution $u = x - 1$, $v = y - 1$ transforms it to the almost linear system

$$u' = 2v + v^2, \qquad v' = 3u - v + 3u^2 + u^3$$

whose linearization has characteristic roots $\lambda_1 = -3$, $\lambda_2 = 2$. Hence $(1, 1)$ is an unstable saddle point of the given system. The substitution $u = x + 1$, $v = y + 1$ transforms it to the almost linear system

$$u' = -2v + v^2, \qquad v' = 3u - v - 3u^2 + u^3$$

whose linearization has characteristic roots $\lambda_1, \lambda_2 = (-1 \pm i\sqrt{23})/2$. Hence $(-1, -1)$ is an asymptotically stable spiral point.

32. The critical points of the given system are $(2, 1)$ and $(-2, -1)$. The substitution $u = x - 2$, $v = y - 1$ transforms it to the almost linear system

$$u' = u + 2v + uv, \qquad v' = u - 2v$$

whose linearized system has characteristic roots $\lambda_1, \lambda_2 = (-1 \pm \sqrt{17})/2$ of opposite sign. Hence $(2, 1)$ is an unstable saddle point of the given system. The substitution $u = x + 2$, $v = y + 1$ transforms it to the almost linear system

$$u' = -u - 2v + uv, \qquad v' = u - 2v$$

whose linearized system has characteristic roots $\lambda_1, \lambda_2 = (-3 \pm i\sqrt{7})/2$. Hence $(-2, -1)$ is an asymptotically stable spiral point of the given system.

33.   The characteristic equation of the given linear system is

$$(\lambda - \varepsilon)^2 + 1 = 0$$

with characteristic roots $\lambda_1, \lambda_2 = \varepsilon \pm i$.

(a)   So if $\varepsilon < 0$ then λ_1, λ_2 are complex conjugates with negative real part, and hence $(0, 0)$ is an asymptotically stable spiral point.

(b)   If $\varepsilon = 0$ then $\lambda_1, \lambda_2 = \pm i$, so $(0,0)$ is a stable center.

(c)   If $\varepsilon > 0$, the situation is the same as in (a) except that the real part is positive, so $(0, 0)$ is an unstable spiral point.

34.   The characteristic equation of the given linear system is

$$(\lambda + 1)^2 - \varepsilon = 0.$$

(a)   If $\varepsilon < 0$ then $\lambda_1, \lambda_2 = -1 \pm i\sqrt{(-\varepsilon)}$, so $(0,0)$ is an asymptotically stable spiral point.

(b)   If $\varepsilon = 0$ then the characteristic roots $\lambda_1 = \lambda_2 = -1$ are equal and negative, so $(0,0)$ is an asymptotically stable node. If $0 < \varepsilon < 1$ then $\lambda_1, \lambda_2 = -1 \pm \sqrt{\varepsilon}$ are both negative, so $(0,0)$ is an asymptotically stable improper node.

35.   **(a)**   If $h = 0$ we have the familiar system $x' = y$, $y' = -x$ with circular trajectories about the origin, which is therefore a center.

(b)   The change to polar coordinates as in Example 6 of Section 6.1 is routine, yielding $r' = hr^3$ and $\theta' = -1$.

(c)   If $h = -1$, then $r' = -r^3$ integrates to give $2r^2 = 1/(t + C)$ where C is a positive constant, so clearly $r \to 0$ as $t \to +\infty$, and thus the origin is a stable spiral point.

(d)   If $h = +1$, then $r' = r^3$ integrates to give $2r^2 = -1/(t + C)$ where $C = -B$ is a positive constant. It follows that $2r^2 = 1/(B - t)$, so now r increases as t starts at 0 and increases.

36.   **(a)**   Again, the change of variables is essentially the same as in Example 6 of Section 6.1.

(b)   If $\varepsilon = -a^2$ then the equation $r' = -r(a^2 + r^2)$ integrates to give the equation

$$t + C = -\frac{\ln r}{a^2} + \frac{\ln(a^2 + r^2)}{2a^2}$$

that (after exponentiating) we readily solve for

$$r^2 = \frac{a^2 \exp(-2ta^2 - 2Ca^2)}{1 - \exp(-2ta^2 - 2Ca^2)}.$$

This makes it clear that $r \to 0$ as $t \to +\infty$, so the origin is an asymptotically stable spiral point in this case.

(c)   If $\varepsilon = a^2$ then the equation $r' = r(a^2 - r^2)$ integrates to give the equation

$$t + C = \frac{2\ln r - \ln(a - r) - \ln(a + r)}{2a^2}$$

that (after exponentiating) we solve for

$$r^2 = \frac{a^2}{1 + \exp(-2ta^2 - 2Ca^2)}.$$

It therefore follows that $r \to a$ as $t \to +\infty$.

37.   The substitution $y = vx$ in the homogeneous first-order equation

$$\frac{dy}{dx} = \frac{y(2x^3 - y^3)}{x(x^3 - 2y^3)}$$

yields

$$x\frac{dv}{dx} = -\frac{v^4 + v}{2v^3 - 1}.$$

Separating the variables and integrating by partial fractions, we get

$$\int \left(-\frac{1}{v} + \frac{1}{v+1} + \frac{2v-1}{v^2 - v + 1} \right) dv = -\int \frac{dx}{x}$$

$$\ln((v+1)(v^2 - v + 1)) = \ln v - \ln x + \ln C$$

$$(v+1)(v^2 - v + 1) = \frac{Cv}{x}$$

$$v^3 + 1 = \frac{Cv}{x}.$$

Finally, the replacement $v = y/x$ yields $x^3 + y^3 = Cxy$.

SECTION 6.3

ECOLOGICAL APPLICATIONS: PREDATORS AND COMPETITORS

1. If $x = u + b/q$, $y = v + a/p$ then $x' = u'$ and $y' = v'$ so the first predator-prey equation in

$$x' = ax - pxy, \quad y' = -by + qxy \qquad (1)$$

yields

$$u' = a(u + b/q) - p(u + b/q)(v + a/p)$$
$$= au + ab/q - puv - au - bpv/q - ab/q = -bpv/q - puv.$$

upon cancellation of a couple of pairs of terms. In a quite similar way the second predator-prey equation transforms to $v' = aqu/p + quv$.

2. The predator-prey equations $x' = ax - pxy$, $y' = -by + qxy$ yield

$$\frac{dy}{dx} = \frac{y'}{x'} = \frac{y(-b + qx)}{x(a - py)},$$

$$\int \left(\frac{a}{y} - p\right) dy = \int \left(-\frac{b}{x} + q\right) dx,$$

$$a \ln y - py = -b \ln x + qx + C.$$

3. The effect of using the insecticide is to replace b by $b + f$ and a by $a - f$ in the predator-prey equations, while leaving p and q unchanged. Hence the new harmful population is $(b + f)/q > b/q = x_E$, and the new benign population is $(a - f)/p < a/p = y_E$.

Problems 4-7 deal with the competition system

$$x' = 60x - 4x^2 - 3xy, \quad y' = 42y - 2y^2 - 3xy. \qquad (2)$$

In each problem we denote by **A** the coefficient matrix of the linearized system.

4. We simply delete the quadratic terms in (2) to linearize at $(0,0)$. Then it is quite obvious that the coefficient matrix $\mathbf{A} = \begin{bmatrix} 60 & 0 \\ 0 & 42 \end{bmatrix}$ has eigenvalues $\lambda_1 = 60$ and $\lambda_2 = 42$.

5. The substitution $x = u$, $y = v + 21$ gives the linearization $u' = -3u$, $v' = -63u - 42v$ at $(0, 21)$. Then the characteristic equation

$$|\mathbf{A} - \lambda\mathbf{I}| = \begin{vmatrix} -3-\lambda & 0 \\ -63 & -42-\lambda \end{vmatrix} = (\lambda+3)(\lambda+42) = 0$$

has roots $\lambda_1 = -3$ and $\lambda_2 = -42$.

6. The substitution $x = u + 15$, $y = v$ gives the linearization $u' = -60u - 45v$, $v' = -3v$ at $(15, 0)$. Then the characteristic equation

$$|\mathbf{A} - \lambda\mathbf{I}| = \begin{vmatrix} -60-\lambda & -45 \\ 0 & -3-\lambda \end{vmatrix} = (\lambda+60)(\lambda+3) = 0$$

has roots $\lambda_1 = -60$ and $\lambda_2 = -3$.

7. The substitution $x = u + 6$, $y = v + 12$ gives the linearization $u' = -24u - 18v$, $v' = -36u - 24v$ at $(6, 12)$. Then the characteristic equation

$$|\mathbf{A} - \lambda\mathbf{I}| = \begin{vmatrix} -24-\lambda & -18 \\ -36 & -24-\lambda \end{vmatrix} = (-24-\lambda)^2 - 2(18)^2 = 0$$

has roots $\lambda = -24 \pm 18\sqrt{2}$.

Problems 8-10 deal with the competition system

$$x' = 60x - 3x^2 - 4xy, \quad y' = 42y - 3y^2 - 2xy \tag{3}$$

8. The substitution $x = u$, $y = v + 14$ gives the linearization $u' = 4u$, $v' = -28u - 42v$ at $(0, 14)$. Then the characteristic equation

$$|\mathbf{A} - \lambda\mathbf{I}| = \begin{vmatrix} 4-\lambda & 0 \\ -28 & -42-\lambda \end{vmatrix} = (\lambda-4)(\lambda+42) = 0$$

has roots $\lambda_1 = 4$ and $\lambda_2 = -42$.

9. The substitution $x = u + 20$, $y = v$ gives the linearization $u' = -60u - 80v$, $v' = 2v$ at $(20, 0)$. Then the characteristic equation

$$|A - \lambda I| = \begin{vmatrix} -60 - \lambda & -80 \\ 0 & 2 - \lambda \end{vmatrix} = (\lambda + 60)(\lambda - 2) = 0$$

has roots $\lambda_1 = -60$ and $\lambda_2 = 2$.

10. The substitution $x = u + 12$, $y = u + 6$ gives the linearization $u' = -36u - 48v$, $v' = -12u - 18v$ at $(12, 6)$. Then the characteristic equation

$$|A - \lambda I| = \begin{vmatrix} -36 - \lambda & -48 \\ -12 & -18 - \lambda \end{vmatrix} = (\lambda + 36)(\lambda + 18) - 576 = 0$$

has roots $\lambda = -27 \pm 3\sqrt{73}$.

Problems 11-13 deal with the predator-prey system

$$x' = 5x - x^2 - xy, \quad y' = -2y + xy. \tag{4}$$

11. We simply delete the quadratic terms in (4) to linearize at $(0,0)$. Then it is quite obvious that the coefficient matrix $A = \begin{bmatrix} 5 & 0 \\ 0 & -2 \end{bmatrix}$ has eigenvalues $\lambda_1 = 5$ and $\lambda_2 = -2$.

12. The substitution $x = u + 5$, $y = v$ gives the linearization $u' = -5u - 5v$, $v' = 3v$ at $(5, 0)$. Then the characteristic equation

$$|A - \lambda I| = \begin{vmatrix} -5 - \lambda & -5 \\ 0 & 3 - \lambda \end{vmatrix} = (\lambda + 5)(\lambda - 3) = 0$$

has roots $\lambda_1 = -5$ and $\lambda_2 = 3$.

13. The substitution $x = u + 2$, $y = v + 3$ gives the linearization $u' = -2u - 2v$, $v' = 3u$. at $(2, 3)$. Then the characteristic equation

$$|A - \lambda I| = \begin{vmatrix} -2 - \lambda & -2 \\ 3 & -\lambda \end{vmatrix} = \lambda^2 + 2\lambda + 6 = 0$$

has roots $\lambda = -1 \pm i\sqrt{5}$.

Problems 14-17 deal with the predator-prey system

$$x' = x^2 - 2x - xy, \quad y' = y^2 - 4y + xy. \tag{5}$$

14. We simply delete the quadratic terms in (5) to linearize at $(0,0)$. Then it is quite obvious that the coefficient matrix $\mathbf{A} = \begin{bmatrix} -2 & 0 \\ 0 & -4 \end{bmatrix}$ has eigenvalues $\lambda_1 = -2$ and $\lambda_2 = -4$.

15. The substitution $x = u$, $y = v + 4$ gives the linearization $u' = -6u$, $v' = 4u + 4v$ at $(0, 4)$. Then the characteristic equation

$$|\mathbf{A} - \lambda \mathbf{I}| = \begin{vmatrix} -6-\lambda & 0 \\ 4 & 4-\lambda \end{vmatrix} = (\lambda + 6)(\lambda - 4) = 0$$

has roots $\lambda_1 = -6$ and $\lambda_2 = 4$.

16. The substitution $x = u + 2$, $y = v$ gives the linearization $u' = 2u - 2v$, $v' = -2v$ at $(2, 0)$. Then the characteristic equation

$$|\mathbf{A} - \lambda \mathbf{I}| = \begin{vmatrix} 2-\lambda & -2 \\ 0 & -2-\lambda \end{vmatrix} = (\lambda - 2)(\lambda + 2) = 0$$

has roots $\lambda = \pm 2$.

17. The substitution $x = u + 3$, $y = v + 1$ gives the linearization $u' = 3u - 3v$, $v' = u + v$ at $(3, 1)$. Then the characteristic equation

$$|\mathbf{A} - \lambda \mathbf{I}| = \begin{vmatrix} 3-\lambda & -3 \\ 1 & 1-\lambda \end{vmatrix} = \lambda^2 - 4\lambda + 6 = 0$$

has roots $\lambda = 2 \pm i\sqrt{2}$.

Problems 18 and 19 deal with the predator-prey system

$$x' = 2x - xy, \quad y' = -5y + xy \tag{7}$$

18. We simply delete the quadratic terms in (7) to linearize at $(0,0)$. Then it is quite obvious that the coefficient matrix $\mathbf{A} = \begin{bmatrix} 2 & 0 \\ 0 & -5 \end{bmatrix}$ has eigenvalues $\lambda_1 = 2$ and $\lambda_2 = -5$.

19. The substitution $x = u + 5$, $y = v + 2$ gives the linearization $u' = -5v$, $v' = 2u$ at $(5, 2)$. Then the characteristic equation

$$|\mathbf{A} - \lambda \mathbf{I}| = \begin{vmatrix} -\lambda & -5 \\ 2 & -\lambda \end{vmatrix} = \lambda^2 + 10 = 0$$

has roots $\lambda = \pm i\sqrt{10}$.

Problems 20-22 deal with the predator-prey system

$$x' = -3x + x^2 - xy, \quad y' = -5y + xy \tag{8}$$

20. We simply delete the quadratic terms in (8) to linearize at $(0,0)$. Then it is quite obvious that the coefficient matrix $\mathbf{A} = \begin{bmatrix} -3 & 0 \\ 0 & -5 \end{bmatrix}$ has eigenvalues $\lambda_1 = -3$ and $\lambda_2 = -5$.

21. The substitution $x = u + 3, \ y = v$ gives the linearization $u' = 3u - 3v, \ v' = -2v$ at $(3, 0)$. Then the characteristic equation

$$|\mathbf{A} - \lambda\mathbf{I}| = \begin{vmatrix} 3-\lambda & -3 \\ 0 & -2-\lambda \end{vmatrix} = (\lambda - 3)(\lambda + 2) = 0$$

has roots $\lambda_1 = 3$ and $\lambda_2 = -2$.

22. The substitution $x = u + 5, \ y = u + 2$ gives the linearization $u' = 5u - 5v, \ v' = 2u$ at $(5, 2)$. Then the characteristic equation

$$|\mathbf{A} - \lambda\mathbf{I}| = \begin{vmatrix} 5-\lambda & -5 \\ 2 & -\lambda \end{vmatrix} = \lambda^2 - 5\lambda + 10 = 0$$

has roots $\lambda = \frac{1}{2}\left(5 \pm i\sqrt{15}\right)$.

Problems 23-25 deal with the predator-prey system

$$x' = 7x - x^2 - xy, \quad y' = -5y + xy \tag{9}$$

23. We simply delete the quadratic terms in (9) to linearize at $(0,0)$. Then it is quite obvious that the coefficient matrix $\mathbf{A} = \begin{bmatrix} 7 & 0 \\ 0 & -5 \end{bmatrix}$ has eigenvalues $\lambda_1 = 7$ and $\lambda_2 = -5$.

24. The substitution $x = u + 7, \ y = v$ gives the linearization $u' = -7u - 7v, \ v' = 2v$ at $(7, 0)$. Then the characteristic equation

$$|\mathbf{A} - \lambda\mathbf{I}| = \begin{vmatrix} -7-\lambda & -7 \\ 0 & 2-\lambda \end{vmatrix} = (\lambda + 7)(\lambda - 2) = 0$$

has roots $\lambda_1 = -7$ and $\lambda_2 = 2$.

25. The substitution $x = u + 5, \ y = u + 2$ gives the linearization $u' = -5u - 5v, \ v' = 2u$ at $(5, 2)$. Then the characteristic equation

$$|A - \lambda I| = \begin{vmatrix} -5-\lambda & -5 \\ 2 & -\lambda \end{vmatrix} = \lambda^2 + 5\lambda + 10 = 0$$

has roots $\lambda = \frac{1}{2}\left(-5 \pm i\sqrt{15}\right)$.

SECTION 6.4

NONLINEAR MECHANICAL SYSTEMS

In each of Problems 1–4 we need only substitute the familiar power series for the exponential, sine, and cosine functions, and then discard all higher-order terms. For each problem we give the corresponding linear system, the eigenvalues λ_1 and λ_2, and the type of this critical point.

1. $x' = -x + 2y$, $y' = -x - 4y$; $\lambda_1 = -2$, $\lambda_2 = -3$; stable node

2. $x' = 2x + y$, $y' = x + 2y$; $\lambda_1 = 1$, $\lambda_2 = 3$; unstable node

3. $x' = x + 2y$, $y' = 8x + y$; $\lambda_1 = -3$, $\lambda_2 = 5$; unstable saddle point

4. The linear system is $x' = x - 2y$, $y' = 4x - 3y$ because

$$\sin x \cos y = (x - x^3/3! + \cdots)(1 - y^2/2! + \cdots) = x + \cdots.$$

$\lambda_1, \lambda_2 = -1 \pm 2i$, stable spiral point

5. The critical points are of the form $(0, n\pi)$ where n is an integer. The linearized system at $(0, n\pi)$ is

$$u' = -u \pm v, \quad v' = 2u$$

where we take the plus sign if n is even, the minus sign if n is odd. If n is even the eigenvalues are $\lambda_1 = 1$ and $\lambda_2 = -2$, so $(0, n\pi)$ is an unstable saddle point. If n is odd the eigenvalues are $\lambda_1, \lambda_2 = (-1 \pm i\sqrt{7})/2$, so $(0, n\pi)$ is a stable spiral point.

6. The critical points are of the form $(n, 0)$ where n is an integer. The linearized system at $(n, 0)$ is

$$u' = v, \quad v' = \pm\pi u - v$$

where we take the plus sign if n is even, the minus sign if n is odd. The characteristic equation

$$\lambda^2 + \lambda - \pi = 0$$

has one positive and one negative root, so $(n, 0)$ is an unstable saddle point if n is even.

The equation

$$\lambda^2 + \lambda + \pi = 0$$

has complex conjugate roots with negative real part, so $(n, 0)$ is a stable spiral point if n is odd.

7. The critical points are of the form $(n\pi, n\pi)$ where n is an integer. The linearized system at $(n\pi, n\pi)$ is

$$u' = -u + v, \qquad v' = \pm 2u$$

where we take the plus sign if n is even, the minus sign if n is odd. The characteristic equation is $\lambda^2 + \lambda \mp 2 = 0$. If n is even the eigenvalues are $\lambda_1 = 1$ and $\lambda_2 = -2$, so $(n\pi, n\pi)$ is an unstable saddle point. If n is odd the eigenvalues are $\lambda_1, \lambda_2 = (-1 \pm i\sqrt{7})/2$, so $(n\pi, n\pi)$ is a stable spiral point.

8. The critical points are of the form $(n\pi, 0)$ where n is an integer. The linearized system at $(n\pi, 0)$ is

$$u' = \pm 3u + v, \qquad v' = \pm u + 2v$$

where we take the plus signs if n is even, the minus signs if n is odd. If n is even then the eigenvalues $\lambda_1, \lambda_2 = (5 \pm \sqrt{5})/2$ are both positive, so $(n\pi, 0)$ is an unstable node. If n is odd then the eigenvalues $\lambda_1, \lambda_2 = (-1 \pm \sqrt{21})/2$ have different signs, so $(n\pi, 0)$ is an unstable saddle point.

For Problems 9–11 the linearization of the damped pendulum system at the critical point $(n\pi, 0)$ is

$$u' = v, \qquad v' = \pm \omega^2 u - cv$$

where we take the plus sign if n is odd, the minus sign if n is even.

9. If n is odd then the characteristic equation $\lambda^2 + c\lambda - \omega^2 = 0$ has real roots

$$\lambda_1, \lambda_2 = \frac{-c \pm \sqrt{c^2 + 4\omega^2}}{2}$$

with opposite signs, so $(n\pi, 0)$ is an unstable saddle point.

10. If n is odd then the characteristic equation $\lambda^2 + c\lambda + \omega^2 = 0$ has roots

$$\lambda_1, \lambda_2 = \frac{-c \pm \sqrt{c^2 - 4\omega^2}}{2}.$$

If $c^2 > 4\omega^2$ then λ_1 and λ_2 are both negative so $(n\pi, 0)$ is a stable node.

11. If $c^2 < 4\omega^2$ then the two eigenvalues

$$\lambda_1, \lambda_2 = \frac{-c \pm \sqrt{c^2 - 4\omega^2}}{2} = -\frac{c}{2} \pm \frac{i}{2}\sqrt{4\omega^2 - c^2}$$

are complex conjugates with negative real part, so $(n\pi, 0)$ is a stable spiral point.

Problems 12–16 call for us to find and classify the critical points of the first order-system $x' = y$, $y' = -f(x, y)$ that corresponds to the given equation $x'' + f(x, x') = 0$. We give here only the answers.

12. The critical points $(\pm 2, 0)$ are unstable saddle points, whereas $(0, 0)$ is a stable center of the linearized system.

13. The critical points $(\pm 2, 0)$ are unstable saddle points, whereas $(0, 0)$ is a stable spiral point.

14. The critical points $(\pm 2, 0)$ are stable centers of the linearized system, while $(0, 0)$ is an unstable saddle point.

15. The origin $(0, 0)$ is a stable center of the linearized system, whereas $(-4, 0)$ is an unstable saddle point.

16. The critical points $(\pm 2, 0)$ and $(0, 0)$ are stable centers of the linearized system, whereas the critical points $(\pm 1, 0)$ are unstable saddle points.

The statements of Problems 17-22 in the text include their answers and outline their solutions, which therefore are omitted here.

SECTION 6.5

CHAOS IN DYNAMICAL SYSTEMS

We list here some programs that may be useful in the projects for this section. Further discussion of these projects can be found in the computer lab manual that accompanies this text.

As indicated in Fig. 6.5.1 in the text, you can use the Maple commands

```
r := 1.5:
x = array(1..200):
x[1] := 0.5:
for n from 2 to 200 do
    z := x[n-1]:
    x[n] := r*z*(1-z):
od:
```

the Mathematica commands

```
r = 1.5;
x = Table[n,{n,1,200}];
x[[1]] = 0.5;
For[n=2, n<=200,
    n=n+1,
    z = x[[n-1]];
    x[[n]] = r*z*(1-z)];
```

or the MATLAB commands

```
r = 1.5;
x = 1:200;
x(1) = 0.5;
for n = 2:200
    z = x(n-1);
    x(n) = r*z*(1-z);
    end
```

to calculate and assemble a list of the successive iterates given by $x_{n+1} = r x_n (1 - x_n)$, as illustrated in Figures 6.5.2 through 6.5.7 in the text. The following BASIC program can be used to investigate periodic cycles for this iteration.

```
100  'Program PERIODS
110  '
120  'The period-doubling iteration
130  '
140  '           x    =    rx(1 - x)
150  '
160  '  r  =  2.75  :   Period  1
170  '  r  =  3.25  :   Period  2
180  '  r  =  3.50  :   Period  4
190  '  r  =  3.55  :   Period  8
200  '  r  =  3.565 :   Period 16
210  '  r  =  3.57  :   CHAOS
220  '  r  =  3.84  :   Period  3
230  '  r  =  3.845 :   Period  6
240  '  r  =  3.848 :   Period 12
250  '
260   DEFDBL R,X
270   INPUT "Value of r"; R
280   INPUT "Print in blocks of k  =  "; K
290   P$  =  "#.####       "
300   X  =  .5                     'Initial seed
310  '
320   FOR I  =   1 TO 500          '500 initial
330      X  =  R*X*(1 - X)         'iterations to
340   NEXT I                       'stabilize.
```

```
350 '
360  FOR  I  =  1  TO  K
370      X  =  R*X*(1 - X)        'Final iterations
380      PRINT USING P$; X;
390  NEXT
400  IF K <> 8 THEN PRINT
410  '
420  'Press any key but Q to continue:
430  A$  =   INKEY$
440  IF A$  =   "" THEN GOTO 430
450  IF A$  =  "q" OR A$  =  "Q" THEN END
460  GOTO 360                    'End of loop
470  '
480  END
```

The next BASIC program below can be used to plot pitchfork diagrams as in Figures 6.5.8 and
6.5.9 in the text. As written, it runs well in Borland TurboBasic, but may have to be fine-tuned
to run in other dialects of BASIC.

```
100 'Program PICHFORK
110 '
120 'Exhibits the period-doubling toward chaos
130 'generated by the Verhulst iteration
140 '
150 '          x  =  rx(1 - x)
160 '
170 'as the growth parameter  r  is increased
180 'in the range from about  3  to about  4.
190 '
200  DEFDBL H,K,R,X
210  DEFINT I,J,M,N,P,Q
220  INPUT "Rmin,Rmax"; RMIN, RMAX       'Try 2.8 and 4.0
230  INPUT "Xmin,Xmax"; XMIN, XMAX       'Try 0 and 1
240  '
250  KEY OFF  : CLS
260 'SCREEN 1  :  N  =  319            'For med resolution
270  SCREEN 2  :  N  =  639            'For hi  resolution
280  M  =  200                         'Hor rows for either
290  H  =  (RMAX - RMIN)/N
300  K  =  (XMAX - XMIN)/M
310  '
320  LINE (0,0) - (N,0)                'Draws a box
330  LINE - (N,199)                    'around
340  LINE - (0,199)                    'the screen
350  LINE - (  0,0)
360  '
370  FOR P  =  1 TO 9                  'Tick marks on
380      Q  =  (P*(N+1)/10) - 1        'top and bottom
390      LINE (Q,0) - (Q,5)            'of box
400      LINE (Q,195) - (Q,199)
```

```
410   NEXT P
420   '
430   FOR J  =  0 TO  N                'Jth vertical column
440       R  =  RMIN + J*H             'of pixels on screen
450       X  =  .5
460       FOR P  =  0 TO 1000          'These iterations
470           X  =  R*X*(1-X)          'to settle down.
480       NEXT P
490       FOR Q  =  0 TO 250           'These iterations
500           X  =  R*X*(1-X)          'are recorded.
510           I  =  INT((X - XMIN)/K)
520           I  =  200 - I
530           IF (0< = I) AND (I<200) THEN PSET (J,I)
540       NEXT Q
550   NEXT J
560   '
570   WHILE INKEY$  =  ""              'Press a key when
580   WEND                             'finished looking.
590   SCREEN 0  :  CLS  :  KEY ON
600   END
```

A more elaborate construction of these pitchfork diagrams is given by the following Mathematica program, a slight elaboration of one found on page 102 of T. Gray and J. Glynn, *Exploring Mathematics with Mathematica*, Addison-Wesley, 1991.

```
g[x_] : =  r x (1 - x);
Clear[r];
a  =  2.8;  b  =  4.0.    (* r-range for Fig 6.5.8 *)
c  =  0;    d  =  1;           (* x-range *)
m  =  250;                     (* no of x-points *)
n  =  500;                     (* no of r-values *)
ListPlot[
   Flatten[Table[
      Transpose[{
         Table[r, {m+1}],
            NestList[g, Nest[q, 0.5, 2m], m] }],
            {r, a, b, (b-a)/n} ],
             1],
      PlotStyle -> PointSize[0.001],
      PlotRange -> {{a,b},{c,d}},
      AspectRatio -> 0.75,
      Frame -> True,
      AxesLabel -> {"r","x"} ]
```

This Mathematica program runs slowly, and requires a fast machine with plenty of memory to finish within a reasonable waiting time. The following MATLAB program (which was actually used to construct Figs 6.5.8 and 6.5.9) runs much faster on a comparable computer, and may be easier to understand.

```
% pitchfork diagram script
% for Figures 6.5.8 and 6.5.9

hold off
m   =   400;                        % no of r-subintervals
n   =   400;                        % no of x-subintervals

 a  =  2.8;     b  =   4.0;         % r-range for 6.5.9
dr  =   (b - a)/m;
R   =  a+dr/2 : dr : b;             % vector of r-values
c   =  0;        d  =  1;           % x-range
dx  =  (d - c)/n
X   =  c+dx/2 : dx : d;             % vector of x-values
[rr,xx]   =   meshgrid(R,X);        % matrices of r- and x-coords
                                    % of grid points in rx-rect


C = zeros(m,n);
for j  =  1 : m                     % Cycle through r-values
   r  =  a - dr/2 + j*dr;
   x  =  0.5;                       % Initialize x-value
   for k  =  1:1000                 % 1000 iterations to stabilize
      x  =  r*x*(1-x);
   end
   for k  =  1:1000                 % 1000 more iterations
      x  =  r*x*(1-x);
      i = ceil(x/dx);
      C(i,j) = 1;                   % lattice point to plot
      end
   end

C = C + 1;
C = flipud(C);                      % matrix of points for image
image(R,X,C)
colormap([1 1 1; 0 0 0])           % color them black or white
axis square
```

The following MATLAB function defines the forced Duffing equation for Figures 6.5.13 through 6.5.16.

```
function  yp = ypduffing(t,x)
F0 = 0.80;
yp = x;
y = x(2);    x = x(1);
yp(1) = y;
yp(2) = F0*cos(t)-y+x-x.^3;
```

Then the following MATLAB script can be used to construct Fig. 6.5.16.

```matlab
% fig6_5_16.m script
options = odeset('RelTol',1e-8,'AbsTol',1e-8);
[t,y] = ode45('ypduffing', [0 100], [1;0],options);
n = length(t);
y100 = y(n,:)';
[t,y] = ode45('ypduffing', [100 300], y100,options);
hold off
plot(y(:,1),y(:,2),'b')           % Fig. 6.5.16(a)
axis([-1.5 1.5 -1.5 1.5])
axis square
hold on
plot([-1.5 1.5],[0 0],'k')
plot([0 0],[-1.5 1.5],'k')
pause
hold off
plot(t,y(:,1),'b')                % Fig. 6.5.16(b)
axis([100 300 -1.5 1.5])
axis square
hold on
plot([100 300],[0 0],'k')
plot([0 0],[-1.5 1.5],'k')
```

CHAPTER 7

LAPLACE TRANSFORM METHODS

SECTION 7.1

LAPLACE TRANSFORMS AND INVERSE TRANSFORMS

The objectives of this section are especially clearcut. They include familiarity with the definition of the Laplace transform $\mathcal{L}\{f(t)\} = F(s)$ that is given in Equation (1) in the text, the direct application of this definition to calculate Laplace transforms of simple functions (as in Examples 1-3), and the use of known transforms (those listed in Figure 7.1.2) to find Laplace transforms and inverse transforms (as in Examples 4-6). Perhaps students need to be told explicitly to memorize the transforms that are listed in the short table that appears in Figure 7.1.2.

1.　　$\mathcal{L}\{t\} = \displaystyle\int_0^\infty e^{-st} t\, dt$　　　　$(u = -st,\quad du = -s\, dt)$

$$= \int_0^{-\infty} \left[\frac{1}{s^2}\right] u e^u\, du = \frac{1}{s^2}\left[(u-1)e^u\right]_0^{-\infty} = \frac{1}{s^2}$$

2.　　We substitute $u = -st$ in the tabulated integral

$$\int u^2 e^u\, du = e^u\left(u^2 - 2u + 2\right) + C$$

(or, alternatively, integrate by parts) and get

$$\mathcal{L}\{t^2\} = \int_0^\infty e^{-st} t^2\, dt = \left[-e^{-st}\left(\frac{t^2}{s} + \frac{2t}{s^2} + \frac{2}{s^3}\right)\right]_{t=0}^\infty = \frac{2}{s^3}.$$

3.　　$\mathcal{L}\{e^{3t+1}\} = \displaystyle\int_0^\infty e^{-st} e^{3t+1}\, dt = e\int_0^\infty e^{-(s-3)t}\, dt = \frac{e}{s-3}$

4.　　With $a = -s$ and $b = 1$ the tabulated integral

$$\int e^{au} \cos bu\, du = e^{au}\left[\frac{a\cos bu + b\sin bu}{a^2 + b^2}\right] + C$$

yields

$$\mathcal{L}\{\cos t\} = \int_0^\infty e^{-st} \cos t\, dt = \left[\frac{e^{-st}(-s\cos t + \sin t)}{s^2 + 1}\right]_{t=0}^\infty = \frac{s}{s^2 + 1}$$

5. $\mathcal{L}\{\sinh t\} = \tfrac{1}{2}\mathcal{L}\{e^t - e^{-t}\} = \tfrac{1}{2}\int_0^\infty e^{-st}(e^t - e^{-t})\,dt = \tfrac{1}{2}\int_0^\infty (e^{-(s-1)t} - e^{-(s+1)t})\,dt$

$$= \frac{1}{2}\left[\frac{1}{s-1} - \frac{1}{s+1}\right] = \frac{1}{s^2-1}$$

6. $\mathcal{L}\{\sin^2 t\} = \int_0^\infty e^{-st}\sin^2 t\,dt = \tfrac{1}{2}\int_0^\infty e^{-st}(1 - \cos 2t)\,dt$

$$= \frac{1}{2}\left[e^{-st}\left(-\frac{1}{s}\right) - e^{-st}\cdot\frac{-s\cos 2t + 2\sin 2t}{s^2+4}\right]_{t=0}^\infty = \frac{1}{2}\left[\frac{1}{s} - \frac{s}{s^2+4}\right]$$

7. $\mathcal{L}\{f(t)\} = \int_0^1 e^{-st}\,dt = \left[-\frac{1}{s}e^{-st}\right]_0^1 = \frac{1-e^{-s}}{s}$

8. $\mathcal{L}\{f(t)\} = \int_1^2 e^{-st}\,dt = \left[-\frac{e^{-st}}{s}\right]_1^2 = \frac{e^{-s} - e^{-2s}}{s}$

9. $\mathcal{L}\{f(t)\} = \int_0^1 e^{-st}t\,dt = \frac{1-e^{-s} - se^{-s}}{s^2}$

10. $\mathcal{L}\{f(t)\} = \int_0^1 (1-t)e^{-st}\,dt = \left[-e^{-st}\left(\frac{1}{s} - \frac{t}{s} - \frac{1}{s^2}\right)\right]_0^1 = \frac{1}{s} - \frac{1}{s^2} + \frac{e^{-s}}{s^2}$

11. $s^{-3/2}\Gamma(3/2) + 3s^{-2} = (1/2)\sqrt{\pi}\,s^{-3/2} + 3s^{-2}$

12. $3\cdot\Gamma(7/2)/s^{7/2} - 4\cdot3!/s^4 = 45\sqrt{\pi}/8s^{7/2} - 24/s^4$

13. $\mathcal{L}\{t - 2e^{3t}\} = 1/s^2 - 2/(s-3)$

14. $\mathcal{L}\{t^{3/2} + e^{-10t}\} = 3\sqrt{\pi}/4s^{5/2} + 1/(s+10)$

15. $\mathcal{L}\{1 + \cosh 5t\} = 1/s + s/(s^2 - 25)$

16. $\mathcal{L}\{\sin 2t + \cos 2t\} = (s+2)/(s^2+4)$

17. $\mathcal{L}\{\cos^2 2t\} = (1/2)\mathcal{L}\{1 + \cos 4t\} = (1/2)[1/s + s/(s^2 + 16)]$

18. $\mathcal{L}\{\sin 3t\cos 3t\} = \mathcal{L}\{(1/2)\sin 6t\} = 3/(s^2 + 36)$

19. $\mathcal{L}\{(1+t)^3\} = \mathcal{L}\{1 + 3t + 3t^2 + t^3\} = 1/s + 3/s^2 + 6/s^3 + 6/s^4$

20. Integrating by parts with $u = t$, $dv = e^{-(s-1)t}\,dt$, we get

$$\mathcal{L}\{te^t\} = \int_0^\infty e^{-st} te^t \, dt = \int_0^\infty te^{-(s-1)t} \, dt$$

$$= \left[\frac{-te^{-(s-1)t}}{s-1}\right]_0^\infty + \frac{1}{s-1}\int_0^\infty e^{-st}e^t \, dt = \frac{1}{s-1}\mathcal{L}\{t\} = \frac{1}{(s-1)^2}$$

21. Integration by parts with $u = t$ and $dv = e^{-st}\cos 2t \, dt$ yields

$$\mathcal{L}\{t\cos 2t\} = \int_0^\infty te^{-st}\cos 2t \, dt = -\frac{1}{s^2+4}\int_0^\infty e^{-st}(-s\cos 2t + 2\sin 2t) \, dt$$

$$= -\frac{1}{s^2+4}\left[-s\mathcal{L}\{\cos 2t\} + 2\mathcal{L}\{\sin 2t\}\right]$$

$$= -\frac{1}{s^2+4}\left[\frac{-s^2}{s^2+4} + \frac{4}{s^2+4}\right] = \frac{s^2-4}{\left(s^2+4\right)^2}$$

22. $\mathcal{L}\{\sinh^2 3t\} = \mathcal{L}\{(1/2)(\cosh 6t - 1)\} = (1/2)[s/(s^2 - 36) - 1/s]$

23. $\mathcal{L}^{-1}\{3/s^4\} = t^3/2$

24. $\mathcal{L}^{-1}\{s^{-3/2}\} = 2t^{1/2}/\sqrt{\pi}$

25. $\mathcal{L}^{-1}\{1/s - 2/s^{5/2}\} = 1 - 8t^{3/2}/3\sqrt{\pi}$

26. $\mathcal{L}^{-1}\{1/(s+5)\} = e^{-5t}$

27. $\mathcal{L}^{-1}\{3/(s-4)\} = 3e^{4t}$

28. $\mathcal{L}^{-1}\{(3s+1)/(s^2+4)\}$

$\qquad = 3\mathcal{L}^{-1}\{s/(s^2+4)\} + (1/2)\mathcal{L}^{-1}\{2/(s^2+4)\} = 3\cos 2t + (1/2)\sin 2t$

29. $\mathcal{L}^{-1}\{(5-3s)/(s^2+9)\} = (5/3)\sin 3t - 3\cos 3t$

30. $\mathcal{L}^{-1}\{(9+s)/(4-s^2)\}$

$\qquad = -\mathcal{L}^{-1}\{s/(s^2-4)\} - (9/2)\mathcal{L}^{-1}\{2/(s^2-4) = -\cosh 2t - (9/2)\sinh 2t$

31. $\mathcal{L}^{-1}\{(10s-3)/(25-s^2)\} = (3/5)\sinh 5t - 10\cosh 5t$

32. $\mathcal{L}^{-1}\{2s^{-1}e^{-3s}\} = 2u(t-3)$

34. $\mathcal{L}\{\sinh kt\} = (1/2)\mathcal{L}\{e^{kt}\} - (1/2)\mathcal{L}\{e^{-kt}\} = (1/2)[1/(s-k) - 1/(s+k)] = k/(s^2 - k^2)$

37. $f(t) = 1 - u_a(t) = 1 - u(t-a)$

38. $\mathcal{L}\{f(t)\} = \mathcal{L}\{u(t-a) - u(t-b)\} = s^{-1}(e^{-as} - e^{-bs})$

39. $\mathcal{L}\{f(t)\} = \Sigma \mathcal{L}\{u(t-n)\} = \Sigma s^{-1}e^{-ns}$

$$= s^{-1}(1 + e^{-s} + e^{-2s} + e^{-3s} + \cdots) = s^{-1}/(1 - e^{-s})$$

40. $\mathcal{L}\{f(t)\} = \Sigma(-1)^n \mathcal{L}\{u(t-n)\} = \Sigma(-1)^n s^{-1}e^{-ns}$

$$= s^{-1}(1 - e^{-s} + e^{-2s} - e^{-3s} + \cdots) = s^{-1}/(1 + e^{-s})$$

41. $\mathcal{L}\{g(t)\} = \mathcal{L}\{2f(t) - 1\} = 2/s(1 + e^{-s}) - 1/s$

$$= s^{-1}[(1 - e^{-s})/(1 + e^{-s})]$$

$$= s^{-1}[(e^{s/2} - e^{-s/2})/(e^{s/2} + e^{-s/2})] = s^{-1}\tanh(s/2)$$

SECTION 7.2

TRANSFORMATION OF INITIAL VALUE PROBLEMS

The focus of this section is on the use of transforms of derivatives (Theorem 1) to solve initial value problems (as in Examples 1 and 2). Transforms of integrals (Theorem 2) appear less frequently in practice, and the extension of Theorem 1 at the end of Section 7.2 may be considered entirely optional (except perhaps for electrical engineering students).

1. $[s^2 X(s) - 5s] + 4\{X(s)\} = 0$

$X(s) = 5s/(s^2 + 4) = 5[s/(s^2 + 4)]$

$x(t) = \mathcal{L}^{-1}\{X(s)\} = 5\cos 2t$

2. $[s^2 X(s) - 3s - 4] + 9[X(s)] = 0$

$X(s) = (3s + 4)/(s^2 + 9) = 3[s/(s^2 + 9)] + (4/3)[3/(s^2 + 9)]$

$x(t) = \mathcal{L}^{-1}\{X(s)\} = 3\cos 3t + (4/3)\sin 3t$

3. $[s^2 X(s) - 2] - [sX(s)] - 2[X(s)] = 0$

$X(s) = 2/(s^2 - s - 2) = (2/3)[1/(s - 2) - 1/(s + 1)]$

$x(t) = (2/3)(e^{2t} - e^{-t})$

4. $[s^2 X(s) - 2s + 3] + 8[s\, X(s) - 2] + 15[X(s)] = 0$

$X(s) = (2s + 13)/(s^2 + 8s + 15) = (7/2)/(s + 3) - (3/2)/(s + 5)$

$x(t) = \mathcal{L}^{-1}\{X(s)\} = (7/2)e^{-3t} - (3/2)e^{-5t}$

5. $[s^2X(s)] + [X(s)] = 2/(s^2+4)$

$X(s) = 2/[(s^2+1)(s^2+4)] = (1/3)[2/(s^2+1) - 2/(s^2+4)]$

$x(t) = (2\sin t - \sin 2t)/3$

6. $[s^2X(s)] + 4[X(s)] = \mathcal{L}\{\cos t\} = s/(s^2+1)$

$X(s) = s/[(s^2+1)(s^2+4)] = (1/3)s/(s^2+1) - (1/3)s/(s^2+4)$

$x(t) = \mathcal{L}^{-1}\{X(s)\} = (\cos t - \cos 2t)/3$

7. $[s^2X(s) - s] + [X(s)] = s/s^2+9)$

$(s^2+1)X(s) = s + s/(s^2+9) = (s^3+10s)/(s^2+9)$

$X(s) = (s^3+10s)/[(s^2+1)(s^2+9)] = (1/8)[9s/(s^2+1) - s/(s^2+9)]$

$x(t) = (9\cos t - \cos 3t)/8$

8. $[s^2X(s)] + 9[X(s)] = \mathcal{L}\{1\} = 1/s$

$X(s) = 1/[s(s^2+9)] = (1/9)/s - (1/9)s/(s^2+9)$

$x(t) = \mathcal{L}^{-1}\{X(s)\} = (1 - \cos 3t)/9$

9. $s^2X(s) + 4sX(s) + 3X(s) = 1/s$

$X(s) = 1/[s(s^2+4s+3)] = (1/6)[2/s - 3/(s+1) + 1/(s+3)]$

$x(t) = (2 - 3e^{-t} + e^{-3t})/6$

10. $[s^2X(s) - 2] + 3[sX(s)] + 2[X(s)] = \mathcal{L}\{t\} = 1/s^2$

$(s^2+3s+2)X(s) = 2 + 1/s^2 = (2s^2+1)/s^2$

$X(s) = (2s^2+1)/[s^2(s^2+3s+2)] = -(3/4)/s + (1/2)/s^2 + 3/(s+1) - (9/4)/(s+2)$

$x(t) = \mathcal{L}^{-1}\{X(s)\} = (-3 + 2t + 12e^{-t} - 9e^{-2t})/4$

11.   The transformed equations are

$$sX(s) - 1 = 2X(s) + Y(s)$$
$$sY(s) + 2 = 6X(s) + 3Y(s).$$

We solve for the Laplace transforms

$$X(s) = (s-5)/[s(s-5)] = 1/s$$
$$Y(s) = (-2s+10)/[s(s-5)] = -2/s.$$

Hence the solution is given by

$$x(t) = 1, \qquad y(t) = -2.$$

12. The transformed equations are

$$s\,X(s) = X(s) + 2Y(s)$$
$$s\,Y(s) = X(s) + 1/(s+1),$$

which we solve for

$$X(s) = 2/(s-2)(s+1)^2 = (2/9)[1/(s-2) - 1/(s+1) - 3/(s+1)^2]$$
$$Y(s) = (s-1)/[(s-2)(s+1)^2] = (1/9)[1/(s-2) - 1/(s+1) + 6/(s+1)^2].$$

Hence the solution is

$$x(t) = (2/9)(e^{2t} - e^{-t} - 3t\,e^{-t})$$
$$y(t) = (1/9)(e^{2t} - e^{-t} + 6t\,e^{-t}).$$

13. $sX(s) + 2[sY(s) - 1] + X(s) = 0$
$sX(s) - [sY(s) - 1] + Y(s) = 0$

$X(s) = -2/(3s^2 - 1)$
$Y(s) = (3s + 1)/(3s^2 - 1)$

$x(t) = -(2/\sqrt{3})\sinh(t/\sqrt{3})$
$y(t) = \cosh(t/\sqrt{3}) + (1/\sqrt{3})\sinh(t/\sqrt{3})$

14. The transformed equations are

$$s^2 X(s) + 1 + 2X(s) + 4Y(s) = 0$$
$$s^2 Y(s) + 1 + X(s) + 2Y(s) = 0,$$

which we solve for

$$X(s) = (-s^2 + 2)/[s^2(s^2 + 4)] = (1/4)[2/s^2 - 6/(s^2 + 4)]$$
$$Y(s) = (-s^2 - 1)/[s^2(s^2 + 4)] = (-1/8)[2/s^2 + 6/(s^2 + 4)].$$

Hence the solution is

$$x(t) = (1/4)(2t - 3\sin 2t)$$
$$y(t) = (-1/8)(2t + 3\sin 2t).$$

15. $[s^2 X - s] + [sX - 1] + [sY - 1] + 2X - Y = 0$
$[s^2 Y - s] + [sX - 1] + [sY - 1] + 4X - 2Y = 0$

$$X(s) = (2s^2 - 2)/[s(s^3 + 2s^2 - 3)] = (2s + 2)/[s(s^2 + 3s + 3)]$$
$$= (1/3)[2/s + (s + 3)/(s^2 + 3s + 3)]$$

$$Y(s) = (s^3 + 2s^2 - 2s - 4)/[s(s - 1)(s^2 + 3s + 3)]$$
$$= (1/21)[28/s - 9/(s - 1) + (2s + 15)/(s^2 + 3s + 3)]$$

$$x(t) = (1/3)\{2 + e^{-3t/2}[\cos(t/2)\sqrt{3} + \sqrt{3}\sin(t/2)\sqrt{3}]\}$$

$$y(t) = (1/21)\{28 - 9e^t + 2e^{-3t/2}[\cos(t/2)\sqrt{3} + 4\sqrt{3}\sin(t/2)\sqrt{3}]\}$$

16. The transformed equations are

$$s\,X(s) - 1 = X(s) + Z(s)$$
$$s\,Y(s) = X(s) + Y(s)$$
$$s\,Z(s) = -2X(s) - Z(s),$$

which we solve for

$$X(s) = (s^2 - 1)/[(s - 1)(s^2 + 1)] = (s + 1)/(s^2 + 1)$$
$$Y(s) = (s + 1)/[(s - 1)(s^2 + 1)] = 1/(s - 1) - s/(s^2 + 1)$$
$$Z(s) = -2(s - 1)/[(s - 1)(s^2 + 1)] = -2/(s^2 + 1).$$

Hence the solution is

$$x(t) = \cos t + \sin t$$
$$y(t) = e^t - \cos t$$
$$z(t) = -2\sin t.$$

17. $\quad f(t) = \displaystyle\int_0^t e^{3t}\,dt = \tfrac{1}{3}\left(e^{3t} - 1\right)$

18. $\quad f(t) = \displaystyle\int_0^t 3e^{-5t}\,dt = \tfrac{3}{5}\left(1 - e^{-5t}\right)$

19. $\quad f(t) = \displaystyle\int_0^t \tfrac{1}{2}\sin 2t\,dt = \tfrac{1}{4}(1 - \cos 2t)$

20. $\quad f(t) = \displaystyle\int_0^t \left(2\cos 3t + \tfrac{1}{3}\sin 3t\right) = \tfrac{1}{9}(6\sin 3t - \cos 3t + 1)$

21. $\quad f(t) = \displaystyle\int_0^t \left[\int_0^t \sin t\,dt\right]dt = \int_0^t (1 - \cos t)\,dt = t - \sin t$

22. $f(t) = \int_0^t \frac{1}{3}\sinh 3t \, dt = \frac{1}{9}(\cosh 3t - 1)$

23. $f(t) = \int_0^t \left[\int_0^t \sinh t \, dt \right] dt = \int_0^t (\cosh t - 1) \, dt = \sinh t - t$

24. $f(t) = \int_0^t \left(e^{-t} - e^{-2t} \right) dt = \frac{1}{2}\left(e^{-2t} - 2e^{-t} + 1 \right)$

25. With $f(t) = \cos kt$ and $F(s) = s/(s^2 + k^2)$, Theorem 1 in this section yields

$$\mathcal{L}\{-k \sin kt\} = \mathcal{L}\{f'(t)\} = sF(s) - 1$$
$$= [s^2/(s^2 + k^2)] - 1 = -k^2/(s^2 + k^2),$$

so division by $-k$ yields $\mathcal{L}\{\sin kt\} = k/(s^2 + k^2)$.

26. With $f(t) = \sinh kt$ and $F(s) = k/(s^2 - k^2)$, Theorem 1 yields

$$\mathcal{L}\{f'(t)\} = \mathcal{L}\{k \cosh kt\} = ks/(s^2 - k^2) = sF(s),$$

so it follows that $\mathcal{L}\{\cosh kt\} = s/(s^2 - k^2)$.

27. (a) With $f(t) = t^n e^{at}$ and $f'(t) = nt^{n-1}e^{at} + at^n e^{at}$, Theorem 1 yields

$$\mathcal{L}\{nt^{n-1}e^{at} + at^n e^{at}\} = s\,\mathcal{L}\{t^n e^{at}\}$$

so

$$n\,\mathcal{L}\{t^{n-1}e^{at}\} = (s - a)\mathcal{L}\{t^n e^{at}\}$$

28. Problems 28 and 30 are the trigonometric and hyperbolic versions of essentially the same computation. For Problem 30 we let $f(t) = t \cosh kt$, so $f(0) = 0$. Then

$$f'(t) = \cosh kt + kt \sinh kt$$
$$f''(t) = 2k \sinh kt + k^2 t \cosh kt,$$

and $f'(0) = 1$, so Formula (5) in this section yields

$$\mathcal{L}\{2k \sinh kt + k^2 t \cosh kt\} = s^2 \mathcal{L}\{t \cosh kt\} - 1,$$
$$2k^2/(s^2 - k^2) = k^2 F(s) = s^2 F(s) - 1.$$

We readily solve this last equation for

$$\mathcal{L}\{t \cosh kt\} = F(s) = (s^2 + k^2)/(s^2 - k^2)^2.$$

32. If $f(t) = u(t - a)$, then the only jump in $f(t)$ is $j_1 = 1$ at $t_1 = a$. Since $f(0) = 0$ and

$f'(t) = 0$, Formula (21) in this section yields

$$0 = s\, F(s) - 0 - e^{as}(1).$$

Hence $\mathcal{L}\{u(t-a)\} = F(s) = s^{-1}e^{-as}$.

34. The square wave function of Figure 7.2.6 has a sequence $\{t_n\}$ of jumps with $t_n = n$ and $j_n = 2(-1)^n$ for $n = 1, 2, 3, \ldots$. Hence Formula (21) yields

$$0 = s\, F(s) - 1 - \Sigma\,(-1)^n 2e^{-ns}.$$

It follows that

$$
\begin{aligned}
s\, F(s) &= 1 + 2\,\Sigma(-1)^n e^{-ns} \\
&= -1 + 2(1 - e^{-s} + e^{-2s} - e^{-3s} + \cdots) \\
&= -1 + 2/(1 + e^{-s}) \\
&= (1 - e^{-s})/(1 + e^{-s}) \\
&= (e^{s/2} - e^{-s/2})/(e^{s/2} + e^{-s/2}) \\
s\, F(s) &= \tanh(s/2),
\end{aligned}
$$

because $2\cosh(s/2) = e^{s/2} + e^{-s/2}$ and $2\sinh(s/2) = e^{s/2} - e^{-s/2}$.

36. If $g(t)$ is the triangular wave function of Figure 7.2.8 and $f(t)$ is the square wave function of Problem 28, then $g'(t) = f(t)$. Hence Theorem 1 and the result of Problem 28 yield

$$\mathcal{L}\{g'(t)\} = s\,\mathcal{L}\{g(t)\} - g(0),$$

$$F(s) = s\, G(s),$$

$$\mathcal{L}\{g(t)\} = s^{-1}F(s) = s^{-2}\tanh(s/2).$$

SECTION 7.3

TRANSLATION AND PARTIAL FRACTIONS

This section is devoted to the computational nuts and bolts of the staple technique for the inversion of Laplace transforms -- partial fraction decompositions. If time does not permit going further in this chapter, Sections 7.1–7.3 provide a self-contained introduction to Laplace transforms that suffices for the most common elementary applications.

1. $\mathcal{L}\{t^4\} = 24/s^5$, so $\mathcal{L}\{t^4 e^{\pi t}\} = 24/(s - \pi)^5$.

2. $\mathcal{L}\{t^{3/2}\} = (3\sqrt{\pi}/4)s^{-5/2}$, so $\mathcal{L}\{t^{3/2}e^{-4t}\} = (3\sqrt{\pi}/4)(s+4)^{-5/2}$.

3. $\mathcal{L}\{\sin 3\pi t\} = 3\pi/(s^2 + 9\pi^2)$, so $\mathcal{L}\{e^{-2t}\sin 3\pi t\} = 3\pi/[(s+2)^2 + 9\pi^2]$.

4. $\cos(2t - \pi/4) = (1/\sqrt{2})(\cos 2t + \sin 2t)$

$\mathcal{L}\{\cos(2t - \pi/4)\} = (1/\sqrt{2})(s+2)/(s^2+4)$

$\mathcal{L}\{f(t)\} = (1/\sqrt{2})(s+1/2+2)/[(s+1/2)^2+4] = (\sqrt{2})(2s+5)/(4s^2+4s+17)$

5. $F(s) = 3/(2s-4) = (3/2)/(s-2)$, $f(t) = (3/2)e^{2t}$

6. $F(s) = [(s+1)-2]/(s+1)^3 = 1/(s+1)^2 - 2/(s+1)^3$

$f(t) = e^{-t}(t - t^2)$

7. $F(s) = 1/(s+2)^2$; $f(t) = te^{-2t}$

8. $F(s) = (s+2)/[(s+2)^2+1]$; $f(t) = e^{-2t}\cos t$

9. $F(s) = [3(s-3) + (7/2)(4)]/[(s-3)^2+16]$

$f(t) = e^{3t}[3\cos 4t + (7/2)\sin 4t]$

10. $F(s) = (2s-3)/[(3s-2)^2+16] = [(2/9)(s-2/3) - (5/36)(4/3)]/[(s-2/3)^2 + (4/3)^2]$

$f(t) = (1/36)e^{2t/3}(8\cos 4t/3 - 5\sin 4t/3)$

11. $f(t) = \mathcal{L}^{-1}\{(1/4)[1/(s-2) - 1/(s+2)]\} = (1/4)(e^{2t} - e^{-2t}) = (1/2)\sinh 2t$

12. $f(t) = \mathcal{L}^{-1}\{2/s + 3/(s-3)\} = 2 + 3e^{3t}$

13. $f(t) = \mathcal{L}^{-1}\{3/(s+2) - 5/(s+5)\} = 3e^{-2t} - 5e^{-5t}$

14. $F(s) = 2/s + 1/(s-2) - 3/(s+1)$, $f(t) = 2 + e^{2t} - 3e^{-t}$

15. $f(t) = \mathcal{L}^{-1}\{(1/25)[1/(s-5) - 1/s - 5/s^2]\} = (e^{5t} - 1 - 5t)/25$

16. $F(s) = (1/125)[-2/(s-2) + 5/(s-2)^2 + 2/(s+3) + 5/(s+3)^2]$

$f(t) = (1/125)[e^{2t}(-2+5t) + e^{-3t}(2+5t)]$

17. $f(t) = (1/8)\mathcal{L}^{-1}\{1/(s^2-4) - 1/(s^2+4)\} = (\sinh 2t - \sin 2t)/16$

18. $F(s) = 1/(s-4) + 12/(s-4)^2 + 48/(s-4)^3 + 64/(s-4)^4$

$f(t) = e^{4t}(1 + 12t + 24t^2 + 32t^3/3)$

19. $F(s) = (1/3)[(2s + 4)/(s^2 + 4) - (2s + 1)/s^2 + 1)]$

$f(t) = (1/3)(2 \cos 2t + 2 \sin 2t - 2 \cos t - \sin t)$

20. $F(s) = (1/32)[-1/(s - 2) + 2/(s - 2)^2 + 1/(s + 2) + 2/(s + 2)^2]$

$f(t) = (1/32)[e^{2t}(-1 + 2t) + e^{-2t}(1 + 2t)]$

21. $f(t) = (1/2)e^{-t}(5 \sin t - 3t \cos t - 2t \sin t)$

22. First we need to find A, B, C, D so that

$$\frac{2s^3 - s^2}{\left(4s^2 - 4s + 5\right)^2} = \frac{As + B}{4s^2 - 4s + 5} + \frac{Cs + D}{\left(4s^2 - 4s + 5\right)^2}.$$

When we multiply each side by the quadratic factor we get the identity

$$2s^3 - s^2 = (As + B)(4s^2 - 4s + 5) + Cs + D.$$

When we substitute the root $s = 1/2 + i$ of the quadratic into this identity, we find that $C = -3/2$ and $D = -5/4$. When we first differentiate each side of the identity and then substitute the root, we find that $A = 1/2$ and $B = 1/4$. Writing

$$4s^2 - 4s + 5 = 4[(s - 1/2)^2 + 1],$$

it follows that

$$F(s) = \frac{1}{8} \cdot \frac{(s - \frac{1}{2}) + 1}{(s - \frac{1}{2})^2 + 1} - \frac{1}{32} \cdot \frac{3(s - \frac{1}{2}) + 4}{\left[(s - \frac{1}{2})^2 + 1\right]^2}.$$

Finally the results

$$\mathcal{L}^{-1}\{2s/(s^2 + 1)^2\} = t \sin t$$

$$\mathcal{L}^{-1}\{2/(s^2 + 1)^2\} = \sin t - t \cos t$$

of Example 5 and Problem 31 in Section 7.2, together with the translation theorem, yield

$$f(t) = (1/64)e^{t/2}[(8 + 4t)\cos t + (4 - 3t)\sin t].$$

24. $\dfrac{4as}{s^4 + 4a^4} = \dfrac{1}{s^2 - 2as + 2a^2} - \dfrac{1}{s^2 + 2as + 2a^2}$

and $s^2 \pm 2as + 2a^2 = (s \pm a)^2 + a^2$, so it follows that

$$\mathcal{L}^{-1}\{s/(s^4 + 4a^4)\} = (1/4a^2)(e^{at} - e^{-at})\sin at = (1/2a^2)\sinh at \sin at.$$

27. $[s^2X(s) - 2s - 3] + 6[sX(s) - 2] + 2sX(s) = 0$

$X(s) = [2(s + 3) + 9]/[(s + 3)^2 + 16]$

$x(t) = e^{-3t}[2\cos 4t + (9/4)\sin 4t]$

28. $X(s) = 2/[s(s - 2)(s - 4)] = (1/4)/s - (1/2)/(s - 2) + (1/4)/(s - 4)$

$x(t) = (1 - 2e^{2t} + e^{4t})/4$

29. $(s^2 - 4)X(s) = 3/s^2$

$X(s) = (3/4)[1/(s^2 - 4) - 1/s^2]$

$x(t) = (3\sinh 2t - 6t)/8$

30. $X(s) = 1/[(s + 1)(s^2 + 4s + 8)] = (1/5)/(s + 1) - (1/5)(s + 3)/[(s + 2)^2 + 4]$

$x(t) = (1/10)[2e^{-t} - e^{-2t}(2\cos 2t + \sin 2t)]$

31. $[s^3X(s) - s - 1] + [s^2X(s) - 1] - 6[sX(s)] = 0$

$X(s) = (1/15)[-5/s + 6/(s - 2) - 1/(s + 3)]$

$x(t) = (-5 + 6e^{2t} - e^{-3t})/15$

32. $X(s) = s^3/(s^4 - 1) = (1/2)s/(s^2 + 1) + (1/2)s/(s^2 - 1)$

$x(t) = (\cos t + \cosh t)/2$

33. $[s^4X(s) - 1] + X(s) = 0$

$X(s) = 1/(s^4 + 1)$

It therefore follows from Problem 26 with $a = 1/\sqrt{2}$ that

$$x(t) = a(\cosh at \sin at - \sinh at \cos at).$$

34. $[s^4X(s) - 2s^2 + 13] + 13[s^2X(s) - 2] + 36 X(s) = 0$

$X(s) = (2s^2 + 13)/(s^4 + 13s^2 + 36) = 1/(s^2 + 4) + 1/(s^2 + 9)$

$x(t) = (1/2)\sin 2t + (1/3)\sin 3t$

35. $X(s) = 1/(s^2 + 4)^2$, so Equation (16) in this section yields

$$x(t) = (\sin 2t - 2t \cos 2t)/16.$$

36. $X(s) = 1/[(s-2)(s^4+2s^2+1)] = \dfrac{1}{25}\cdot\dfrac{1}{s-2} - \dfrac{1}{25}\cdot\dfrac{s+2}{s^2+1} - \dfrac{1}{5}\cdot\dfrac{s+2}{(s^2+1)^2}$

$x(t) = (1/25)e^{2t} - (1/25)\cos t - (2/25)\sin t - (1/10)(t\sin t) - (1/5)(\sin t - t\cos t)$

$\qquad = (1/50)[2e^{2t} + (10t-2)\cos t - (5t+14)\sin t]$

37. $X(s) = (2s^2+4s+3)/[(s+1)^2(s^2+4s+13)]$

$\qquad = [-1/(s+1) + 5/(s+1)^2 + (s+98)/(s^2+4s+13)]/50$

$x(t) = [(-1+5t)e^{-t} + e^{-2t}(\cos 3t + 32\sin 3t)]/50$

38. $[s^2X(0) - s + 1] + 6[s\,X(s) - 1] + 18X(s) = s/(s^2+4)$

$X(s) = (s+5)/(s^2+6s+18) + s/[(s^2+4)(s^2+6s+18)]$

$\qquad = \dfrac{1}{170}\cdot\dfrac{163(s+3)+307}{(s+3)^2+9} + \dfrac{1}{170}\cdot\dfrac{7s+12}{s^2+4}$

$x(t) = (1/510)e^{-3t}(489\cos 3t + 307\sin 3t) + (1/170)(7\cos 2t + 6\sin 2t)$

39. $x'' + 9x = 6\cos 3t$

$(s^2+9)X(s) = 6s/(s^2+9)$

$x(t) = \mathcal{L}^{-1}\{6s/(s^2+9)^2\} = t\sin 3t$

40. $x'' + 0.4\,x' + 9.04\,x = 6e^{-t/5}\cos 3t$

$(s^2+0.4s+9.04)X(s) = 6(s+0.2)/[s+0.2)^2+9]$

$x(t) = \mathcal{L}^{-1}\{6(s+0.2)/[(s+0.2)^2+9]^2\} = te^{-t/5}\sin 3t$

SECTION 7.4

DERIVATIVES, INTEGRALS, AND PRODUCTS OF TRANSFORMS

This section completes the presentation of the standard "operational properties" of Laplace transforms, the most important one here being the convolution property $\mathcal{L}\{f*g\} = \mathcal{L}\{f\}\cdot\mathcal{L}\{g\}$, where the **convolution** $f*g$ is defined by

$$f*g(t) = \int_0^t f(x)g(t-x)\,dx.$$

In an applied course the proofs may (as marked in the text) be regarded as optional.

1. $t*1 = t^2/2$

2. To compute $\int x\,e^{a(t-x)}\,dx = e^{at}\int xe^{-ax}\,dx$, substitute $u = -ax$ and use the integral

formula $\int ue^u\,du = (u-1)e^u + C$.

Answer: $(e^{at} - at - 1)/a^2$

3. To compute $\int \sin x\sin(t-x)\,dx$, first apply the identity

$$\sin A \sin B = [\cos(A - B) - \cos(A + B)]/2.$$

Answer: $(\sin t - t\cos t)/2$

4. To compute $\int x^2\cos(t-x)\,dx$, first substitute

$$\cos(t - x) = \cos t\cos x + \sin t\sin x,$$

and then use the integral formulas

$$\int x^2\cos x\,dx = x^2\sin x + 2x\cos x - 2\sin x + C,$$

$$\int x^2\sin x\,dx = -x^2\cos x + 2x\sin x + 2\cos x + C.$$

Answer: $2(t - \sin t)$

5. $e^{at} * e^{at} = te^{at}$

6. $(e^{at} - e^{bt})/(a - b)$

7. $f(t) = 1*e^{3t} = (e^{3t} - 1)/3$

8. $f(t) = (1)*(\sin 2t)/2 = (1 - \cos 2t)/4$

9. $f(t) = (1/9)(\sin 3t)*(\sin 3t) = (\sin 3t - 3t\cos 3t)/54$

10. $f(t) = (t)*(\sin kt)/k = (kt - \sin kt)/k^3$

11. $f(t) = (\cos 2t)*(\cos 2t) = (\sin 2t + 2t\cos 2t)/4$

12. $f(t) = (e^{-2t}\sin t)*(1) = \int_0^t e^{-2x}\sin x\,dx = \frac{1}{5}\left[1 - e^{-2t}(\cos t + 2\sin t)\right]$

13. $f(t) = e^{3t}*\cos t = (-3\cos t + \sin t + 3e^{3t})/10$

14. $f(t) = (\cos 2t)*(\sin t) = (\cos t - \cos 2t)/3$ with much use of the trigonometric addition formulas.

15. $\mathcal{L}\{t \sin t\} = -(d/ds)\mathcal{L}\{\sin 3t\} = -(d/ds)(3/(s^2 + 9)) = 6s/(s^2 + 9)^2$

16. $\mathcal{L}\{t^2\cos 2t\} = (d^2/ds^2)\mathcal{L}\{\cos 2t\} = (d^2/ds^2)[s/(s^2 + 4)] = (2s^3 - 24s)/(s^2 + 4)^3$

17. $\mathcal{L}\{e^{2t}\cos 3t\} = (s - 2)/(s^2 - 4s + 13)$

      $\mathcal{L}\{te^{2t}\cos 3t\} = -(d/ds)[(s - 2)/(s^2 - 4s + 13)] = (s^2 - 4s - 5)/(s^2 - 4s + 13)^2$

18. $\mathcal{L}\{\sin^2 t\} = \mathcal{L}\{(1 - \cos 2t)/2\} = 2/s(s^2 + 4)$

      $\mathcal{L}\{e^{-t}\sin^2 t\} = 2/[(s + 1)(s^2 + 2s + 5)]$

      $\mathcal{L}\{te^{-t}\sin^2 t\} = -(d/ds)[2/((s + 1)(s^2 + 2s + 5))]$

               $= 2(3s^2 + 6s + 7)/[(s + 1)^2(s^2 + 2s + 5)^2]$

19. $\mathcal{L}\left\{\dfrac{\sin t}{t}\right\} = \displaystyle\int_s^\infty \dfrac{ds}{s^2 + 1} = \left[\tan^{-1} s\right]_s^\infty = \dfrac{\pi}{2} - \tan^{-1} s = \tan^{-1}(1/s)$

20. $\mathcal{L}\{1 - \cos 2t\} = \dfrac{1}{s} - \dfrac{s}{s^2 + 4}$

      $\mathcal{L}\left\{\dfrac{1 - \cos 2t}{t}\right\} = \displaystyle\int_s^\infty \left(\dfrac{1}{s} - \dfrac{s}{s^2 + 4}\right)ds = \left[\dfrac{\ln s}{\sqrt{s^2 + 4}}\right]_s^\infty = \ln\left((1/s)\sqrt{s^2 + 4}\right)$

21. $\mathcal{L}\{e^{3t} - 1\} = 1/(s - 3) - 1/s$

      $\int [1/(s - 3) - 1/s]\, ds = \ln[(s - 3)/s] + C$

      $\mathcal{L}[(e^{3t} - 1)/t] = \ln[s/(s - 3)]$

22. $\mathcal{L}\{e^t - e^{-t}\} = \mathcal{L}\{2 \sinh t\} = 2/(s^2 - 1)$

      $\int [2/(s^2 - 1)]\, ds = \ln[(s - 1)/(s + 1)] + C$

      $\mathcal{L}\{(e^t - e^{-t})/t\} = \ln[(s + 1)/(s - 1)]$

23. $f(t) = -(1/t)\mathcal{L}^{-1}\{F'(s)\}$

      $= -(1/t)\mathcal{L}^{-1}\{1/(s - 2) - 1/(s + 2)\}$

      $= -(1/t)(e^{2t} - e^{-2t}) = -(2 \sinh 2t)/t$

24. $f(t) = -(1/t)\mathcal{L}^{-1}\{F'(s)\}$

      $= -(1/t)\mathcal{L}^{-1}\{2s/(s^2 + 1) - 2s/(s^2 + 4)\} = (2/t)(\cos 2t - \cos t)$

25. $f(t) = -(1/t)\mathcal{L}^{-1}\{2s/(s^2+1) - 1/(s+2) - 1/(s-3)\}$

  $= (e^{-2t} + e^{3t} - 2\cos t)/t$

26. $f(t) = -(1/t)\mathcal{L}^{-1}\{F'(s)\}$

  $= -(1/t)\mathcal{L}^{-1}\{-3/[(s+2)^2+9]\} = t^{-1}e^{-2t}\sin 3t$

27. $f(t) = -(1/t)\mathcal{L}^{-1}\{(-2/s^3)/(1+1/s^2)\}$

  $= (2/t)\mathcal{L}^{-1}\{1/(s^3+s)\}$

  $= (2/t)\mathcal{L}^{-1}\{1/s - s/(s^2+1)\} = (2/t)(1 - \cos t)$

28. An empirical approach works best with this one. We can construct transforms with powers of (s^2+1) in their denominators by differentiating the transforms of $\sin t$ and $\cos t$. Thus,

$$\mathcal{L}\{t\sin t\} = -(d/ds)[1/(s^2+1)] = 2s/(s^2+1)^2,$$

$$\mathcal{L}\{t\cos t\} = -(d/ds)[s/(s^2+1)] = (s^2-1)/(s^2+1)^2,$$

$$\mathcal{L}\{t^2\cos t\} = -(d/ds)[(s^2-1)/(s^2+1)^2] = (2s^3-6s)/(s^2+1)^3.$$

From the first and last of these formulas it follows readily that

$$\mathcal{L}^{-1}\{s/(s^2+1)^3\} = (t\sin t - t^2\cos t)/8.$$

Alternatively, one could work out the repeated convolution

$$\mathcal{L}^{-1}\{s/(s^2+1)^3\} = (\cos t)*((\sin t)*(\sin t)).$$

29. $-[s^2X - x'(0)]' - [sX]' - 2[sX] + [X] = 0$

  $s(s+1)X'(s) + 4sX(s) = 0 \quad$ (separable)

  $X(s) = A/(s+1)^4 \quad$ with $A \neq 0$

  $x(t) = Ct^3e^{-t} \quad$ with $C \neq 0$

30. $-[s^2X(s) - x'(0)]' - 3[sX(s)]' - [sX(s)] + 3X(s) = 0$

  $-(s^2+3s)X'(s) - 3sX(s) = 0 \quad$ (separable)

  $X(s) = A/(s+3)^3 \quad$ with $A \neq 0$

  $x(t) = Ct^2e^{-3t} \quad$ with $C \neq 0$

31. $-[s^2X - x'(0)]' + 4[sX]' - [sX] - 4[X]' + 2X = 0$

  $(s^2 - 4s + 4)X' + (3s - 6)X = 0 \quad$ (separable)

$$(s - 2)X' + 3X = 0$$

$$X(s) = A/(s - 2)^3 \text{ with } A \neq 0$$

$$x(t) = Ct^2 e^{2t} \text{ with } C \neq 0$$

32. $-[s^2 X(s) - x'(0)]' - 2[s X(s)]' - 2[s X(s)] - 2X(s) = 0$

$-(s^2 + 2s)X'(s) - (4s + 4)X(s) = 0$ (separable)

$X(s) = A/[s^2(s + 2)^2] = C[1/s - 1/s^2 - 1/(s + 2) - 1/(s + 2)^2]$

$x(t) = C(1 - t - e^{-2t} - te^{-2t})$ with $C = -A/4 \neq 0$

33. $-[s^2 X - x(0)]' - 2[sX] - [X]' = 0$

$(s^2 + 1)X' + 4sX = 0$ (separable)

$X(s) = A/(s^2 + 1)^2$ with $A \neq 0$

$x(t) = C(\sin t - t \cos t)$ with $C \neq 0$

34. $-(s^2 + 4s + 13)X'(s) - (4s + 8)X(s) = 0$

$X(s) = C/(s^2 + 4s + 13)^2 = C/[(s + 2)^2 + 9]^2$

It now follows from Problem 31 in Section 7.2 that

$$x(t) = Ae^{-2t}(\sin 3t - 3t \cos 3t) \text{ with } A \neq 0.$$

36. $s^2 X(s) + 4X(s) = F(s)$

$X(s) = (1/2)F(s) \cdot [2/(s^2 + 4)]$

$x(t) = (1/2)f(t) * (\sin 2t)$

38. $X(s) = (1/3)F(s) \cdot [3/(s^2 + 4s + 13)]$

$x(t) = (1/3)f(t) * (e^{-2t} \sin 3t)$

SECTION 7.5

PERIODIC AND PIECEWISE CONTINUOUS FORCING FUNCTIONS

1. $f(t) = (t - 3)u_3(t)$

2. $f(t) = (t - 1)u_1(t) - (t - 3)u_3(t)$. Hence

$$f(t) = 0 \text{ if } t < 1;$$

$$f(t) = t - 1 \text{ if } 1 \le t < 3;$$

$$f(t) = 2 \text{ if } t \ge 3.$$

3. $f(t) = e^{-2(t-1)} u_1(t)$

4. $f(t) = e^{t-1} u_1(t) - e^2 e^{t-2} u_2(t)$. Hence

$$f(t) = 0 \text{ if } t < 1;$$
$$f(t) = e^{t-1} \text{ if } 1 \le t < 2;$$
$$f(t) = e^{t-1} - e^t \text{ if } t > 2.$$

5. $f(t) = u_\pi(t) \sin(t - \pi) = -u_\pi(t) \sin t$

6. $f(t) = u_1(t) \cos \pi(t - 1)$. Hence

$$f(t) = 0 \text{ if } t < 1;$$

$$f(t) = \cos \pi(t - 1) = -\cos \pi t \text{ if } t \ge 1.$$

7. $f(t) = \sin t - u_{2\pi}(t) \sin(t - 2\pi) = [1 - u_{2\pi}(t)] \sin t$

8. $f(t) = \cos \pi t - u_2(t) \cos \pi(t - 2) = [1 - u_2(t)] \cos \pi t$. Hence

$$f(t) = \cos \pi t \text{ if } t < 2;$$

$$f(t) = 0 \text{ if } t \ge 2.$$

9. $f(t) = \cos \pi t + u_3(t) \cos \pi(t - 3) = [1 - u_3(t)] \cos \pi t$

10. $f(t) = 2 u_\pi(t) \cos 2(t - \pi) - 2 u_{2\pi}(t) \cos 2(t - 2\pi) = 2[u_\pi(t) - u_{2\pi}(t)] \cos 2t$
    Hence
$$f(t) = 0 \text{ if } t < \pi \text{ or } t \ge 2\pi;$$

$$f(t) = 2 \cos 2t \text{ if } \pi \le t < 2\pi.$$

11. $f(t) = 2[1 - u_3(t)]; \quad F(s) = (2/s)(1 - e^{-3s})$

12. $f(t) = 3[u_1(t) - u_4(t)]; \qquad F(s) = 3(e^{-s} - e^{-4s})/s$

13. $f(t) = [1 - u_{2\pi}(t)] \sin t; \qquad F(s) = (1 - e^{-2\pi s})/(s^2 + 1)$

14. $f(t) = [1 - u_2(t)] \cos \pi t = \cos \pi t - u_2(t) \cos \pi(t - 2)$
    $F(s) = s(1 - e^{-2s})/(s^2 + \pi^2)$

15. $f(t) = [1 - u_{3\pi}(t)]\sin t = \sin t + u_{3\pi}(t)\sin(t - 3\pi)$

$F(s) = (1 + e^{-3\pi s})/(s^2 + 1)$

16. $f(t) = [u_\pi(t) - u_{2\pi}(t)]\sin 2t = u_\pi(t)\sin 2(t - \pi) - u_{2\pi}(t)\sin 2(t - 2\pi)$

$F(s) = 2(e^{-\pi s} - e^{-2\pi s})/(s^2 + 4)$

17. $f(t) = [u_2(t) - u_3(t)]\sin \pi t = u_2(t)\sin \pi(t - 2) + u_3(t)\sin \pi(t - 3)$

$F(s) = \pi(e^{-2s} + e^{-3s})/(s^2 + \pi^2)$

18. $f(t) = [u_3(t) - u_5(t)]\cos \pi t/2 = u_3(t)\sin \pi(t - 3)/2 + u_5(t)\sin \pi(t - 5)/2$

$F(s) = 2\pi(e^{-3s} + e^{-5s})/(4s^2 + \pi^2)$

19. $f(t) = (t + 1)u_1(t); \quad F(s) = e^{-s}(1/s + 1/s^2)$

20. $f(t) = [1 - u_1(t)]t + u_1(t) = t + u_1(t) - u_1(t)g(t - 1)$ where $g(t) = t + 1$. Hence

$$F(s) = 1/s^2 + e^{-s}/s - e^{-s}(1/s^2 + 1/s) = (1 - e^{-s})/s^2.$$

21. $f(t) = t[1 - u_1(t)] + (2 - t)[u_1(t) - u_2(t)]$

$= t + 2u_1(t) - 2u_2(t) - 2u_1(t)g(t - 1) + u_2(t)h(t - 2)$

where $g(t) = t + 1$ and $h(t) = t + 2$.

$F(s) = 1/s^2 + 2e^{-s}/s - 2e^{-2s}/s - 2e^{-s}(1/s + 1/s^2) - e^{-2s}(2/s + 1/s^2)$

$= (1 - 2e^{-s} + e^{-2s})/s^2$

22. $f(t) = [u_1(t) - u_2(t)]t^3 = u_1(t)g(t - 1) - u_2(t)h(t - 2)$ where

$$g(t) = (t + 1)^3 = t^3 + 3t^2 + 3t + 1,$$
$$h(t) = (t + 2)^3 = t^3 + 6t^2 + 12t + 8.$$

It follows that

$$F(s) = e^{-s}G(s) - e^{-2s}H(s)$$
$$= [(s^3 + 3s^2 + 6s + 6)e^{-s} - (8s^3 + 12s^2 + 12s + 6)e^{-2s}]/s^4.$$

23. Simply apply Formula (12) in the text with $p = 1$ and $f(t) = 1$.

24. $f(t) = \cos kt$ is periodic with period $p = 2\pi/k$. Apply Formula (12) and use the integral formula

$$\int e^{at} \cos bt \, dt = e^{at} \left[\frac{a\cos bt + b\sin bt}{a^2 + b^2} \right] + C.$$

25. Apply Formula (12) with $p = 2a$ and $f(t) = 1$ if $0 \leq t \leq a$, $f(t) = 0$ if $a < t \leq 2a$.

26. Apply Formula (12) with $f(t) = t/a$ and $p = a$; then use the integral formula $\int ue^u \, du = (u-1)e^u + C.$

27. $G(s) = (1/as^2) - F(s)$. Now substitute for $F(s)$ the result of Problem 26.

28. $F(s) = (1 - e^{-as} - ase^{-as})/[s^2(1 - e^{-2as})]$

29. Apply Formula (12) with $p = 2\pi/k$ and $f(t) = \sin kt$ if $0 \leq t \leq \pi k$, $f(t) = 0$ if $\pi/k \leq t \leq 2\pi/k$; then use the integral formula

$$\int e^{at} \sin bt \, dt = e^{at} \left[\frac{a\sin bt - b\cos bt}{a^2 + b^2} \right] + C.$$

30. $h(t) = f(t) + u(t - \pi/k)\, f(t - \pi/k)$, so

$$H(s) = F(s) + e^{-\pi s/k} F(s) = (1 + e^{-\pi s/k})F(s)$$
$$= (1 + e^{-\pi s/k}) \cdot k/(s^2 + k^2)(1 - e^{-\pi s/k})$$
$$= [k/(s^2 + k^2)] \cdot [(1 + e^{-\pi s/k})/(1 + e^{-\pi s/k})] = [k/(s^2 + k^2)]\coth \pi s/2k$$

31. $x'' + 4x = 1 - u_\pi(t)$

$s^2 X(s) + 4X(s) = (1 - e^{-\pi s})/s$

$X(s) = (1 - e^{-\pi s})/[s(s^2 + 4)] = (1/4)(1 - e^{-\pi s})[1/s - s/(s^2 + 4)]$

$x(t) = (1/4)[1 - u_\pi(t)][1 - \cos 2(t - \pi)] = (1/2)[1 - u_\pi(t)]\sin^2 t$

32. $x'' + 5x' + 4x = 1 - u_2(t)$

$s^2 X(s) + 5s\, X(s) + 4X(s) = (1 - e^{-2s})/s$

$X(s) = (1 - e^{-2s})/[s(s^2 + 5s + 4)] = (1 - e^{-2s})G(s)$

where

$$g(t) = (1/4)(1 - e^{-2t}\cos t - 3e^{-2t}\sin t)$$

It follows that

$$x(t) = g(t) - u_2(t)g(t - 2).$$

Hence

$$x(t) = g(t) \text{ if } t < 2, \text{ and}$$
$$x(t) = g(t) - g(t-2) \text{ if } t \geq 2.$$

33. $x'' + 9x = [1 - u_{2\pi}(t)]\sin t$

$X(s) = (1 - e^{-2\pi s})/[(s^2 + 1)(s^2 + 9)] = (1/8)(1 - e^{-2\pi s})[1/(s^2 + 1) - 1/(s^2 + 9)]$

$x(t) = (1/8)[1 - u_{2\pi}(t)][\sin t - (1/3)\sin 3t]$

34. $x'' + x = [1 - u_1(t)]t$

$s^2 X(s) + X(s) = 1/s^2 - e^{-s}(1/s + 1/s^2)$

It follows that

$$X(s) = \frac{1}{s^2(s^2+1)} - \frac{e^{-s}(s+1)}{s^2(s^2+1)}$$

$$= (1-e^{-s})\left(\frac{1}{s^2} - \frac{1}{s^2+1}\right) - e^{-s}\left(\frac{1}{s} - \frac{s}{s^2+1}\right) = (1-e^{-s})G(s) - e^{-s}H(s)$$

where $g(t) = t - \sin t$, $h(t) = 1 - \cos t$. Hence

$$x(t) = g(t) - u_1(t)g(t-1) - u_1(t)h(t-1)$$

and so
$$x(t) = t - \sin t \text{ if } t < 1,$$
$$x(t) = -\sin t + \sin(t-1) + \cos(t-1) \text{ if } t > 1.$$

35. $x'' + 4x' + 4x = [1 - u_2(t)]t = t - u_2(t)[(t-2) + 2]$

$(s+2)^2 X(s) = 1/s^2 - e^{-2s}(2/s + 1/s^2)$

$X(s) = 1/[s^2(s+2)^2] - e^{-2s}(2s+1)/[s^2(s+2)^2]$

$\qquad = (1/4)[-1/s + 1/s^2 + 1/(s+2) + 1/(s+2)^2]$

$\qquad\quad - (1/4)e^{-2s}[1/s + 1/s^2 - 1/(s+2) - 3/(s+2)^2]$

$x(t) = (1/4)\{-1 + t + (1+t)e^{-2t} + u_2(t)[1 - t + (3t - 5)e^{-2(t-2)}]\}$

36. $100\,I(s) + 1000\,I(s)/s = 100(1/s - e^{-s}/s)$

$I(s) = (1 - e^{-s})/(s + 10) = (1 - e^{-s})G(s)$

where $g(t) = e^{-10t}$. Hence

$$i(t) = e^{-10t} - u_1(t)e^{-10(t-1)}$$

37. $i'(t) + 10^4 \int i(t)\, dt = 100[1 - u_{2\pi}(t)]$

$s\, I(s) + 10^4 I(s)/s = 100(1 - e^{-2\pi s})/s$

$I(s) = 100(1 - e^{-2\pi s})/(s^2 + 10^4)$

$i(t) = \sin 100t - u_{2\pi}(t)\sin 100(t - 2\pi) = [1 - u_{2\pi}(t)]\sin 100t$

38. $i'(t) + 10000 \int i(t)\, dt = [1 - u_\pi(t)](100 \sin 10t)$

$s\, I(s) + 10000\, I(s)/s = 1000(1 - e^{-\pi s})/(s^2 + 100)$

Hence

$$I(s) = (1 - e^{-\pi s}) \cdot 1000s/(s^2 + 100)(s^2 + 10000) = (1 - e^{-\pi s})G(s)$$

with

$$g(t) = (10/99)(\cos 10t - \cos 100t).$$

It follows that

$$i(t) = g(t) - u_\pi(t)g(t - \pi),$$

so

$$i(t) = g(t) \text{ if } t < \pi, \ i(t) = 0 \text{ if } t > \pi.$$

39. $i'(t) + 150\, i(t) + 5000 \int i(t)\, dt = 100t[1 - u_1(t)]$

$s\, I(s) + 150 I(s) + 5000 I(s)/s = 100/s^2 - 100e^{-s}(1/s + 1/s^2)$

$I(s) = 100/[s(s + 50)(s + 100)] - e^{-s} \cdot 100(s + 1)/[s(s + 50)(s + 100)]$

$\qquad = (1/50)[1/s - 2/(s + 50) + 1/(s + 100)]$

$\qquad\quad - (1/50)e^{-s}[1/s + 98/(s + 50) - 99/(s + 100)]$

$i(t) = (1/50)[1 - 2e^{-50t} + e^{-100t}] - (1/50)u_1(t)[1 + 98e^{-50(t-1)} - 99e^{-100(t-1)}]$

40. $i'(t) + 100\, i(t) + 2500 \int i(t)\, dt = 50t[1 - u_1(t)]$

$s\, I(s) + 100\, I(s) + 2500\, I(s)/s = 50/s^2 - 50e^{-s}(1/s + 1/s^2)$

It follows that

$$I(s) = (1 - e^{-s}) \cdot 50/[s(s + 50)^2] - e^{-s} \cdot 50/(s + 50)^2 = (1 - e^{-s})G(s) - e^{-s}H(s)$$

where

$$g(t) = (1 - e^{-50t} - 50te^{-50t})/50,$$
$$h(t) = 50te^{-50t}.$$

Hence

$$i(t) = g(t) - u_1(t)g(t - 1) - u_1(t)h(t - 1).$$

41. $x'' + 4x = f(t)$, $x(0) = x'(0) = 0$

$(s^2 + 4)X(s) = (4s)[(1 - e^{-\pi s})/(1 + e^{-\pi s})]$ (by Example 6)

By a computation like that in the solution of Example 8 in the text, it follows that

$$(s^2 + 4)X(s) = (4/s) + (8/s) \sum (-1)^n e^{-n\pi s}.$$

Now let

$$g(t) = \mathcal{L}^{-1}\{4/s(s^2 + 4)\} = 1 - \cos 2t = 2 \sin^2 t.$$

Then it follows that

$$x(t) = g(t) + 2 \sum (-1)^n u_{n\pi}(t) g(t - n\pi) = 2 \sin^2 t + 4 \sum (-1)^n u_{n\pi}(t) \sin^2 t.$$

Hence

$$x(t) = 2 \sin^2 t \text{ if } 2n\pi \le t < (2n + 1)\pi,$$
$$x(t) = -2 \sin^2 t \text{ if } (2n - 1)\pi \le t < 2n\pi.$$

Consequently the complete solution

$$x(t) = 2|\sin t| \sin t$$

is periodic, so the transient solution is zero.

42. $x'' + 2x' + 10x = f(t)$, $x(0) = x'(0) = 0$

As in the solution of Example 8 we find first that

$$(s^2 + 2s + 10)X(s) = (10/s) + (20/s) \sum (-1)^n e^{-n\pi s}.$$

If

$$g(t) = \mathcal{L}^{-1}\{10/s[(s + 1)^2 + 9]\}$$
$$= 1 - (1/3)e^{-t}(3 \cos 3t + \sin 3t)$$

then it follows that

$$x(t) = g(t) + 2 \sum (-1)^n u_{n\pi}(t) g(t - n\pi).$$

SECTION 7.6

IMPULSES AND DELTA FUNCTIONS

Among the several ways of introducing delta functions, we consider the physical approach of the first two pages of this section to be the most tangible one for elementary students. Whatever the approach, however, the practical consequences are the same -- as described in the discussion associated with equations (11)–(19) in the text. That is, in order to solve a differential equation of the form

$$ax''(t) + bx'(t) + cx(t) = f(t)$$

where $f(t)$ involves delta functions, we transform the equation using the operational principle $\mathcal{L}\{\delta_a(t)\} = e^{-as}$, then solve for $X(s)$, and finally invert as usual to find the formal solution $x(t)$.

1. $s^2 X(s) + 4X(s) = 1$

    $X(s) = 1/(s^2 + 4)$

    $x(t) = (1/2)\sin 2t$

2. $s^2 X(s) + 4X(s) = 1 + e^{-\pi s}$

    $X(s) = 1/(s^2 + 4) + e^{-\pi s}/(s^2 + 4)$

    $x(t) = (1/2)\sin 2t + (1/2)u_\pi(t)\sin 2t$

    Hence

    $$x(t) = (1/2)\sin 2t \text{ if } t < \pi$$
    $$x(t) = \quad \sin 2t \text{ if } t > \pi.$$

3. $s^2 X(s) + 4sX(s) + 4X(s) = (1/s) + e^{-2s}$

    $X(s) = 1/[s(s+2)^2] + e^{-2s}/(s+2)^2$

    $\quad = (1/4)[1/s - 1/(s+2) - 2/(s+2)^2] + e^{-2s}/(s+2)^2$

    $x(t) = (1/4)[1 - e^{-2t} - 2te^{-2t}] + u_2(t)(t-2)e^{-2(t-2)}$

4. $[s^2 X(s) - 1] + 2sX(s) + X(s) = 1 + 1/s^2$

    $X(s) = (2s^2 + 1)/[s^2(s+1)^2] = -2/s + 1/s^2 + 2/(s+1) + 3/(s+1)^2$

    $x(t) = -2 + t + 2e^{-t} + 3te^{-t}$

5. $(s^2 + 2s + 2)X(s) = 2e^{-\pi s}$

    $X(s) = 2e^{-\pi s}/[(s+1)^2 + 1]$

    $x(t) = 2u_\pi(t)e^{-(t-\pi)}\sin(t - \pi)$

    Hence

    $$x(t) = 0 \text{ if } 0 \le t \le \pi,$$
    $$x(t) = -2e^{-(t-\pi)}\sin t \text{ if } t \ge \pi.$$

6. $s^2X(s) + 9X(s) = e^{-3\pi s} + s/(s^2+9)$

$X(s) = e^{-3\pi s}/(s^2+9) + s/(s^2+9)^2$

$x(t) = u_{3\pi}(t)\cdot(1/3)\sin 3(t-3\pi) + (1/6)t\sin 3t = -(1/3)u_{3\pi}(t)\sin 3t + (1/6)t\sin t$

7. $[s^2X(s) - 2] + 4sX(s) + 5X(s) = e^{-\pi s} + e^{-2\pi s}$

$X(s) = [2 + e^{-\pi s} + e^{-2\pi s}]/[(s+2)^2+1]$

$x(t) = 2e^{-2t}\sin t + u_\pi(t)e^{-2(t-\pi)}\sin(t-\pi) + u_{2\pi}(t)e^{-2(t-2\pi)}\sin(t-2\pi)$

$\quad = [2 - e^{2\pi}u_\pi(t) + e^{4\pi}u_{2\pi}(t)]e^{-2t}\sin t$

8. $[s^2X(s) - 2s - 2] + 2[sX(s) - 2] + X(s) = 1 - e^{-2s}$

$X(s) = (2s + 7 - e^{-2s})/(s+1)^2 = 2/(s+1) + 5/(s+1)^2 - e^{-2s}/(s+1)^2$

$x(t) = (2 + 5t)e^{-t} - u_2(t)(t-2)e^{-(t-2)}$

9. $s^2X(s) + 4X(s) = F(s)$

$X(s) = [1/(s^2+4)]\cdot F(s)$

$x(t) = \frac{1}{2}\int_0^t (\sin 2u)\,f(t-u)\,du$

10. $s^2X(s) + 6s\,X(s) + 9X(s) = F(s)$

$X(s) = [1/(s+3)^2]\cdot F(s)$

$x(t) = \int_0^t ue^{-3u}\,f(t-u)\,du$

11. $(s^2 + 6s + 8)X(s) = F(s)$

$X(s) = \{1/[(s+3)^2 - 1]\}\cdot F(s)$

$x(t) = \int_0^t e^{-3u}(\sinh u)\,f(t-u)\,du$

12. $s^2X(s) + 4sX(s) + 8X(s) = F(s)$

$X(s) = \{1/[(s+2)^2 + 4]\}\cdot F(s)$

$x(t) = \frac{1}{2}\int_0^t e^{-2u}(\sin 2u)\,f(t-u)\,du$

13. **(a)** $mx_\varepsilon''(t) = (p/\varepsilon)[u_0(t) - u_\varepsilon(t)]$

$\quad ms^2X_\varepsilon(s) = (p/\varepsilon)[1/s - e^{-\varepsilon s}/s]$

$\quad mX_\varepsilon(s) = (p/\varepsilon)[(1 - e^{-\varepsilon s})/s^3]$

$\quad mx_\varepsilon(t) = (p/2\varepsilon)[t^2 - u_\varepsilon(t)(t-\varepsilon)^2]$

(b)   If $\underline{t} > \varepsilon$ then

$$mx_\varepsilon(t) = (p/2\varepsilon)[t^2 - (t^2 - 2\varepsilon t + \varepsilon^2)] = (p/2\varepsilon)(2\varepsilon t - \varepsilon^2).$$

Hence $mx_\varepsilon(t) \to pt$ as $\varepsilon \to 0$.

(c) $mv = (mx)' = (pt)' = p.$

14. $sX(s) = e^{-as}; \quad X(s) = e^{-as}/s; \quad x(t) = u(t - a)$

15.   Each of the two given initial value problems transforms to

$$(ms^2 + k)X(s) = mv_0 = p_0.$$

16.   Each of the two given initial value problems transforms to

$$(as^2 + bs + c)X(s) = F(s) + av_0$$

17.   **(b)** $i' + 100i = \delta_1(t) - \delta_2(t), \quad i(0) = 0$

$$I(s) = (e^{-s} - e^{-2s})/(s + 100)$$

$$i(t) = u_1(t)e^{-100(t-1)} - u_2(t)e^{-100(t-2)} = e^{-100t}[e^{100}u_1(t) - e^{200}u_2(t)]$$

18.   **(b)** $i''(t) + 100\, i(t) = 10\, \delta(t) - 10\, \delta(t - \pi)$

$$(s^2 + 100)\, I(s) = 10 - 10\, e^{-\pi s}$$

$$I(s) = 10/(s^2 + 100) - 10\, e^{-\pi s}/(s^2 + 100)$$

$$i(t) = \sin 10t - u_\pi(t)\sin 10(t - \pi) = [1 - u_\pi(t)]\sin 10t$$

19. $(s^2 + 100)I(s) = 10 \sum (-1)^n e^{-n\pi s/10}$

$$I(s) = \sum (-1)^n e^{-n\pi s/10}[10/(s^2 + 100)]$$

$$i(t) = \sum (-1)^n u_{n\pi/10}(t)\sin(10t - n\pi) = \sum u_{n\pi/10}(t)\sin 10t$$

because $\sin(10t - n\pi) = (-1)^n \sin 10t$. Hence

$$i(t) = (n + 1)\sin 10t$$

if $n\pi/10 < t < (n + 1)\pi/10$.

20. $(s^2 + 100)I(s) = 10 \sum (-1)^n e^{-n\pi s/5}$

$$I(s) = \sum (-1)^n e^{-n\pi s/5}[10/(s^2 + 100)]$$

$$i(t) = \Sigma (-1)^n u_{n\pi/5}(t) \sin(10t - 2n\pi) = \Sigma (-1)^n u_{n\pi/5}(t) \sin 10t.$$

Hence

$$i(t) = \sin 10t - \sin 10t + \cdots + (-1)^n \sin 10t$$

if $n\pi/5 < (n+1)\pi/5$, $n \geq 0$.

21. (b) $(s^2 + 60s + 1000)I(s) = 10\Sigma(-1)^n e^{-n\pi s/10}$

where the summation is from $n = 0$ to ∞. Hence

$$I(s) = \Sigma (-1)^n 10\, e^{-n\pi s/10}/[(s+30)^2 + 100]$$
$$i(t) = \Sigma (-1)^n u_{n\pi/10}(t)\, g(t - n\pi/10)$$

where $g(t) = e^{-30t} \sin 10t$, and so

$$g(t - n\pi/10) = \exp[-30(t - n\pi/10)] \sin 10(t - n\pi/10)$$
$$= e^{3n\pi} e^{-30t} \cdot (-1)^n \sin 10t$$

Therefore

$$i(t) = \Sigma u_{n\pi/10}(t)\, e^{3n\pi} e^{-30t} \sin 10t.$$

If $n\pi/10 < t < (n+1)\pi/10$ then it follows that

$$i(t) = (1 + e^{3\pi} + \cdots + e^{3n\pi})e^{-30t} \sin 10t$$
$$= [(e^{3n\pi+3\pi} - 1)/(e^{3\pi} - 1)]e^{-30t} \sin 10t.$$

22. $(s^2 + 1)X(s) = \Sigma e^{-2n\pi s}$

$X(s) = \Sigma e^{-2n\pi s}[1/(s^2 + 1)]$

$x(t) = \Sigma u_{2n\pi}(t)\sin(t - 2n\pi) = \Sigma u_{2n\pi}(t)\sin t$

Hence $x(t) = (n+1)\sin t$ if $2n\pi < t < 2(n+1)\pi$.

CHAPTER 8

POWER SERIES METHODS

SECTION 8.1

INTRODUCTION AND REVIEW OF POWER SERIES

The power series method consists of substituting a series $\Sigma c_n x^n$ into a given differential equation in order to determine what the coefficients $\{c_n\}$ must be in order that the power series will satisfy the equation. It might be pointed out that, if we find a recurrence relation in the form $c_{n+1} = \phi(n)c_n$, then we can determine the radius of convergence ρ of the series solution directly from the recurrence relation,

$$\rho = \lim_{n \to \infty} \left| \frac{c_n}{c_{n+1}} \right| = \lim_{n \to \infty} \left| \frac{1}{\phi(n)} \right|.$$

1. $c_{n+1} = c_n/(n+1)$; it follows that $c_n = c_0/n!$; $\rho = \infty$

$$y = c_0(1 + x + x^2/2! + x^3/3! + \cdots) = c_0 e^x$$

2. $c_{n+1} = 4c_n/(n+1)$; $\rho = \infty$

$$y = c_0(1 + 4x + 4^2 x^2/2! + 4^3 x^3/3! + \cdots) = c_0 e^{4x}$$

3. $c_{n+1} = -3c_n / 2(n+1)$

It follows that $c_n = (-1)^n 3^n c_0/2^n (n!)$; $\rho = \infty$.

$$y = c_0(1 - 3x/2 + 3^2 x^2/2!2^2 - 3^3 x^3/3!2^3 + 3^4 x^4/4!2^4 - \cdots) = c_0 e^{-3x/2}$$

4.   When we substitute $y = \Sigma c_n x^n$ into the equation $y' + 2xy = 0$, we find that

$$c_1 + \Sigma \left[(n+2)c_{n+2} + 2c_n \right] x^{n+1} = 0.$$

Hence $c_1 = 0$ and $c_{n+2} = -2c_n/(n+2)$. It follows that $c_{odd} = 0$ and $c_{2k} = (-1)^k c_0/k!$, so the solution is

$$y = c_0(1 - x^2 + x^4/2! - x^6/3! + \cdots) = c_0 \exp(-x^2).$$

5. $c_{n+3} = c_n/(n+3)$ and $c_1 = c_2 = 0$. It follows that $c_{3k+1} = c_{3k+2} = 0$ and $c_{3k} = c_0/(3 \cdot 6 \cdots (3k)) = c_0/k! \, 3^k$.

$$y = c_0(1 + x^3/3 + x^6/2!3^2 + x^9/3!3^3 + \cdots) = c_0 \exp(x^3/3); \quad \rho = \infty$$

6. $c_{n+1} = c_n/2; \; \rho = 2$

$$y = c_0(1 + x/2 + x^2/2^2 + x^3/2^3 + \cdots) = 2c_0/(2 - x)$$

7. $c_{n+1} = 2c_n, \text{ so } c_n = 2^n c_0; \; \rho = 1/2$

$$y = c_0(1 + 2x + 4x^2 + 8x^3 + \cdots) = c_0/(1 - 2x)$$

8. $c_{n+1} = -(2n - 1)c_n/(2n + 2); \; \rho = 1$

$$y = c_0(1 + x/2 - x^2/8 + x^3/16 + \cdots) = c_0(1 + x)^{1/2}$$

9. $c_{n+1} = (n + 2)c_n/(n + 1); \text{ it follows that } c_n = (n + 1)c_0.$

$$y = c_0(1 + 2x + 3x^2 + 4x^3 + \cdots) = c_0(1 - x)^{-2}; \; \rho = 1$$

10. $c_{n+1} = (2n - 3)c_n/(2n + 2); \; \rho = 1$

$$y = c_0(1 - 3x/2 + 3x^2/8 + x^3/16 + \cdots) = c_0(1 - x)^{3/2}$$

11. $c_{n+2} = c_n/(n + 1)(n + 2); \text{ it follows that } c_{2k} = c_0/(2k)! \text{ and } c_{2k+1} = c_1/(2k + 1)!.$

$$y = c_0(1 + x^2/2! + x^4/4! + x^6/6! + \cdots) + c_1(x + x^3/3! + x^5/5! + x^7/7! + \cdots)$$

$$= c_0 \cosh x + c_1 \sinh x$$

12. $c_{n+2} = 4c_n/(n + 1)(n + 2)$

$$y = c_0(1 + 2^2 x^2/2! + 2^4 x^4/4! + \cdots) + (c_1/2)(2x + 2^3 x^3/3! + 2^5 x^5/5! + \cdots)$$

$$= c_0 \cosh 2x + (c_1/2)\sinh 2x$$

13. $c_{n+2} = -9c_n/(n + 1)(n + 2)$

$$y = c_0(1 - 3^2 x^2/2! + 3^4 x^4/4! - 3^6 x^6/6! + \cdots)$$

$$+ (c_1/3)(3x - 3^3 x^3/3! + 3^5 x^5/5! - 3^7 x^7/7! + \cdots)$$

$$= c_0 \cos 3x + (c_1/3)\sin 3x$$

14.   When we substitute $y = \Sigma c_n x^n$ into $y'' + y - x = 0$ and split off the terms of degrees 0 and 1, we get

$$(2c_2 + c_0) + (6c_3 + c_1 - 1) + \Sigma \left[(n + 1)(n + 2)c_{n+2} + c_n \right] x^n = 0.$$

Hence $c_2 = -c_0/2, \; c_3 = -(c_1 - 1)/3!$ and $c_{n+2} = -c_n/(n + 1)(n + 2).$ It follows that

$$y = x + c_0(1 - x^2/2! + x^4/4! - \cdots) + (c_1 - 1)(x - x^3/3! + x^5/5! - \cdots)$$

$$= x + c_0 \cos x + (c_1 - 1)\sin x$$

15.   We find that $(n + 1)c_n = 0$ for all $n \geq 0$, so $c_n = 0$ for all $n \geq 0$.

16. When we substitute $y = \Sigma c_n x^n$ into the differential equation $2xy' = y$, we find that $2nc_n = c_n$ for $n \geq 0$. This can be so only if $c_n = 0$ for all n.

17. We find that $c_0 = c_1 = 0$ and that $c_{n+1} = -nc_n$ for $n \geq 1$; it follows that $c_n = 0$ for all $n \geq 0$.

18. When we substitute $y = \Sigma c_n x^n$ into $x^3 y' = 2y$ we find that $c_0 = c_1 = c_2 = 0$ and that $c_{n+2} = nc_n/2$ for $n \geq 1$. Hence $c_n = 0$ for all n.

19. $c_n = -2^2 c_{n-2} / n(n-1)$ for $n \geq 2$; $c_0 = 0$ and $c_1 = 3$; $y = (3/2)\sin 2x$

20. $c_{n+2} = 4c_n / (n+1)(n+2)$; $c_0 = 2$, $c_1 = 0$

$y = 2(1 + 2^2 x^2/2! + 2^4 x^4/4! + \cdots) = 2\cosh 2x$

21. $c_{n+1} = (2nc_n - c_{n-1}) / n(n+1)$ for $n \geq 1$; $c_0 = 0$ and $c_1 = 1$; $y = xe^x$

22. $c_{n+2} = -[(n+1)c_{n+1} - 2c_n] / (n+1)(n+2)$; $c_0 = 1$, $c_1 = -2$

$y = 1 - 2x + 2x^2 - 4x^3/3 + 2x^4/3 + \cdots$

$ = 1 - 2x + 2^2 x^2/2! - 2^3 x^3/3! + 2^4 x^4/4! - \cdots = e^{-2x}$

23. $c_0 = c_1 = 0$ and the recursion relation

$$(n^2 - n + 1)c_n + (n-1)c_{n-1} = 0$$

for $n \geq 2$ imply that $c_n = 0$ for $n \geq 0$.

24. **(a)** The fact that $y = (1+x)^\alpha$ satisfies the differential equation $(1+x)y' = \alpha y$ follows immediately from the fact that $y' = \alpha(1+x)^{\alpha-1}$.

(b) When we substitute $y = \Sigma c_n x^n$ into the differential equation $(1+x)y' = \alpha y$ we get the recurrence formula

$$c_{n+1} = (\alpha - n)c_n/(n+1).$$

Since $c_0 = 1$ because of the initial condition $y(0) = 1$, the binomial series (Equation (12) in the text) follows.

(c) The function $(1+x)^\alpha$ and the binomial series must agree on $(-1, 1)$ because of the uniqueness of solutions of linear initial value problems.

26. **(b)** The roots of the characteristic equation $r^3 = 1$ are $r_1 = 1$, $r_2 = \alpha = (-1 + i\sqrt{3})/2$, and $r_3 = \beta = (-1 - i\sqrt{3})/2$. Then the general solution is

$$y(x) = Ae^x + Be^{\alpha x} + Ce^{\beta x}. \qquad\qquad (*)$$

Imposing the initial conditions, we get the equations

$$
\begin{aligned}
A + B + C &= 1 \\
A + \alpha B + \beta C &= 1 \\
A + \alpha^2 B + \beta^2 C &= -1.
\end{aligned}
$$

The solution of this system is $A = 1/3$, $B = (1 - i\sqrt{3})/3$, $C = (1 + i\sqrt{3})/3$. Substitution of these coefficients in (*) and use of Euler's relation $e^{i\theta} = \cos\theta + i\sin\theta$ finally yields the desired result.

SECTION 8.2

SERIES SOLUTIONS NEAR ORDINARY POINTS

Instead of deriving in detail the recurrence relations and solution series for Problems 1 through 15, we indicate where some of these problems and answers originally came from. Each of the differential equations in Problems 1–10 is of the form

$$(Ax^2 + B)y'' + Cxy' + Dy = 0$$

with selected values of the constants A, B, C, D. When we substitute $y = \Sigma c_n x^n$, shift indices where appropriate, and collect coefficients, we get

$$\Sigma\,[An(n-1)c_n + B(n+1)(n+2)c_{n+2} + Cnc_n + Dc_n]\,x^n = 0.$$

Thus the recurrence relation is

$$c_{n+2} = -\frac{An + (C-A)n + D}{B(n+1)(n+2)}c_n \qquad \text{for } n \geq 0.$$

It yields a solution of the form

$$y = c_0\,y_{even} + c_1\,y_{odd}$$

where y_{even} and y_{odd} denote series with terms of even and odd degrees, respectively. The even series $c_0 + c_2 x^2 + c_4 x^4 + \cdots$ converges (by the ratio test) provided that

$$\lim_{n\to\infty}\left|\frac{c_{n+2}x^{n+2}}{c_n x^n}\right| = \left|\frac{Ax^2}{B}\right| < 1.$$

Hence its radius of convergence is $\rho = \sqrt{|B/A|}$, as is that of the odd degree series.

1. $\quad c_{n+2} = c_n; \quad y = c_0 \sum_{n=0}^{\infty} x^{2n} + c_1 \sum_{n=0}^{\infty} x^{2n+1} = \dfrac{c_0 + c_1 x}{1 - x^2}$

2. $\quad c_{n+2} = -\dfrac{1}{2} c_n; \quad y = c_0 \sum_{n=0}^{\infty} (-1)^n \dfrac{x^{2n}}{2^n} + c_1 \sum_{n=0}^{\infty} (-1)^n \dfrac{x^{2n+1}}{2^n}$

3. $\quad c_{n+2} = -\dfrac{c_n}{(n+2)}; \quad y = c_0 \sum_{n=0}^{\infty} (-1)^n \dfrac{x^{2n}}{n! 2^n} + c_1 \sum_{n=0}^{\infty} (-1)^n \dfrac{x^{2n+1}}{(2n+1)!!}$

4. $\quad c_{n+2} = -\dfrac{n+4}{n+2} c_n; \quad y = c_0 \sum_{n=0}^{\infty} (-1)^n (n+1) x^{2n} + \dfrac{1}{3} c_1 \sum_{n=0}^{\infty} (-1)^n (2n+3) x^{2n+1}$

5. $\quad c_{n+2} = \dfrac{nc_n}{3(n+2)}; \quad y = c_0 + c_1 \sum_{n=0}^{\infty} \dfrac{x^{2n+1}}{(2n+1)3^n}$

6. $\quad c_{n+2} = \dfrac{(n-3)(n-4)}{(n+1)(n+2)} c_n; \quad y = c_0(1 + 6x^2 + x^4) + c_1(x + x^3)$

7. $\quad c_{n+2} = -\dfrac{(n-4)^2}{3(n+1)(n+3)} c_n$

$\quad y = c_0 \left(1 - \dfrac{8}{3} x^2 + \dfrac{8}{27} x^4 \right) + c_1 \left[x - \dfrac{1}{2} x^3 + \dfrac{1}{120} x^5 + 9 \sum_{n=3}^{\infty} \dfrac{[(2n-5)!!]^2 (-1)^n}{(2n+1)!\, 3^n} x^{2n+1} \right]$

8. $\quad c_{n+2} = \dfrac{(n-4)(n+4)}{2(n+1)(n+2)} c_n$

$\quad y = c_0(1 - 4x^2 + 2x^4) + c_1 \left[x - \dfrac{5}{4} x^3 + \dfrac{7}{32} x^5 + \sum_{n=3}^{\infty} \dfrac{(2n-5)!!(2n+3)!!}{(2n+1)!\, 2^n} x^{2n+1} \right]$

9. $\quad c_{n+2} = \dfrac{(n+3)(n+4)}{(n+1)(n+2)} c_n; \quad y = c_0 \sum_{n=0}^{\infty} (n+1)(2n+1) x^{2n} + \dfrac{1}{3} c_1 \sum_{n=0}^{\infty} (n+1)(2n+3) x^{2n+1}$

10. $\quad c_{n+2} = -\dfrac{(n-4)}{3(n+1)(n+2)} c_n$

$\quad y = c_0 \left(1 + \dfrac{2}{3} x^2 + \dfrac{1}{27} x^4 \right) + c_1 \left[x + \dfrac{1}{6} x^3 + \dfrac{1}{360} x^5 + 3 \sum_{n=3}^{\infty} \dfrac{(2n-5)!!(-1)^n}{(2n+1)!\, 3^n} x^{2n+1} \right]$

Chapter 8

11. $c_{n+2} = \dfrac{2(n-5)}{5(n+1)(n+2)}c_n$

$$y = c_0\left(x - \frac{4x^3}{15} + \frac{4x^5}{375}\right) + c_1\left[1 - x^2 + \frac{x^4}{10} + \frac{x^6}{750} + 15\sum_{n=4}^{\infty}\frac{(2n-7)!!\,2^n}{(2n)!\,5^n}x^{2n}\right]$$

12. $c_2 = 0;\quad c_{n+3} = \dfrac{c_n}{n+2}$

$$y = c_0\left[1 + \sum_{n=1}^{\infty}\frac{x^{3n}}{2\cdot 5\cdots(3n-1)}\right] + c_1\sum_{n=0}^{\infty}\frac{x^{3n+1}}{n!\,3^n}$$

13. $c_2 = 0;\quad c_{n+3} = -\dfrac{c_n}{n+3}$

$$y = c_0\sum_{n=0}^{\infty}\frac{(-1)^n x^{3n}}{n!\,3^n} + c_1\sum_{n=0}^{\infty}\frac{(-1)^n x^{3n+1}}{1\cdot 4\cdots(3n+1)}$$

14. $c_2 = 0;\quad c_{n+3} = -\dfrac{c_n}{(n+2)(n+3)}$

$$y = c_0\left[1 + \sum_{n=1}^{\infty}\frac{(-1)^n x^{3n}}{3^n\,n!\cdot 2\cdot 5\cdots(3n-1)}\right] + c_1\sum_{n=0}^{\infty}\frac{(-1)^n x^{3n+1}}{3^n\,n!\cdot 1\cdot 4\cdots(3n+1)}$$

15. $c_2 = c_3 = 0;\quad c_{n+4} = -\dfrac{c_n}{(n+3)(n+4)}$

$$y = c_0\left[1 + \sum_{n=1}^{\infty}\frac{(-1)^n x^{4n}}{4^n\,n!\cdot 3\cdot 7\cdots(4n-1)}\right] + c_1\left[x + \sum_{n=1}^{\infty}\frac{(-1)^n x^{4n+1}}{4^n\,n!\cdot 5\cdot 9\cdots(4n+1)}\right]$$

16. The recurrence relation is

$$c_{n+2} = -(n-1)c_n/(n+1)$$

for $n \geq 0$. This yields $c_3 = c_5 = \cdots = 0$ and $c_{2n} = (-1)^{n-1}c_0/(2n-1)$ for $n \geq 1$. Hence

$$y = c_1 x + c_0(1 + x^2 - x^4/3 + x^6/5 - \cdots) = c_1 x + c_0(1 + x\tan^{-1}x).$$

With $c_0 = y(0) = 0$ and $c_1 = y'(0) = 1$ we obtain the desired particular solution $y(x) = x.$

17. The recurrence relation

$$c_{n+2} = -(n-2)c_n / (n+1)(n+2)$$

yields $c_2 = c_0 = y(0) = 1$ and $c_4 = c_6 = \cdots = 0$. Because $c_1 = y'(0) = 0$, it follows also that $c_1 = c_3 = c_5 = \cdots = 0$. Thus the desired particular solution is $y(x) = 1 + x^2$.

18. The substitution $t = x - 1$ yields $y'' + ty' + y = 0$, where primes now denote differentiation with respect to t. When we substitute $y = \Sigma c_n t^n$ we get the recurrence relation

$$c_{n+2} = -c_n/(n+2)$$

for $n \geq 0$. The initial conditions give $c_0 = 2$ and $c_1 = 0$, so $c_{odd} = 0$ and it follows that

$$y = 2(1 - t^2/2 + t^4/2 \cdot 4 - t^6/2 \cdot 4 \cdot 6 + \cdots)$$
$$= 2[1 - (x-1)^2/2 + (x-1)^4/2 \cdot 4 - (x-1)^6/2 \cdot 4 \cdot 6 + \cdots].$$

19. $y = (1/3)\Sigma(2n+3)(x-1)^{2n+1}$; the series converges if $0 < x < 2$.

20. The substitution $t = x - 3$ yields

$$(t^2 + 1)y'' - 4ty' + 6y = 0,$$

where primes now denote differentiation with respect to t. When we substitute $y = \Sigma c_n t^n$ we get the recurrence relation

$$c_{n+2} = -(n-2)(n-3)c_n / (n+1)(n+2)$$

for $n \geq 0$. The initial conditions give $c_0 = 2$ and $c_1 = 0$. It follows that $c_{odd} = 0$, $c_2 = -6$ and $c_4 = c_6 = \cdots = 0$, so the solution reduces to

$$y = 2 - 6t^2 = 2 - 6(x-3)^2.$$

21. $y = 1 + 4(x+2)^2$; the series converges for all x.

22. The differential equation we wish to solve is

$$(x^2 + 6x)y'' + (3x+9)y' - 3y = 0.$$

The substitution $t = x + 3$ yields

$$(t^2 + 9)y'' + 3ty' - 3y = 0,$$

with primes now denoting differentiation with respect to t. When we substitute $y = \Sigma c_n t^n$ we get the recurrence relation

$$c_{n+2} = (n+3)(n-1)c_n / 9(n+1)(n+2)$$

for $n \geq 0$. The initial conditions give $c_0 = 0$ and $c_1 = 2$. It follows that $c_{even} = 0$ and $c_3 = c_5 = \cdots = 0$, so

$$y = 2t = 2x + 6.$$

23. $2c_2 + c_0 = 0;$ $(n+1)(n+2)c_{n+2} + c_n + c_{n-1} = 0$ for $n \geq 1$

$y_1 = 1 - (1/2)x^2 - (1/6)x^3 + \cdots$

$y_2 = x - (1/6)x^3 - (1/12)x^4 + \cdots$

24. Substitution of $y = \Sigma c_n x^n$ yields

$$2c_2 + \Sigma [2c_n + (n+1)(n+2)c_{n+1} - (n+2)(n+3)c_{n+3}]x^{n+1} = 0.$$

Thus $c_2 = 0$ and

$$c_{n+3} = [2c_n + (n+1)(n+2)c_{n+1}] / (n+2)(n+3)$$

for $n \geq 0$. We find that $c_3 = (c_0 + c_1)/3$, $c_4 = c_1/6$, and $c_5 = (c_0 + c_1)/5$, so

$$y = c_0(1 + x^3/3 + x^5/5 + \cdots) + c_1(x + x^3/3 + x^4/6 + \cdots).$$

25. $c_2 = c_3 = 0;$ $(n+3)(n+4)c_{n+4} + (n+1)c_{n+1} + c_n = 0$ for $n \geq 0;$

$y_1 = 1 - (1/12)x^4 + (1/126)x^7 + \cdots$

$y_2 = x - (1/12)x^4 - (1/20)x^5 + \cdots$

26. When we substitute $y = \Sigma c_n x^n$, shift indices and collect coefficients, we find that

$$2c_2 + 6c_3 x + 12c_4 x^2 + (2c_2 + 20c_5)x^3$$
$$+ \Sigma [c_n + (n+2)(n+3)c_{n+3} + (n+5)(n+6)c_{n+6}]x^{n+4} = 0.$$

Hence $c_2 = c_3 = c_4 = c_5 = 0$ and

$$c_{n+6} = -[c_n + (n+2)(n+3)c_{n+3}] / (n+5)(n+6)$$

for $n \geq 0$. It follows that $c_6 = -c_0/30$, $c_7 = -c_1/42$, $c_8 = 0$, $c_9 = c_0/72$, and $c_{10} = c_1/90$, so

$$y = c_0(1 - x^6/30 + x^9/72 + \cdots) + c_1(x - x^7/42 + x^{10}/90 + \cdots).$$

27. $y = 1 - x - (1/2)x^2 + (1/3)x^3 - (1/24)x^4 + (1/30)x^5$
$$+ (29/720)x^6 - (13/630)x^7 - (143/40320)x^8 + \cdots;$$

Substitution of $x = 0.5$ in this series gives $y(0.5) \approx 0.4156$.

28. When we substitute $y = \Sigma c_n x^n$ and $e^{-x} = \Sigma (-1)^n x^n / n!$, and then collect coefficients of the terms involving 1, x, and x^2 we find that

$$c_2 = -c_0/2, \quad c_3 = (c_0 - c_1)/6, \quad \text{and}$$

$$c_4 = (-c_0/2 + c_1 - c_2)/12 = c_1/12.$$

It follows that

$$y = c_0(1 - x^2/2 + x^3/6 + \cdots) + c_1(x - x^3/6 + x^4/12 + \cdots).$$

29. $y_1 = 1 - (1/2)x^2 + (1/720)x^6 + \cdots ; \quad y_2 = x - (1/6)x^3 - (1/60)x^5 + \cdots$

30. When we substitute $y = \Sigma c_n x^n$ and $\sin x = \Sigma (-1)^n x^{2n+1} / (2n+1)!$, and then collect coefficients of the terms involving x, x^2, x^3, and x^4, we find that

$$c_2 = -c_0, \quad c_3 = -c_1/3,$$

$$c_4 = (c_0/6 - 2c_2)/12 = 13c_0/72, \quad \text{and}$$

$$c_5 = (c_1/6 - 2c_3)/20 = c_1/24.$$

It follows that

$$y = c_0(1 - x^2 + 13x^4/72 + \cdots) + c_1(x - x^3/3 + x^5/24 + \cdots).$$

SECTION 8.3

REGULAR SINGULAR POINTS

1. Upon division of the given differential equation by x we see that $P(x) = 1 - x^2$ and $Q(x) = (\sin x)/x$. Because both are analytic at $x = 0$ (in particular, $(\sin x)/x \to 1$ as $x \to 0$) it follows that $x = 0$ is an ordinary point.

2. Division of the differential equation by x yields

$$y'' + xy' + (1/x)(e^x - 1)y = 0.$$

Because the function

$$(1/x)(e^x - 1) = (1/x)(x + x^2/2! + x^3/3! + \cdots) = 1 + x/2! + x^2/3! + \cdots$$

is analytic at the origin, we see that $x = 0$ is an ordinary point.

3. When we rewrite the given equation in the standard form of Equation (3) in this section, we see that $p(x) = (\cos x)/x$ and $q(x) = x$. Because $(\cos x)/x \to \infty$ as $x \to 0$ it follows that $p(x)$ is not analytic, so $x = 0$ is an irregular singular point.

4. When we rewrite the given equation in the standard form of Equation (3), we have $p(x) = 2/3$ and $q(x) = (1 - x^2)/3x$. Since $q(x)$ is not analytic at the origin, $x = 0$ is an irregular singular point.

5. In the standard form of Equation (3) we have $p(x) = 2/(1 + x)$ and $q(x) = 3x^2/(1 + x)$. Both are analytic, so $x = 0$ is a regular singular point. The indicial equation is

$$r(r - 1) + 2r = r^2 + r = r(r + 1) = 0,$$

so the exponents are $r_1 = 0$ and $r_2 = -1$.

6. In the standard form of Equation (3) we have $p(x) = 2/(1 - x^2)$ and $q(x) = -2/(1 - x^2)$, so $x = 0$ is a regular singular point with $p_0 = 2$ and $q_0 = -2$. The indicial equation is $r^2 + r - 2 = 0$, so the exponents are $r = -2, 1$.

7. In the standard form of Equation (3) we have $p(x) = (6 \sin x)/x$ and $q(x) = 6$, so $x = 0$ is a regular singular point with $p_0 = q_0 = 6$. The indicial equation is $r^2 + 5r + 6 = 0$, so the exponents are $r_1 = -2$ and $r_2 = -3$.

8. In the standard form of Equation (3) we have $p(x) = 21/(6 + 2x)$ and $q(x) = 9(x^2 - 1)/(6 + 2x)$, so $x = 0$ is a regular singular point with $p_0 = 7/2$ and $q_0 = -3/2$. The indicial equation simplifies to $2r^2 + 5r - 3 = 0$, so the exponents are $r = -3, 1/2$.

9. The only singular point of the given equation is $x = 1$. Upon substituting $t = x - 1$, $x = t + 1$ we get the transformed equation

$$-ty'' + (t + 1)y' + (t + 1)^2 y = 0$$

where primes now denote differentiation with respect to t. In the standard form of Equation (3) we have $p(t) = -1 - t$ and $q(t) = -t(1 + t)^2$. Both these functions are analytic, so it follows that $x = 1$ is a regular singular point of the original equation.

10. Regular singular point $x = 1$

11. Regular singular points $x = +1$ and $x = -1$

12. Irregular singular point $x = 2$

13. The singular points of the given equation are $x = +2$ and $x = -2$.

$x = +2$: The substitution $t = x - 2$, $x = t + 2$ yields the transformed equation

$$t(t + 4)y'' + ty' + (t + 4)y = 0.$$

In the standard form of Equation (3) we have $p(t) = t/(4 + t)$ and $q(t) = t$. Both are analytic at $t = 0$, so $x = +2$ is a regular singular point of the original equation.

$x = -2$: The substitution $t = x + 2$, $x = t - 2$ yields the transformed equation

$$t(t - 4)y'' + (t - 4)y' + ty = 0.$$

Now $p(t) = 1$ and $q(t) = t^2/(t - 4)$. Both are analytic at $t = 0$, so $x = -2$ is also a regular singular point of the original equation.

14. Irregular singular points $x = -3, 3$

15. Regular singular point $x = 2$

16. Irregular singular point $x = 0$ and regular singular point $x = 1$

Instead of deriving in detail the solutions given below for the differential equations in Problems 17–31, we indicate here where some of these equations and solutions came from. Each of the differential equations in Problems 17–20 is of the form

$$Axy'' + By' + Cy = 0$$

with indicial equation $Ar^2 + (B - A)r = 0$. Substitution of $y = \sum c_n x^{n+r}$ into the differential equation yields the recurrence relation

$$c_n = -Cc_{n-1} / [A(n + r)^2 + (B - A)(n + r)]$$

for $n \geq 1$. In these problems the exponents $r_1 = 0$ and $r_2 = (A - B)/A$ do *not* differ by an integer, so this recurrence relation yields two linearly independent Frobenius series solutions when we apply it separately with $r = r_1$ and with $r = r_2$.

The differential equations in Problems 21–24, 27–29, and 31 are all of the form

$$Ax^2y'' + Bxy' + (C + Dx^2)y = 0$$

with indical equation

$$\phi(r) = Ar^2 + (B - A)r + C = 0.$$

Substitution of $y = \sum c_n x^{n+r}$ into the differential equation yields

$$\phi(r)c_0 x^r + \phi(r + 1)c_1 x^{r+1} + \sum [\phi(n + r)c_n + Dc_{n-2}]x^{n+r} = 0. \qquad (*)$$

In each of Problems 21–24 the exponents r_1 and r_2 do *not* differ by an integer. Hence when we substitute either $r = r_1$ or $r = r_2$ into Equation (*) above, we find that c_0 is arbitrary, that $c_1 = 0$, and that

$$c_n = -Dc_{n-2} / [A(n+r)^2 + (B - A)(n + r) + C]$$

for $n \geq 2$. Thus this recurrence formula yields two linearly independent Frobenius series solutions when we apply it separately with $r = r_1$ and with $r = r_2$.

In Problems 27–29 and 31, by contrast, the exponents r_1 and $r_2 = r_1 - 1$ *do* differ by an integer. Hence when we substitute the smaller exponent $r = r_2$ into Equation (*), we find that c_0 and c_1 are *both* arbitrary, and that c_n is given (for $n \geq 2$) by the recurrence relation above. Thus the smaller exponent yields two linearly independent Frobenius series solutions.

17. $\quad y_1 = \cos\sqrt{x}, \quad y_2 = \sin\sqrt{x}$

18. $\quad y_1 = \sum_{n=0}^{\infty} \frac{x^n}{n!(2n+1)!!}, \quad y_2 = x^{-1/2} \sum_{n=0}^{\infty} \frac{x^n}{n!(2n-1)!!}$

19. $\quad y_1 = x^{3/2}\left[1 + 3\sum_{n=1}^{\infty} \frac{x^n}{n!(2n+3)!!}\right], \quad y_2 = 1 - x - \sum_{n=2}^{\infty} \frac{x^n}{n!(2n-3)!!}$

20. $\quad y_1 = x^{1/3} \sum_{n=0}^{\infty} \frac{(-1)^n 2^n x^n}{n! \cdot 4 \cdot 7 \cdots (3n+1)}, \quad y_2 = \sum_{n=0}^{\infty} \frac{(-1)^n 2^n x^n}{n! \cdot 2 \cdot 5 \cdots (3n-1)}$

21. $\quad y_1 = x\left[1 + \sum_{n=1}^{\infty} \frac{x^{2n}}{n! \cdot 7 \cdot 11 \cdots (4n+3)}\right], \quad y_2 = x^{-1/2} \sum_{n=0}^{\infty} \frac{x^{2n}}{n! \cdot 1 \cdot 5 \cdots (4n+1)}$

22. $\quad y_1 = x^{3/2}\left[1 + \sum_{n=1}^{\infty} \frac{(-1)^n x^{2n}}{n! \cdot 9 \cdot 13 \cdots (4n+5)}\right], \quad y_2 = x^{-1}\left[1 + \sum_{n=1}^{\infty} \frac{(-1)^{n-1} x^{2n}}{n! \cdot 3 \cdot 7 \cdots (4n-1)}\right]$

23. $\quad y_1 = x^{1/2}\left[1 + \sum_{n=1}^{\infty} \frac{x^{2n}}{2^n n! \cdot 19 \cdot 31 \cdots (12n+7)}\right]$

$\qquad y_2 = x^{-2/3}\left[1 + \sum_{n=1}^{\infty} \frac{x^{2n}}{2^n n! \cdot 5 \cdot 17 \cdots (12n-7)}\right]$

24. $\quad y_1 = x^{1/3}\left[1 + \sum_{n=1}^{\infty} \frac{(-1)^n x^{2n}}{2^n n! \cdot 7 \cdot 13 \cdots (6n+1)}\right], \quad y_2 = 1 + \sum_{n=1}^{\infty} \frac{(-1)^n x^{2n}}{2^n n! \cdot 5 \cdot 11 \cdots (6n-1)}$

25. $\quad y_1 = x^{1/2} \sum_{n=0}^{\infty} \frac{(-1)^n x^n}{n! 2^n} = x^{1/2} e^{-x/2}, \quad y_2 = 1 + \sum_{n=1}^{\infty} \frac{(-1)^n x^n}{(2n-1)!!}$

26. $y_1 = x^{1/2} \sum\limits_{n=0}^{\infty} \dfrac{x^{2n}}{n!2^n} = x^{1/2}e^{-x^2/2}, \quad y_2 = 1 + \sum\limits_{n=1}^{\infty} \dfrac{2^n x^{2n}}{3 \cdot 7 \cdots (4n-1)}$

27. $y_1 = (\cos 3x)/x, \quad y_2 = (\sin 3x)/x$

28. $y_1 = (\cosh 2x)/x, \quad y_2 = (\sinh 2x)/x$
$\cdot$

29. $y_1 = (1/x)\cos(x/2), \quad y_2 = (1/x)\sin(x/2)$

30. $y_1 = \cos x^2, \quad y_2 = \sin x^2$

31. $y_1 = x^{1/2}\cosh x, \quad y_2 = x^{1/2}\sinh x$

32. Exponents $r_1 = 1$ and $r_2 = -1/2$

$c_n = -(n - r - 3)c_{n-1}/[2(n + r)^2 - (n + r) - 1]$

$y_1 = x + 3x^2/5 + 3x^3/35 + x^4/315 \quad$ (terminates)

$y_2 = x^{-1/2}(1 - 3x/2 - 3x^2/8 + x^3/48 + \cdots)$

33. $y_1 = x^{-1}(1 + 10x + 5x^2 + 10x^3/9 + \cdots)$

$y_2 = x^{1/2}(1 + 11x/20 - 11x^2/224 + 671x^3/24192 + \cdots)$

34. Exponents $r_1 = 1$ and $r_2 = -1/2$

$y_1 = x(1 - x^2/42 + x^4/1320 + \cdots)$

$y_2 = x^{-1/2}(1 - 7x^2/24 + 19x^4/3200 + \cdots)$

36. **(a)** When we substitute $y = \Sigma c_n x^{n+r}$ we find that $r = 0$ is the only possible value.

(b) Now we find that $r = -B/A$ is the only possible value.

(c) When we substitute $y = \Sigma c_n x^{n+r}$ with $c_0 \neq 0$ the term involving x^r is $Bc_0 x^r$, which cannot vanish.

38. Bessel's equation of order 1/2 is of the same form as the equations in Problems 27–29 and 31 discussed above, with $r_1 = 1/2$ and $r_2 = -1/2$ differing by 1. Hence the smaller exponent $r_2 = -1/2$ yields two linearly independent Frobenius series solutions.

SECTION 8.4

METHOD OF FROBENIUS — THE EXCEPTIONAL CASES

Each of the differential equations in Problems 1–6 is of the form

$$xy'' + (A + Bx)y' + Cy = 0.$$

The origin is a regular singular point with exponents $r = 0$ and $r = 1 - A$, so if A is an integer then we have an exceptional case of the method of Frobenius. When we substitute $y = \Sigma c_n x^{n+r}$ in the differential equation we find that the coefficient of x^{n+r} is

$$[(n + r)^2 + (A - 1)(n + r)]c_n + [B(n + r) + C - B]c_{n-1} = 0. \qquad (*)$$

Case 1: In each of Problems 1–4 we have $A \geq 2$ and $B = C$, so the larger exponent $r_1 = 0$ and the smaller exponent $r_2 = 1 - A = -N$ differ by a positive integer. When we substitute the smaller exponent $r = -N$ in Equation (*) above, it simplifies to

$$n(n - N)c_n + B(n - N)c_{n-1} = 0. \qquad (1)$$

This equation determines $c_1, c_2, \cdots, c_{N-1}$ in terms of c_0, thereby yielding the solution

$$y_1 = x^{-N}(c_0 + c_1 x + \cdots + c_{N-1}x^{n-1}).$$

When $n = N$ Equation (1) reduces to

$$0 \cdot c_n + 0 \cdot c_{N-1} = 0,$$

so c_n may be chosen arbitrarily. For $n > N$, Equation (1) yields the recurrence formula $c_n = -Bc_{n-1}/n$, and the second solution is of the form

$$y_2 = c_n + c_{n+1}x + c_{n+2}x^2 + \cdots$$

Case 2: If $A \leq 0$ then the larger exponent $r_1 = 1 - A = N$ and the smaller exponent $r_2 = 0$ again differ by a positive integer. In Problems 5 and 6 we have this case with $B = -1$. When we substitute the smaller exponent $r = 0$ in Equation (*), it simplifies to

$$n(n - N)c_n - (n - C - 1)c_{n-1} = 0. \qquad (2)$$

This equation determines $c_1, c_2, \cdots, c_{N-1}$ in terms of c_0. When $n = N$ it reduces to

$$0 \cdot c_N - (N - C - 1)c_{N-1} = 0. \qquad (3)$$

If either $N - C - 1 = 0$ or $c_{N-1} = 0$ (the latter happens in Problem 5) then c_N can be chosen arbitrarily, and finally $c_{N+1}, c_{N+2}, \cdots$ are determined in terms of c_N. Thus we get *two* Frobenius series solutions

$$y_1 = c_0 + c_1 x + \cdots + c_{N-1}x^{N-1}, \qquad \text{(terminating)}$$
$$y_2 = c_N x^N + c_{N+1}x^{N+1} + \cdots . \qquad \text{(not terminating)}$$

On the other hand, if (as in Problem 6) neither $N - C - 1 = 0$ nor $c_{N-1} = 0$, then c_N cannot be chosen so as to satisfy Equation (3), and hence there is no Frobenius series solution corresponding to the smaller exponent $r_2 = 0$. We therefore find the *single* Frobenius series solution by substituting the larger exponent $r_1 = N$ in Equation (*) and using the resulting recurrence relation to determine $c_1, c_2, c_3, \cdots$ in terms of c_0.

1. $y_1 = x^{-2}(1+x), \quad y_2 = 1 + 2\sum_{n=1}^{\infty} \dfrac{x^n}{(n+2)!}$

2. $y_1 = x^{-4}\left(1 + x + \dfrac{1}{2}x^2 + \dfrac{1}{6}x^3\right), \quad y_2 = 1 + 24\sum_{n=1}^{\infty} \dfrac{x^n}{(n+4)!}$

3. $y_1 = x^{-4}\left(1 - 3x + \dfrac{9}{2}x^2 - \dfrac{9}{2}x^3\right), \quad y_2 = 1 + 24\sum_{n=1}^{\infty} \dfrac{(-1)^n 3^n x^n}{(n+4)!}$

4. $y_1 = x^{-5}\left(1 - \dfrac{3}{5}x + \dfrac{9}{50}x^2 - \dfrac{9}{250}x^3 + \dfrac{27}{1000}x^4\right), \quad y_2 = 1 + 120\sum_{n=1}^{\infty} \dfrac{(-1)^n 3^n x^n}{(n+5)!\,5^n}$

5. $y_1 = 1 + \dfrac{3}{4}x + \dfrac{1}{4}x^2 + \dfrac{1}{24}x^3, \quad y_2 = x^5\left[1 + 120\sum_{n=1}^{\infty} \dfrac{(n+1)x^n}{(n+5)!}\right]$

6.   Here $A = -3$, $B = -1$, $C = 1/2$, $r_1 = N = 4$, and $r_2 = 0$, so Equation (2) above is

$$n(n - 4)c_n - (n - 3/2)c_{n-1} = 0.$$

Starting with $c_0 = 1$, this equation gives $c_1 = 1/6$, $c_2 = 1/48$, $c_3 = 1/96$. With $n = 4$ it reduces to

$$0 \cdot c_4 - (7/2)(1/96) = 0,$$

so c_4 cannot be chosen. We therefore start over by substituting $r_1 = 4$ in Equation (*) above and get the recurrence relation

$$c_n = (2n + 5)c_{n-1} / 2n(n + 4)$$

for $n \geq 1$. This yields the single Frobenius series solution

$$y_1 = x^4[1 + (8/5)\Sigma (2n + 5)!!x^n / 2^n n!(n + 4)!].$$

7. $y_1 = x^{-2}(2 - 6x + 9x^2); \quad y_2 = \Sigma(-1)^{n-1}3^n x^n/(n + 2)!$

8.   The exponents are $r = 0, 4$. When we substitute $y = \Sigma c_n x^n$ (corresponding to $r = 0$) in the differential equation we get

$$(n-4)c_n - (n-3)c_{n-1} = 0$$

for $n \geq 1$. Starting with $c_0 = 1$, we compute $c_1 = 2/3$, $c_2 = 1/3$, and $c_3 = 0$. Hence

$$y_1 = 3 + 2x + x^2$$

is one solution. Because $c_3 = 0$ we can choose $c_4 = 1$. Then our recurrence formula above yields $c_5 = 2$, $c_6 = 3$, $c_7 = 4$, $\cdots$. Hence the second solution is

$$y_2 = x^4(1 + 2x + 3x^2 + 4x^3 + \cdots) = x^4/(1-x)^2,$$

with the closed form coming from the derivative of the geometric series $1/(1-x) = \Sigma x^n$.

9. $\quad y_1 = 1 + x^2/2^2 + x^4/2^2 4^2 + x^6/2^2 4^2 6^2 + \cdots;$

$\quad y_2 = y_1(\ln x - x^2/4 + 5x^4/128 - 23x^6/3456 + \cdots)$

10. $\quad y_1 = x\left(1 - \dfrac{x^2}{2^2} + \dfrac{x^4}{2^2 4^2} - \dfrac{x^6}{2^2 4^2 6^2} + \cdots\right)$

$\quad y_2 = y_1 \displaystyle\int x \cdot x^{-2}\left(1 - \dfrac{x^2}{4} + \dfrac{x^4}{64} - \dfrac{x^6}{2304} + \cdots\right)^{-2} dx$

$\quad = y_1 \displaystyle\int x^{-1}\left(1 - \dfrac{x^2}{2} + \dfrac{3x^4}{32} - \dfrac{5x^6}{576} + \cdots\right)^{-1} dx$

$\quad = y_1 \displaystyle\int x^{-1}\left(1 + \dfrac{x^2}{2} + \dfrac{5x^4}{32} + \dfrac{23x^6}{576} + \cdots\right) dx$

$\quad y_2 = y_1\left(\ln x + \dfrac{x^2}{4} + \dfrac{5x^4}{128} + \dfrac{23x^6}{3456} + \cdots\right)$

11. $\quad y_1 = x^2[1 - 2x + (3/2)x^2 - (2/3)x^3 + \cdots]$

$\quad y_2 = y_1[\ln x + 3x + (11/4)x^2 + (49/18)x^3 + \cdots]$

12. $\quad y_1 = x^2\left(1 - \dfrac{x}{2} + \dfrac{3x^2}{20} - \dfrac{x^3}{30} + \dfrac{x^4}{168} - \cdots\right)$

$\quad y_2 = y_1 \displaystyle\int e^{-x} x^{-4}\left(1 - \dfrac{x}{2} + \dfrac{3x^2}{20} - \dfrac{x^3}{30} + \dfrac{x^4}{168} - \cdots\right)^{-2} dx$

$\quad = y_1 \displaystyle\int x^{-4} e^{-x}\left(1 - x + \dfrac{11x^2}{20} - \dfrac{13x^3}{60} + \dfrac{569x^4}{8400} - \cdots\right)^{-1} dx$

$$= y_1 \int x^{-4} \left(1 - \frac{x^2}{20} + \frac{3x^4}{100} + \cdots \right) dx$$

$$= y_1 \left(-\frac{1}{3x^3} + \frac{1}{20x} + \frac{3x}{100} + \cdots \right) \qquad \text{(no logarithmic term)}$$

13. $y_1 = x^3 [1 - 2x + 2x^2 - (4/3)x^3 + \cdots]$
   $y_2 = y_1 [2 \ln x - 1/(2x^2) - 2/x + (4/3)x + \cdots]$

14. $y_1 = x^2 \left(1 - \frac{2x}{5} + \frac{x^2}{10} - \frac{2x^3}{105} + \frac{x^4}{336} - \cdots \right)$

   $y_2 = y_1 \int x^{-1} e^{-x} (y_1)^{-2} \, dx$

$$= y_1 \int \left(x^{-5} - \frac{x^{-4}}{5} - \frac{x^{-3}}{50} + \frac{13x^{-2}}{1750} + 0 \cdot x^{-1} + \cdots \right) dx$$

   $y_2 = y_1 \left(-\frac{x^{-4}}{4} + \frac{x^{-3}}{15} + \frac{x^{-2}}{100} - \frac{13x^{-1}}{1750} + 0 \cdot \ln x + \cdots \right)$

Thus y_2 contains no logarithmic term.

16. $y_1 = x^{3/2} \left[1 + \sum_{n=1}^{\infty} \frac{(-1)^n x^{2n}}{2^n n! \cdot 5 \cdot 7 \cdots (2n+3)} \right], \quad y_2 = x^{-3/2} \left[1 + \sum_{n=1}^{\infty} \frac{(-1)^n x^{2n}}{2^n n! \cdot (-1) \cdot 1 \cdot 3 \cdots (2n-3)} \right]$

18. When we substitute

$$y(x) = C \, y_1 \ln x + \Sigma \, b_n x^n$$

in the differential equation $xy'' - x = 0$ we find that $b_1 = -b_0 = -C$ and that

$$n(n+1)b_{n+1} - b_n = -\frac{(2n+1)C}{n!(n+1)!}$$

for $n \geq 1$. To solve this recurrence relation we take $C = 1$ and substitute $b_n = c_n / (n-1)!n!$. The result is

$$c_{n+1} - c_n = -\frac{2n+1}{n(n+1)} = -\frac{1}{n} - \frac{1}{n+1}.$$

Starting with $c_1 = b_1 = -1$, it follows readily by induction on n that
$c_n = -(H_n + H_{n+1})$.

SECTION 8.5

BESSEL'S EQUATION

Of course Bessel's equation is the most important special ordinary differential equation in mathematics, and every student should be exposed at least to Bessel functions of the first kind. Though Bessel functions of integral order can be treated without the gamma function, the subsection on the gamma function is also needed for Chapter 7 on Laplace transforms. The final subsections on Bessel function identities and the parametric Bessel equation will not be needed until Section 10.4, and therefore may be considered optional at this point in the course.

2. **(a)**

$$\Gamma([2n+1]/2) = ([2n-1]/2)\,\Gamma([2n-1]/2)$$

$$= ([2n-1]/2)\cdot([2n-3]/2)\,\Gamma([2n-3]/2)$$

$$= \cdots$$

$$= 2^{-n}(2n-1)(2n-3)\cdots(3)(1)\,\Gamma(1/2)$$

$$\Gamma([2n+1]/2) = 2^{-n}(1)(3)\cdots(2n-1)\sqrt{\pi}$$

(b)

$$J_{1/2}(x) = \sum_{m=0}^{\infty}\frac{(-1)^m\,x^{2m+\frac{1}{2}}}{m!\,\Gamma(m+\frac{3}{2})\,2^{2m+\frac{1}{2}}} = \sqrt{\frac{2}{x}}\sum_{m=0}^{\infty}\frac{(-1)^m\,x^{2m+1}}{m!\,2^{-m-1}(2m+1)!!\,\sqrt{\pi}\,2^{2m+1}}$$

$$= \sqrt{\frac{2}{\pi x}}\sum_{m=0}^{\infty}\frac{(-1)^m\,x^{2m+1}}{(2\cdot4\cdots2m)(1\cdot3\cdots(2m+1))}$$

$$= \sqrt{\frac{2}{\pi x}}\sum_{m=0}^{\infty}\frac{(-1)^m\,x^{2m+1}}{(2m+1)!}$$

$$J_{1/2}(x) = \sqrt{\frac{2}{\pi x}}\sin x$$

4. With $p = 1/2$ in Equation (26) in the text we have

$$J_{3/2}(x) = (1/x)J_{1/2}(x) - J_{-1/2}(x)$$

$$= (1/x)\sqrt{(2/\pi x)}\sin x - \sqrt{(2/\pi x)}\cos x$$

$$J_{3/2}(x) = \sqrt{(2/\pi x^3)}(\sin x - x\cos x)$$

5. Starting with $p = 3$ in Equation (26) we get

$$J_4(x) = (6/x)J_3(x) - J_2(x)$$

$$= (6/x)[(4/x)J_2(x) - J_1(x)] - J_2(x)$$

$$= (24/x^2 - 1)[(2/x)J_1(x) - J_0(x)] - (6/x)J_1(x)$$

$$J_4(x) = (1/x^2)(x^2 - 24)J_0(x) + (8/x^3)(6 - x^2)J_1(x)$$

8. When we carry out the differentiations indicated in Equations (22) and (23) in the text, we get

$$p\,x^{p-1}J_p(x) + x^p J_p'(x) = x^p J_{p-1}(x),$$

$$-p\,x^{-p-1}J_p(x) + x^{-p}J_p'(x) = -x^{-p}J_{p+1}(x).$$

When we solve these two equations for $J_p'(x)$ we get Equations (24) and (25) in the text.

10. When we add equations (24) and (25) we get

$$J_p'(x) = (1/2)[J_{p-1}(x) - J_{p+1}(x)],$$

so

$$J_p''(x) = (1/2)[J_{p-1}'(x) - J_{p+1}'(x)].$$

Replacing p with $p-1$ and with $p+1$ in the first equation, we get

$$J_{p-1}'(x) = (1/2)[J_{p-2}(x) - J_p(x)]$$

and

$$J_{p+1}'(x) = (1/2)[J_p(x) - J_{p+2}(x)].$$

When we use these equations to substitute for $J_{p-1}'(x)$ and $J_{p+1}(x)$ in the equation for $J_p''(x)$ above, we find that

$$J_p''(x) = (1/4)[J_{p-2}(x) - 2\,J_p(x) + J_{p+2}(x)].$$

11. $\Gamma(p+m+1) = (p+m)(p+m-1)\cdots(p+2)(p+1)\Gamma(p+1)$

12. Substitution of the power series of Problem 11 yields

$$y(x) = x^2 \cdot \frac{x^{5/2}(A+\cdots) + x^{-5/2}(B+\cdots)}{x^{1/2}(C+\cdots) + x^{-1/2}(D+\cdots)} = \frac{x^5(A+\cdots) + (B+\cdots)}{x(C+\cdots) + (D+\cdots)}$$

where $A = 1/2^{5/2}\Gamma(7/2)$, $B = 1/2^{-5/2}\Gamma(-3/2)$, $C = 1/2^{1/2}\Gamma(3/2)$, and $D = 1/2^{-1/2}\Gamma(1/2)$. Hence

$$y(0) = B/D = [2^{5/2}\Gamma(1/2)]/[2^{1/2}\Gamma(-3/2)] = [2^2\Gamma(1/2)]/[(4/3)\Gamma(1/2)] = 3.$$

We will not include here detailed solutions for Problems 13–21. The solution of Problem 18 is fairly typical.

13. $x^2 J_1(x) + xJ_0(x) - \int J_0(x)\,dx + C$

14. $(x^3 - 4x)J_1(x) + 2x^2 J_0(x) + C$

15. $(x^4 - 9x^2)J_1(x) + (3x^3 - 9x)J_0(x) + 9\int J_0(x)\,dx + C$

16. $-xJ_0(x) + \int J_0(x)\,dx + C$

17. $2xJ_1(x) - x^2 J_0(x) + C$

18. First we integrate by parts with

$$
\begin{array}{ll}
u = x^3 & dv = J_1(x)\,dx \\
du = 3x^2 dx & v = -J_0(x)
\end{array}
$$

using the result of Example 1 in the text. This yields

$$\int x^3 J_1(x)\,dx = -x^3 J_0(x) + 3\int x^2 J_0(x)\,dx.$$

Next we integrate by parts with

$$
\begin{array}{ll}
u = x & dv = xJ_0(x)\,dx \\
du = dx & v = xJ_1(x)
\end{array}
$$

and get

$$\int x^3 J_1(x)\,dx = -x^3 J_0(x) + 3x^2 J_1(X) - 3\int xJ_1(x)\,dx.$$

Finally we integrate by parts with

$$
\begin{array}{ll}
u = x & dv = J_1(x)\,dx \\
du = dx & v = -J_0(x)
\end{array}
$$

and get

$$\int x^3 J_1(x)\,dx = -x^3 J_0(x) + 3x^2 J_1(x) + 3xJ_0(x) - 3\int J_0(x)\,dx.$$

19. $(4x^3 - 16x)J_1(x) + (8x^2 - x^4)J_0(x) + C$

20. $-2J_1(x) + \int J_0(x)\,dx$

21. $J_0(x) - (4/x)J_1(x) + C$

22. Let us define

$$g(x) = \int_0^\pi \cos(x\sin\theta)\,d\theta$$

and note first that

$$g(0) = \int_0^\pi \cos(0)\,d\theta = \pi = \pi J_0(0).$$

Differentiation under the integral sign yields

$$g'(x) = -\int_0^\pi \sin(x\sin\theta)\sin\theta\,d\theta.$$

When we integrate by parts with

$$u = \sin(x\sin\theta) \qquad dv = \sin\theta\,d\theta$$
$$du = (x\cos\theta)\cos(x\sin\theta)\,d\theta \qquad v = -\cos\theta$$

we get

$$g'(x) = -x\int_0^\pi \cos^2\theta\,\cos(x\sin\theta)\,d\theta.$$

But differentiation of the first equation for $g'(x)$ yields

$$g''(x) = -\int_0^\pi \sin^2\theta\cos(x\sin\theta)\,d\theta.$$

Finally, because $\cos^2\theta + \sin^2\theta = 1$, it follows that

$$g''(x)+\frac{1}{x}g'(x) = -\int_0^\pi \cos(x\sin\theta)\,d\theta = -g(x).$$

Thus $y = g(x)$ satisfies Bessel's equation of order zero in the form $y'' + (1/x)y' + y = 0$. Therefore the function g takes the form

$$g(x) = a\,J_0(x) + b\,Y_0(x).$$

Since $g(0) = \pi$ is finite and $J_0(0) = 1$, we must have $a = \pi$ and $b = 0$, so $g(x) = \pi\,J_0(x)$, as desired.

23.   This is a special case of the discussion below in Problem 24.

24.   Given an integer $n \geq 1$, let us define

$$g_n(x) = \int_0^\pi \cos(n\theta - x\sin\theta)\,d\theta.$$

Differentiation yields

$$g_n'(x) = \int_0^\pi \sin(n\theta - x\sin\theta)\sin\theta\,d\theta.$$

Integration by parts with $u = \sin(n\theta - x\sin\theta)$ and $dv = \sin\theta\,d\theta$ yields

$$g_n'(x) = n\int_0^\pi \cos\theta\,\cos(n\theta - x\sin\theta)\,d\theta - x\int_0^\pi \cos^2\theta\,\cos(n\theta - x\sin\theta)\,d\theta.$$

But differentiation of the first equation for $g_n'(x)$ yields

$$g_n''(x) = -\int_0^\pi \sin^2\theta \, \cos(n\theta - x\sin\theta) \, d\theta.$$

It follows that

$$g_n''(x) + \frac{1}{x}g_n'(x) = -g_n(x) + \frac{n}{x}\int_0^\pi \cos\theta \, \cos(n\theta - x\sin\theta) \, d\theta$$

$$= -g_n(x) - \frac{n}{x^2}\int_0^\pi \left[(n - x\cos\theta) - n\right]\cos(n\theta - x\sin\theta) \, d\theta$$

$$= -g_n(x) - \frac{n}{x^2}\left[\sin(n\theta - x\sin\theta)\right]_0^\pi + \frac{n^2}{x^2}g_n(x) = -\left(1 - \frac{n^2}{x^2}\right)g_n(x).$$

Upon equating the first and last members of this continued inequality and multiplying by x^2, we see that $y = g_n(x)$ satisfies Bessel's equation of order $n \geq 1$. The initial values of $g_n(x)$ are

$$g_n(0) = \int_0^\pi \cos(n\theta) \, d\theta = 0 \quad \text{and} \quad g_n'(0) = \int_0^\pi \sin(\theta)\sin(n\theta) \, d\theta = 0.$$

If $n = 1$ then $g_1'(0) = \pi/2$, whereas $g_n'(0) = 0$ if $n \geq 1$. In either case the values of $g_n(0)$ and $g_n'(0)$ are π times those of $J_n(0)$ and $J_n'(0)$, respectively. Now we know from the general solution of Bessel's equation that $g_n(x) = c \, J_n(x)$ for some constant c. If $n = 1$ than the fact that

$$\pi/2 = g_n'(0) = c \, J_1'(0) = c/2$$

implies that $c = \pi$, as desired. But if $n > 1$ the fact that

$$0 = g_n'(0) = c \, J_n'(0) = c \cdot 0$$

does not suffice to determine c.

SECTION 8.6

APPLICATIONS OF BESSEL FUNCTIONS

Problems 1–12 are routine applications of the theorem in this section. In each case it is necessary only to identify the coefficients A, B, C and the exponent q in Equation (3) of this section in the text. Then we can calculate the values of α, β, k, p using the formulas in (5), and finally write the general solution specified in Equation (6).

1. $\quad y = x[c_1J_0(x) + c_2Y_0(x)]$

2. $\quad y = x^{-1}[c_1J_1(x) + c_2Y_1(x)]$

3. $\quad y = x[c_1J_{1/2}(3x^2) + c_2J_{-1/2}(3x^2)]$

4. $\quad y = x^3[c_1J_2(2x^{1/2}) + c_2Y_2(2x^{1/2})]$

5. $\quad y = x^{-1/3}[c_1 J_{1/3}(x^{3/2}/3) + c_2 J_{-1/3}(x^{3/2}/3)]$

6. $\quad y = x^{-1/4}[c_1 J_0(2x^{3/2}) + c_2 Y_0(2x^{3/2})]$

7. $\quad y = x^{-1}[c_1 J_0(x) + c_2 Y_0(x)]$ $\qquad$ **8.** $\quad y = x^2[c_1 J_1(4x^{1/2}) + c_2 Y_1(4x^{1/2})]$

9. $\quad y = x^{1/2}[c_1 J_{1/2}(2x^{3/2}) + c_2 J_{-1/2}(2x^{3/2})]$

10. $\quad y = x^{-1/4}[c_1 J_{3/2}(2x^{5/2}/5) + c_2 J_{-3/2}(2x^{5/2}/5)]$

11. $\quad y = x^{1/2}[c_1 J_{1/6}(x^3/3) + c_2 J_{-1/6}(x^3/3)]$

12. $\quad y = x^{1/2}[c_1 J_{1/5}(4x^{5/2}/5) + c_2 J_{-1/5}(4x^{5/2}/5)]$

13. $\quad$ We want to solve the equation $xy'' + 2y' + xy = 0$. If we rewrite it as

$$x^2 y'' + 2xy' + x^2 y = 0$$

then we have the form in Equation (3) with $A = 2$, $B = 0$, $C = 1$, and $q = 2$. Then Equation (5) gives $\alpha = -1/2$, $\beta = 1$, $k = 1$, and $p = 1/2$, so by Equation (6) the general solution is

$$y = x^{-1/2}[c_1 J_{1/2}(x) + c_2 J_{-1/2}(x)]$$
$$= x^{-1/2}(2/\pi x)^{1/2}[c_1 \cos x + c_2 \sin x]$$
$$y = x^{-1}(A \cos x + B \sin x),$$

using Equations (19) in Section 3.5.

15. $\quad$ The substitution

$$y = -u'/u, \quad y' = (u')^2/u^2 - u''/u$$

immediately transforms $y' = x^2 + y^2$ to $u'' + x^2 u = 0$. The equation

$$x^2 u'' + x^4 u = 0$$

is of the form in (3) with $A = B = 0$, $C = 1$, and $q = 4$. Equations (5) give $\alpha = 1/2$, $\beta = 2$, $k = 1/2$, and $p = 1/4$, so the general solution is

$$u = x^{1/2}[c_1 J_{1/4}(x^2/2) + c_2 J_{-1/4}(x^2/2)].$$

To compute u', let $z = x^2/2$ so $x = 2^{1/2} z^{1/2}$. Then Equation (22) in Section 8.5 with $p = 1/4$ yields

$$D_x[x^{1/2} J_{1/4}(x^2/2)] = D_z[2^{1/4} z^{1/4} J_{1/4}(z)] \cdot (dz/dx)$$

$$= 2^{1/4} z^{1/4} J_{-3/4}(x^2/2) \cdot x = x^{3/2} J_{-3/4}(x^2/2).$$

Similarly, Equation (23) in Section 8.5 with $p = -1/4$ yields

$$D_x[x^{1/2} J_{-1/4}(x^2/2)] = D_z[2^{1/4} z^{1/4} J_{-1/4}(z)] \cdot (dz/dx)$$
$$= -2^{1/4} z^{1/4} J_{3/4}(z) \cdot x = -x^{3/2} J_{3/4}(x^2/2).$$

Therefore

$$u' = x^{3/2}[c_1 J_{-3/4}(x^2/2) - c_2 J_{3/4}(x^2/2)].$$

It follows finally that the general solution of the Riccati equation $y' = x^2 + y^2$ is

$$y(x) = -\frac{u'}{u} = x \cdot \frac{J_{3/4}(\frac{1}{2}x^2) - c J_{-3/4}(\frac{1}{2}x^2)}{c J_{1/4}(\frac{1}{2}x^2) + J_{-1/4}(\frac{1}{2}x^2)}$$

where the arbitrary constant is $c = c_1/c_2$.

16. Substitution of the series expressions for the Bessel functions in the formula for $y(x)$ in Problem 15 yields

$$y(x) = x \cdot \frac{A(\frac{1}{2}x^2)^{3/4}(1 + \cdots) - c B(\frac{1}{2}x^2)^{-3/4}(1 + \cdots)}{c C(\frac{1}{2}x^2)^{1/4}(1 + \cdots) + D(\frac{1}{2}x^2)^{-1/4}(1 + \cdots)}$$

where each pair of parentheses encloses a power series in x with constant term 1, and

$$A = 2^{-3/4}/\Gamma(7/4) \qquad\qquad B = 2^{3/4}/\Gamma(1/4)$$
$$C = 2^{-1/4}/\Gamma(5/4) \qquad\qquad D = 2^{1/4}/\Gamma(3/4).$$

Multiplication of numerator and denominator by $x^{1/2}$ and a bit of simplification gives

$$y(x) = \frac{2^{-3/4} A x^3 (1 + \cdots) - 2^{3/4} c B(1 + \cdots)}{2^{-1/4} c C x(1 + \cdots) + 2^{1/4} D(1 + \cdots)}.$$

It now follows that

$$y(0) = -2^{1/2} cB/D$$
$$= -2^{1/2} c \cdot [2^{3/4}/\Gamma(1/4)]/[2^{1/4}/\Gamma(3/4)] = -2c \cdot \Gamma(3/4)/\Gamma(1/4). \qquad (*)$$

(a) If $y(0) = 0$ then (*) gives $c = 0$ in the general solution formula of Problem 15.

(b) If $y(0) = 1$ then (*) gives $c = -\Gamma(1/4)/2\Gamma(3/4)$. More generally, (*) yields the formula

$$y(x) = x \cdot \frac{2\Gamma(\frac{3}{4})J_{3/4}(\frac{1}{2}x^2) + y_0\, \Gamma(\frac{1}{4})J_{-3/4}(\frac{1}{2}x^2)}{2\Gamma(\frac{3}{4})J_{-1/4}(\frac{1}{2}x^2) - y_0\, \Gamma(\frac{1}{4})J_{1/4}(\frac{1}{2}x^2)}$$

for the solution of the initial value problem

$$y' = x^2 + y^2, \qquad y(0) = y_0.$$

17. If we write the equation $x^4 y'' + \gamma^2 y = 0$ in the form

$$x^2 y'' + \gamma^2 x^{-2} y = 0,$$

then we see that it is of the form in Equation (3) of this section with $A = B = 0$, $C = \gamma^2$, and $q = -2$. Then Equations (5) give $\alpha = 1/2$, $\beta = -1$, $k = \gamma$, and $p = -1/2$, so the theorem yields the general solution

$$y(x) = x^{1/2}[c_1 J_{1/2}(\gamma/x) + c_2 J_{-1/2}(\gamma/x)] = x[A\cos(\gamma/x) + B\sin(\gamma/x)],$$

using Equations (19) in Section 8.5 for $J_{1/2}(x)$ and $J_{-1/2}(x)$. With a and b both nonzero, the initial conditions $y(a) = y(b) = 0$ yield the equations

$$A\cos(\gamma/a) + B\sin(\gamma/a) = 0$$
$$A\cos(\gamma/b) + B\sin(\gamma/b) = 0.$$

These equations have a nontrivial solution for A and B only if the coefficient determinant

$$\Delta = \sin(\gamma/b)\cos(\gamma/a) - \sin(\gamma/a)\cos(\gamma/b)$$
$$= \sin(\gamma/b - \gamma/a) = \sin(\gamma L/ab)$$

is nonzero. Hence $\gamma L/ab$ must be an integral multiple $n\pi$ of π, and then the nth buckling force is

$$P_n = EI_0\gamma_n^2/b^4 = EI_0(n\pi ab/L)^2 b^4 = (n^2\pi^2 EI_0/L^2)(a/b)^2.$$

18. The substitution $L = a + bt$ in $L\theta'' + 2L'\theta' + g\theta = 0$ yields the transformed equation

$$L^2\theta''(L) + 2L\theta'(L) + (g/b^2)L\theta = 0$$

with independent variable L that is of the form in (3) with $A = 2$, $B = 0$, $q = 1$, and $C = g/b^2$. Hence

$$\alpha = -1/2, \quad \beta = 1/2, \quad k = 2g^{1/2}/b, \quad \text{and} \quad p = 1,$$

so

$$\theta(L) = L^{-1/2}[A\, J_1(2g^{1/2}L^{1/2}/b) + B\, Y_1(2g^{1/2}L^{1/2}/b)].$$

CHAPTER 9

FOURIER SERIES AND SEPARATION OF VARIABLES

SECTION 9.1

PERIODIC FUNCTIONS AND TRIGONOMETRIC SERIES

1. Smallest period $P = 2\pi/3$

2. Smallest period $P = 1$

3. Smallest period $P = 4\pi/3$

4. Smallest period $P = 6$

5. Smallest period $P = \pi$

6. Smallest period $P = 1/2$

7. Not periodic

8. Not periodic

9. Smallest period $P = \pi$

10. Smallest period $P = \pi/3$

11. With $f(t) = 1$ the integral formulas of Eqs. (16) and (17) in the text give $a_0 = 2$ and $a_n = b_n = 0$ for $n \geq 0$. Thus the Fourier series of f is the single term series $f(t) = 1$.

12. $-\dfrac{12}{\pi}\left[\dfrac{\sin t}{1} + \dfrac{\sin 3t}{3} + \dfrac{\sin 5t}{5} + \dfrac{\sin 7t}{7} + \cdots\right]$

13. $\dfrac{1}{2} + \dfrac{2}{\pi}\left[\dfrac{\sin t}{1} + \dfrac{\sin 3t}{3} + \dfrac{\sin 5t}{5} + \dfrac{\sin 7t}{7} + \cdots\right]$

14. $\dfrac{1}{2} - \dfrac{10}{\pi}\left[\dfrac{\sin t}{1} + \dfrac{\sin 3t}{3} + \dfrac{\sin 5t}{5} + \dfrac{\sin 7t}{7} + \cdots\right]$

15. $2\left[\dfrac{\sin t}{1} - \dfrac{\sin 2t}{2} + \dfrac{\sin 3t}{3} - \dfrac{\sin 4t}{4} + \cdots\right]$

16. $\pi - 2\left[\dfrac{\sin t}{1} + \dfrac{\sin 2t}{2} + \dfrac{\sin 3t}{3} + \dfrac{\sin 4t}{4} + \cdots\right]$

17. $\dfrac{\pi}{2} - \dfrac{4}{\pi}\left[\dfrac{\cos t}{1} + \dfrac{\cos 3t}{9} + \dfrac{\cos 5t}{25} + \dfrac{\cos 7t}{49} + \cdots\right]$

18. $\dfrac{\pi}{2} + \dfrac{4}{\pi}\left[\dfrac{\cos t}{1} + \dfrac{\cos 3t}{9} + \dfrac{\cos 5t}{25} + \dfrac{\cos 7t}{49} + \cdots\right]$

19. $\dfrac{\pi}{2} + \dfrac{2}{\pi}\left[\dfrac{\cos t}{1} + \dfrac{\cos 3t}{9} + \dfrac{\cos 5t}{25} + \dfrac{\cos 7t}{49} + \cdots\right] - \left[\dfrac{\sin t}{1} + \dfrac{\sin 2t}{2} + \dfrac{\sin 3t}{3} + \dfrac{\sin 4t}{4} + \cdots\right]$

20. $\dfrac{1}{2} + \dfrac{2}{\pi}\left[\dfrac{\cos t}{1} - \dfrac{\cos 3t}{3} + \dfrac{\cos 5t}{5} - \dfrac{\cos 7t}{7} + \cdots\right]$

21. $\dfrac{\pi^2}{3} - 4\left[\dfrac{\cos t}{1} - \dfrac{\cos 2t}{4} + \dfrac{\cos 3t}{9} - \dfrac{\cos 4t}{16} + \cdots\right]$

22. $\dfrac{4\pi^2}{3} + 4\left[\dfrac{\cos t}{1} + \dfrac{\cos 2t}{4} + \dfrac{\cos 3t}{9} + \dfrac{\cos 4t}{16} + \cdots\right] - 4\pi\left[\dfrac{\sin t}{1} + \dfrac{\sin 2t}{2} + \dfrac{\sin 3t}{3} + \dfrac{\sin 4t}{4} + \cdots\right]$

23. $\dfrac{\pi^2}{6} - 2\left[\dfrac{\cos t}{1} - \dfrac{\cos 2t}{4} + \dfrac{\cos 3t}{9} - \dfrac{\cos 4t}{16} + \cdots\right]$

$+ \pi\left[\dfrac{\sin t}{1} - \dfrac{\sin 2t}{2} + \dfrac{\sin 3t}{3} - \dfrac{\sin 4t}{4} + \cdots\right] - \dfrac{2}{\pi}\left[\dfrac{\sin t}{1} + \dfrac{\sin 3t}{27} + \dfrac{\sin 5t}{125} + \dfrac{\sin 7t}{343} + \cdots\right]$

The trigonometric identities

$$2\cos A \cos B = \cos(A+B) + \cos(A-B)$$
$$2\sin A \cos B = \sin(A+B) + \sin(A-B)$$
$$2\sin A \sin B = \cos(A-B) - \cos(A+B)$$

are needed to evaluate the integrals that appear in Problems 24–26.

24. $b_n = 0$ for $n = 1, 2, 3, \cdots$, $a_n = 0$ for n odd, and

$a_n = -4/\pi(n^2 - 1)$ if $n = 0, 2, 4, \cdots$; the series is

$$\dfrac{2}{\pi} - \dfrac{4}{\pi}\left[\dfrac{\cos 2t}{1} + \dfrac{\cos 4t}{15} + \dfrac{\cos 6t}{35} + \dfrac{\cos 8t}{63} + \cdots\right]$$

25. In order to evaluate the coefficient integrals in Eqs. (16) and (17) of the text we would need the trigonometric identity

$$\cos^2 2t = (1/2)(1 + \cos 4t)$$

which, however, tells us in advance that the coefficients in the Fourier series of $f(t) = \cos^2 2t$ are given by $a_0 = 1$, $a_4 = 1/2$, $a_n = 0$ otherwise, and $b_n = 0$ for all $n \geq 1$.

26. $\dfrac{1}{2}\sin t + \dfrac{1}{\pi} - \dfrac{2}{\pi}\left[\dfrac{\cos 2t}{1} + \dfrac{\cos 4t}{15} + \dfrac{\cos 6t}{35} + \dfrac{\cos 8t}{63} + \cdots\right]$

Note that $f(t) = (\sin t + \sin 4t)/2$, so this answer agrees with the answer to Problem 24.

SECTION 9.2

GENERAL FOURIER SERIES AND CONVERGENCE

1. $\quad \dfrac{8}{\pi}\left[\sin\dfrac{\pi t}{3}+\dfrac{1}{3}\sin\dfrac{3\pi t}{3}+\dfrac{1}{5}\sin\dfrac{5\pi t}{3}+\dfrac{1}{7}\sin\dfrac{7\pi t}{3}+\cdots\right]$

2. $\quad \dfrac{1}{2}+\dfrac{2}{\pi}\left[\sin\dfrac{\pi t}{5}+\dfrac{1}{3}\sin\dfrac{3\pi t}{5}+\dfrac{1}{5}\sin\dfrac{5\pi t}{5}+\dfrac{1}{7}\sin\dfrac{7\pi t}{5}+\cdots\right]$

3. $\quad \dfrac{1}{2}-\dfrac{6}{\pi}\left[\sin\dfrac{t}{2}+\dfrac{1}{3}\sin\dfrac{3t}{2}+\dfrac{1}{5}\sin\dfrac{5t}{2}+\dfrac{1}{7}\sin\dfrac{7t}{2}+\cdots\right]$

4. $\quad \dfrac{4}{\pi}\left[\sin\dfrac{\pi t}{2}-\dfrac{1}{2}\sin\dfrac{2\pi t}{2}+\dfrac{1}{3}\sin\dfrac{3\pi t}{2}-\dfrac{1}{4}\sin\dfrac{4\pi t}{2}+\cdots\right]$

5. $\quad 4\left[\sin\dfrac{t}{2}-\dfrac{1}{2}\sin\dfrac{2t}{2}+\dfrac{1}{3}\sin\dfrac{3t}{2}-\dfrac{1}{4}\sin\dfrac{4t}{2}+\cdots\right]$

6. $\quad \dfrac{3}{2}-\dfrac{3}{\pi}\left[\sin\dfrac{2\pi t}{3}+\dfrac{1}{2}\sin\dfrac{4\pi t}{3}+\dfrac{1}{3}\sin\dfrac{6\pi t}{3}+\dfrac{1}{4}\sin\dfrac{8\pi t}{3}+\cdots\right]$

7. $\quad \dfrac{1}{2}-\dfrac{4}{\pi^2}\left[\cos\pi t+\dfrac{1}{9}\cos 3\pi t+\dfrac{1}{25}\cos 5\pi t+\dfrac{1}{49}\cos 7\pi t+\cdots\right]$

8. $\quad L = 3/2$ and $a_0 = 2/3$. We find that

$$a_n = \frac{1}{n\pi}\left[\sin\frac{4n\pi}{3}-\sin\frac{2n\pi}{3}\right], \quad b_n = \frac{1}{n\pi}\left[\cos\frac{2n\pi}{3}-\cos\frac{4n\pi}{3}\right].$$

Analyzing separately the cases $n = 3k$, $n = 3k+1$, and $n = 3k+2$, we find that $a_{3k} = 0$, $a_{3k+1} = -\sqrt{3}/\pi n$, $a_{3k+2} = +\sqrt{3}/\pi n$, and that $b_n = 0$ for all n. Hence the Fourier series of $f(t)$ is

$$\frac{1}{3}-\frac{\sqrt{3}}{\pi}\left[\cos\frac{2\pi t}{3}-\frac{1}{2}\cos\frac{4\pi t}{3}+\frac{1}{4}\cos\frac{8\pi t}{3}-\frac{1}{5}\cos\frac{10\pi t}{3}+\cdots\right].$$

9. $\quad \dfrac{1}{3}-\dfrac{4}{\pi^2}\left[\cos\pi t-\dfrac{1}{4}\cos 2\pi t+\dfrac{1}{9}\cos 3\pi t-\dfrac{1}{16}\cos 4\pi t+\cdots\right]$

10.
$$\frac{2}{3} - \frac{8}{\pi^2}\left[\cos\frac{\pi t}{2} - \frac{1}{4}\cos\frac{2\pi t}{2} + \frac{1}{9}\cos\frac{3\pi t}{2} - \frac{1}{16}\cos\frac{4\pi t}{2} + \cdots\right]$$
$$+ \frac{4}{\pi}\left[\sin\frac{\pi t}{2} - \frac{1}{2}\sin\frac{2\pi t}{2} + \frac{1}{3}\sin\frac{3\pi t}{2} - \cdots\right] - \frac{16}{\pi^3}\left[\sin\frac{\pi t}{2} + \frac{1}{27}\sin\frac{3\pi t}{2} + \frac{1}{125}\sin\frac{5\pi t}{2} + \cdots\right]$$

To calculate the Fourier coefficients in Problems 11–14 we use the trigonometric identities for $\sin A \cos B$ and $\sin A \sin B$ that are listed above in Section 9.1.

11. $a_0 = 4/\pi$, $a_n = (4/\pi)(-1)^{n+1}/(4n^2 - 1)$ for $n \geq 1$, and $b_n = 0$ for $n \geq 1$, so the Fourier series is

$$\frac{2}{\pi} + \frac{4}{\pi}\left[\frac{1}{3}\cos\pi t - \frac{1}{15}\cos 2\pi t + \frac{1}{35}\cos 3\pi t - \frac{1}{63}\cos 4\pi t + \cdots\right]$$

12. $L = 1/2$, $a_0 = 4/\pi$ and $a_n = -(4/\pi)/(4n^2 - 1)$, $b_n = 0$ for $n = 1, 2, 3, \cdots$, so the period 1 Fourier series of $f(t) = \sin \pi t$ is

$$\frac{2}{\pi} - \frac{4}{\pi}\left[\frac{1}{3}\cos 2\pi t + \frac{1}{15}\cos 4\pi t + \frac{1}{35}\cos 6\pi t + \frac{1}{63}\cos 8\pi t + \cdots\right]$$

13. We find that $a_0 = 2/\pi$, $a_1 = 0$, and

$$a_n = [(-1)^{n+1} - 1]/[\pi(n^2 - 1)]$$

for $n \geq 2$, whereas $b_1 = 1/2$ and $b_n = 0$ for $n \geq 2$. Hence the Fourier series of $f(t)$ is

$$\frac{1}{\pi} + \frac{1}{2\pi}\sin\pi t - \frac{2}{\pi}\left[\frac{1}{3}\cos 2\pi t + \frac{1}{15}\cos 4\pi t + \frac{1}{35}\cos 6\pi t + \frac{1}{63}\cos 8\pi t + \cdots\right]$$

14. $L = 2\pi$ and $a_0 = 0$. If $n \neq 2$ then $a_n = 0$ if n is even, whereas $a_n = -4/\pi(n^2 - 4)$ if n is odd, and $b_n = 0$. Working separately with $n = 2$ we calculate $a_2 = 0$ and $b_2 = 1/2$. Hence the desired Fourier series is

$$\frac{1}{2}\sin t + \frac{4}{\pi}\left[\frac{1}{3}\cos\frac{t}{2} - \frac{1}{5}\cos\frac{3t}{2} - \frac{1}{21}\cos\frac{5t}{2} - \frac{1}{45}\cos\frac{7t}{2} - \cdots\right]$$

15. **(b)** Substitute $t = 0$ in the Fourier series of part (a) to obtain the series in (16). Note that

$$f(0) = [f(0-) + f(0+)]/2 = [(2\pi)^2 + (0)^2]/2 = 2\pi^2.$$

Substitute $t = \pi$ and $f(\pi) = \pi^2$ to obtain the series in (17).

16. **(b)** Substitute $t = 0$.

17. **(b)** Substitute $t = 1/2$.

The most efficient approach to Problems 18 and 20 is to derive first the expansions

$$t = \pi - 2\left[\sin t + \frac{\sin 2t}{2} + \frac{\sin 3t}{3} + \frac{\sin 4t}{4} + \cdots\right],$$

$$t^2 = \frac{4\pi^2}{3} + 4\left[\cos t + \frac{\cos 2t}{4} + \frac{\cos 3t}{9} + \frac{\cos 4t}{16} + \cdots\right]$$
$$- 4\pi\left[\sin t + \frac{\sin 2t}{2} + \frac{\sin 3t}{3} + \frac{\sin 4t}{4} + \cdots\right].$$

for $0 < t < 2\pi$, as the Fourier series of the functions $f(t)$ and $g(t)$ of period 2π defined for $0 < t < 2\pi$ by $f(t) = t$ and $g(t) = t^2$. The first series above yields the series in Problem 18, and a combination of the two yields the series in Problem 20.

The expansions in Problems 19 and 21 are valid on the interval $-\pi < t < \pi$ rather than the interval $0 < t < 2\pi$. When we calculate the Fourier series of the functions $f(t)$ and $g(t)$ of period 2π defined for $-\pi < t < \pi$ by $f(t) = t$ and $g(t) = t^2$, we find that

$$t = 2\left[\sin t - \frac{\sin 2t}{2} + \frac{\sin 3t}{3} - \frac{\sin 4t}{4} + \cdots\right],$$

$$t^2 = \frac{\pi^2}{3} - 4\left[\cos t - \frac{\cos 2t}{4} + \frac{\cos 3t}{9} - \frac{\cos 4t}{16} + \cdots\right]$$

if $-\pi < t < \pi$.

24. **(b)** When we substitute $t = 0$ in the series of part (a) we get

$$8\pi^4 = 16\pi^4/5 + 32\pi^2 \Sigma(1/n^2) - 48 \Sigma(1/n^4).$$

After substituting $\Sigma(1/n^2) = \pi^2/6$ we solve this equation for $\Sigma(1/n^4) = \pi^4/90$. Similarly, we find that $\Sigma(-1)^{n+1}/n^4 = 7\pi^4/720$ by substituting $t = \pi$ in the series of part (a). Finally, addition of the first two series in part (b) yields the third one.

25. Now we want to sum the alternating series

$$1 - \frac{1}{3^3} + \frac{1}{5^3} - \frac{1}{7^3} + \frac{1}{9^3} + \cdots$$

of reciprocals of odd cubes. Having used a Fourier series of t^4 in Problem 24 to evaluate $\Sigma(1/n^4)$, it is natural to look at a Fourier series of t^3. Let $f(t)$ be the period 2π

function with $f(t) = t^3$ if $-\pi < t < \pi$. We use Formulas (22)–(25) in Section 9.1 to calculate the Fourier coefficients of $f(t)$, and find that

$$t^3 = 2\pi^2 \sum_{n=1}^{\infty} (-1)^{n+1} \frac{\sin nt}{n} - 12 \sum_{n=1}^{\infty} (-1)^{n+1} \frac{\sin nt}{n^3}.$$

If we substitute $t = \pi/2$ and use Leibniz's series $\Sigma(-1)^{n+1}/n = \pi/4$ of Problem 17 we find that

$$1 - \frac{1}{3^3} + \frac{1}{5^3} - \frac{1}{7^3} + \frac{1}{9^3} + \cdots = \frac{\pi^3}{32}.$$

There is no value of t whose substitution in the Fourier series of $f(t) = t^3$ yields the series $\Sigma(1/n^3)$ containing the reciprocal cubes of both the odd and even integers. Indeed, the summation in "closed form" of the series

$$1 + \frac{1}{2^3} + \frac{1}{3^3} + \frac{1}{4^3} + \frac{1}{5^3} + \cdots$$

is a problem that has challenged many fine mathematicians since the time of Euler. Only fairly recently (by R. Apery in 1978) has it been shown that this sum is an irrational number. For a delightful account of this work, see the article "A Proof that Euler Missed ... An Informal Report" by Alfred van der Poorten in the *The Mathematical Intelligencer*, Volume 1 (1979), pages 195–203.

SECTION 9.3

FOURIER SINE AND COSINE SERIES

1. *Cosine series*: $a_0 = 2$; the coefficient of $\cos n\pi t/L$ is $a_n = 0$ for $n \geq 1$.

    Sine series: The coefficient of $\sin n\pi t/L$ is $b_n = 4/n\pi$ for n odd, $b_n = 0$ for n even.

2. *Cosine series*: $a_0 = 1$; the coefficient of $\cos n\pi t$ is $a_n = 4/n^2\pi^2$ for n odd, $a_n = 0$ for n even.

    Sine series: The coefficient of $\sin n\pi t$ is $b_n = 2/n\pi$ for $n = 1, 2, 3, \cdots$.

3. *Cosine series*: $a_0 = 0$; the coefficient of $\cos n\pi t/2$ is

    $$a_n = [1 - (-1)^n](4/n^2\pi^2)$$

    for $n \geq 1$, so $a_n = 8/n^2\pi^2$ for n odd, $a_n = 0$ for n even.

Sine series: The coefficient of $\sin n\pi t/2$ is

$$b_n = [1 + (-1)^n](2/n\pi)$$

for $n \geq 1$, so $b_n = 4/n\pi$ for n even, $b_n = 0$ for n odd.

4. *Cosine series*: $a_0 = 1$; the coefficient of $\cos(n\pi t/2)$ is $a_n = 0$ for n odd, $a_n = 0$ if $n = 4k$, $a_n = -16/n^2\pi^2$ if $n = 4k + 2$.

Sine series: The coefficient of $\sin(n\pi t/2)$ is given by $b_n = 0$ for n even, $b_n = 8/n^2\pi^2$ if $n = 4k + 1$, and $b_n = -8/n^2\pi^2$ if $n = 4k + 3$.

5. *Cosine series*: $a_0 = 2/3$; the coefficient of $\cos n\pi t/3$ is $a_n = -(2\sqrt{3})/n\pi$ if n is of the form $6k + 2$, $a_n = +(2\sqrt{3})/n\pi$ if n is of the form $6k + 4$, and $a_n = 0$ otherwise. Thus the Fourier cosine series of $f(t)$ is

$$\frac{1}{3} - \frac{2\sqrt{3}}{\pi}\left[\frac{1}{2}\cos\frac{2\pi t}{3} - \frac{1}{4}\cos\frac{4\pi t}{3} + \frac{1}{8}\cos\frac{8\pi t}{3} - \frac{1}{10}\cos\frac{10\pi t}{3} + \frac{1}{14}\cos\frac{14\pi t}{3} - \frac{1}{16}\cos\frac{16\pi t}{3} + \cdots\right]$$

Sine series: The coefficient of $\sin n\pi t/3$ is $b_n = 0$ if n is even, $b_n = -4/n\pi$ if n is of the form $6k + 3$, and $b_n = +2/n\pi$ if either $n = 6k + 1$ or $n = 6k + 5$. Thus the Fourier sine series of $f(t)$ is

$$\frac{2}{\pi}\left[\sin\frac{\pi t}{3} - \frac{2}{3}\sin\frac{3\pi t}{3} + \frac{1}{5}\sin\frac{5\pi t}{3} + \frac{1}{7}\sin\frac{7\pi t}{3} - \frac{2}{9}\sin\frac{9\pi t}{3} + \frac{1}{11}\sin\frac{11\pi t}{3} + \cdots\right]$$

6. *Cosine series*: $a_0 = 2L^2/3$; the coefficient of $\cos(n\pi t/L)$ is given by $a_n = 4L^2(-1)^n/n^2\pi^2$ for $n = 1, 2, 3, \cdots$.

Sine series: The coefficient of $\sin(n\pi t/L)$ is $b_n = 2L^2(n^2\pi^2 - 4)/n^3\pi^3$ for n odd, $b_n = -2L^2/n\pi$ for n even.

7. *Cosine series*: $a_0 = \pi^2/3$; the coefficient of $\cos nt$ is $a_n = -[1 + (-1)^n](2/n^2)$ for $n \geq 1$.

Sine series: The coefficient of $\sin nt$ is $b_n = [1 - (-1)^n](4/\pi n^3)$ for $n \geq 1$.

8. *Cosine series*: $a_0 = 1/3$; the coefficient of $\cos n\pi t$ is given by $a_n = -2(-1)^n/n^2\pi^2$ for $n = 1, 2, 3, \cdots$.

Sine series: The coefficient of $\sin n\pi t$ is $b_n = 8/n^3\pi^3$ for n odd, $b_n = 0$ for n even. Thus

$$t - t^2 = \frac{8}{\pi^3}\left[\sin \pi t + \frac{\sin 3\pi t}{27} + \frac{\sin 5\pi t}{125} + \frac{\sin 7\pi t}{343} + \cdots\right]$$

for $0 < t < 1$. Note that $t = 1/2$ yields the summation of Problem 25 in Section 9.2.

9.   *Cosine series*: $a_n = 4/\pi$ and $a_1 = 0$; if $n \geq 2$, then the coefficient of $\cos nt$ is $a_n = -[1 + (-1)^n]/[2/\pi(n^2 - 1)]$.

Sine series: $b_1 = 1$ and $b_n = 0$ for $n \geq 2$.

10.   *Cosine series*: $a_0 = 2/\pi$, the coefficient of $\cos(nt/2)$ is $a_n = -4/\pi(n^2 - 4)$ if n is odd, $a_n = -8/\pi(n^2 - 4)$ if $n = 4k$, and $a_n = 0$ if $n = 4k + 2$.

Sine series: The coefficient of $\sin(nt/2)$ is $b_n = 0$ if n is even, $b_n = -4/\pi(n^2 - 4)$ if $n = 4k + 1$, and $b_n = 4/\pi(n^2 - 4)$ if $n = 4k + 3$.

11. $x(t) = -\dfrac{4}{\pi}\displaystyle\sum_{n \text{ odd}} \dfrac{\sin nt}{n(n^2 - 2)}$

12.   Because of the initial conditions $x(0) = x(\pi) = 0$, we try a sine series solution of the form

$$x(t) = \Sigma\, b_n \sin nt.$$

Then

$$x''(t) - 4x(t) = -\Sigma\, (n^2 + 4)b_n \sin nt,$$

and

$$1 = (4/\pi)[\sin t + (1/3)\sin 3t + (1/5)\sin 5t + \cdots]$$

by Example 1 in Section 9.1. We therefore choose

$$b_n = 0 \text{ if } n \text{ is even,}$$

$$b_n = -4/\pi n(n^2 + 4) \text{ if } n \text{ is odd}$$

to get the formal Fourier series solution

$$x(t) = -\frac{4}{\pi}\left[\frac{\sin t}{5} + \frac{\sin 3t}{39} + \frac{\sin 5t}{145} + \frac{\sin 7t}{371} + \cdots\right].$$

13. $x(t) = \displaystyle\sum_{n=1}^{\infty} \dfrac{2(-1)^n \sin n\pi t}{n\pi(n^2\pi^2 - 1)}$

14.   To solve the endpoint value problem

$$x'' + 2x = t, \qquad\qquad x(0) = x(2) = 0,$$

we try a sine series solution of the form

$$x(t) = \Sigma\, b_n \sin(n\pi t/2).$$

Then

$$x''(t) + 2x(t) = \Sigma\, [2 - n^2\pi^2/4]b_n \sin(n\pi t/2),$$

and Example 1 in this section gives

$$t = (4/\pi) \,\Sigma\, [(-1)^{n+1}/n]\, \sin(n\pi t/2).$$

When we equate the coefficients of $\sin(n\pi t/2)$ in these two series, we find that we must choose

$$b_n = 16(-1)^{n+1} /\, \pi n(8 - n^2\pi^2)$$

to get a formal Fourier series solution.

15. $\quad x(t) = \dfrac{\pi}{2} + \dfrac{2}{\pi}\displaystyle\sum_{n=1}^{\infty}\dfrac{1-(-1)^n}{n^2(n^2-2)}\cos nt$

16. **(b)** The point is simply that the series in (31) is the Fourier sine series of the period 2 function defined by $f(t) = t - (\sin 2t)/(\sin 2)$ for $0 < t < 1$.

17. *Suggestion*: Substitute $u = -t$ in the left-hand integral.

18. The termwise derivative of the given Fourier series is

$$-(4/\pi) \,\Sigma\, (\sin n\pi t)/n - 4\,\Sigma\, \cos n\pi t.$$

But the series $\Sigma \cos n\pi t$ diverges at $t = 0$ (for instance). Hence the derived series does not converge to any function at all, let alone to $f'(t)$.

22. We want to calculate the coefficients in the Fourier cosine series

$$G(t) = \frac{a_0}{2} + \sum_{n=1}^{\infty} a_n \cos\frac{n\pi t}{2L}$$

which agrees with $f(t)$ if $0 < t < L$. Then

$$a_n = \frac{2}{2L}\int_0^L f(t)\cos\frac{n\pi t}{2L}\,dt - \frac{2}{2L}\int_L^{2L} f(2L-t)\cos\frac{n\pi t}{2L}\,dt.$$

The substitution $u = 2L - t$ yields

$$a_n = \frac{1}{L}\int_0^L f(t)\cos\frac{n\pi t}{2L}\,dt + \frac{1}{L}\int_L^0 f(u)\cos\frac{n\pi(2L-u)}{2L}\,du$$

$$= \frac{1}{L}\int_0^L f(t)\cos\frac{n\pi t}{2L}\,dt - \frac{(-1)^n}{L}\int_0^L f(u)\cos\frac{n\pi u}{2L}\,du.$$

Now it is clear that

$$a_n = \frac{2}{L}\int_0^L f(t)\cos\frac{n\pi t}{2L}\,dt$$

if n is odd, whereas $a_n = 0$ if n is even (including $n = 0$).

24.   We want a solution of the form

$$x(t) = \Sigma\, B_n\sin(nt/2)$$

with $B_n = 0$ for n even, because each term of such a series will satisfy the endpoint conditions $x(0) = x'(\pi) = 0$. Then

$$x''(t) - x(t) = -\Sigma\,(1 + n^2/4)B_n\sin(nt/2),$$

and by Problem 23 we have

$$t = \Sigma\, b_n\sin(nt/2)$$

where $b_n = 0$ for n even, and otherwise

$$b_n = 8(-1)^{(n-1)/2}/\pi n^2.$$

When we equate these two series we get

$$B_n = 32(-1)^{(n+1)/2}/\pi n^2(n^2 + 4) \qquad \text{for } n \text{ odd.}$$

SECTION 9.4

APPLICATIONS OF FOURIER SERIES

1. $$x_{sp}(t) = \frac{12}{\pi}\sum_{n\text{ odd}}\frac{\sin nt}{n(5-n^2)}$$

2.   First we calculate the Fourier cosine series of the even period 4 function $F(t)$, and find that

$$F(t) = \Sigma\, a_n\cos(n\pi t/2)$$

where $a_n = (12/n\pi)\sin(n\pi/2)$, so $a_n = 0$ for n even and $a_n = [12(-1)^{(n-1)/2}]/n\pi$ for n odd. Then we substitute this series and the steady periodic trial solution

$$x(t) = \Sigma A_n\cos(n\pi t/2)$$

in $x'' + 10x = F(t)$, and find that we must choose $A_n = 4a_n/(40 - n^2\pi^2)$. Thus

$$A_n = [48(-1)^{(n-1)/2}] / [n\pi(40 - n^2\pi^2)]$$

for n odd, and $A_n = 0$ for n even.

3. $\qquad x_{sp}(t) = 4\sum_{n=1}^{\infty} \dfrac{(-1)^n \sin nt}{n(n^2 - 3)}$

4. $\qquad$ The Fourier cosine series of the period 4 function $F(t)$ is

$$F(t) = a_0 + \Sigma a_n\cos(n\pi t/2)$$

where $a_0 = 2$, $a_n = 0$ for n even $(n > 0)$, and $a_n = -16/n^2\pi^2$ for n odd. When we substitute this series and the steady periodic trial solution

$$x(t) = A_0 + \Sigma A_n\cos(n\pi t/2)$$

in the differential equation $x'' + 4x = F(t)$, we find that $A_0 = a_0/4 = 1/2$ and

$$(4 - n^2\pi^2/4)A_n = a_n$$

for $n > 0$. Therefore we choose

$$A_n = 64/n^2\pi^2(n^2\pi^2 - 16)$$

for n odd, and $A_n = 0$ for n even.

5. $\qquad x_{sp}(t) = \dfrac{8}{\pi^3}\sum_{n\text{ odd}} \dfrac{\sin n\pi t}{n^3(10 - n^2\pi^2)}$

6. $\qquad$ The period 2π Fourier cosine series of $F(t) = \sin t$ is

$$F(t) = a_0 + \Sigma a_n\cos nt$$

where $a_0 = 4/\pi$, $a_n = 0$ for n odd, and $a_n = -4/\pi(n^2 - 1)$ for n even $(n > 0)$. Substitution of this series and the steady periodic trial solution

$$x(t) = A_0 + \Sigma A_n\cos nt$$

in $x'' + 2x = F(t)$ yields $A_0 = a_0/2 = 2/\pi$ and $(2 - n^2)A_n = a_n$ for $n > 0$. Hence we choose

$$A_n = 4/[\pi(n^2 - 1)(n^2 - 2)]$$

for n even and $A_n = 0$ for n odd.

In Problems 7–12 we are dealing with the equation

$$mx'' + kx = F(t)$$

where $F(t)$ is the external periodic force. The natural frequency is $\omega_0 = \sqrt{(k/m)}$. If the Fourier series of $F(t)$ contains a term of the form $\cos(N\pi t/L)$ or $\sin(N\pi t/L)$ with $\omega_0 = N\pi/L$, then pure resonance occurs. Otherwise, it does not.

7.   The natural frequency is $\omega_0 = 3$, and $F(t) = \Sigma b_n \sin nt$ with $b_n = 4/n\pi$ for n odd, $b_n = 0$ for n even. Thus the Fourier series of $F(t)$ contains a $\sin 3t$ term, so resonance does occur.

8.   The natural frequency is $\omega_0 = \sqrt{5}$, and $F(t) = \Sigma b_n \sin n\pi t$. Since $n\pi \neq \sqrt{5}$ for any integer n, pure resonance does not occur.

9.   The natural frequency is $\omega_0 = 2$, and $F(t) = \Sigma b_n \sin nt$ with $b_n = 12/n\pi$ for n odd, $b_n = 0$ for n even. Because the $\sin 2t$ term is missing from the Fourier series of $F(t)$, resonance will not occur.

10.   The natural frequency is $\omega_0 = 2\pi$. From Equation (16) in Section 9.3 of the text we see that the Fourier series of $F(t)$ contains a $\sin 2\pi t$ term. Hence pure resonance occurs.

11.   The natural frequency is $\omega_0 = 4$. From Equation (15) in Section 9.3 we see that

$$F(t) = \pi/2 - (4/\pi)[(\cos t) + (\cos 3t)/9 + (\cos 5t)/25 + \cdots].$$

Because the $\cos 4t$ term is missing, we see that resonance will not occur.

12.   The natural frequency is $\omega_0 = 5$, and the Fourier series of $F(t)$ is of the form

$$F(t) = \Sigma b_n \sin nt.$$

We calculate b_5, and find that $b_5 = 8/125\pi$. Thus the term $\sin 5t$ is present in $F(t)$, and so pure resonance occurs.

Problems 13–18 are based on Equations (14)–(16) in the text, according to which the steady periodic solution of

$$mx'' + cx' + kx = \Sigma B_n \sin(n\pi t/L)$$

is given by

$$x_{sp}(t) = \Sigma\, b_n \sin(\omega_n t - \alpha_n)$$

where

$$\omega_n = n\pi/L, \quad \alpha_n = \tan^{-1}(c\omega_n/[k - m(\omega_n)^2]) \quad \text{in } [0,\pi],$$

$$b_n = B_n/\{[k - m(\omega_n)^2]^2 + (c\omega_n)^2\}^{1/2}.$$

The following BASIC program was written to calculate the coefficients $\{b_n\}$ for Problem 13. The values of m, c, k, L are input, and only line 300 must be changed for problems 14–18.

```
100 REM--Damped Forced Oscillations Program
110 REM--(Problem 13, Section 9.4)
120 REM--Input parameters:
130      DEFINT N
140      INPUT "Mass m"; M
150      INPUT "Dashpot c"; C
160      INPUT "Spring k"; K
170      INPUT "Half-period L"; L
180      PI  =  3.141593  :  EPS  =  .00001
185      PRINT "N        B        OMEGA        ALPHA"
190 REM--Compute displacement coefficients:
200      FOR N  =  1 TO 9
210           GOSUB 300  :  REM••Get BN
220           W  =  N*PI/L :  REM-- W  =  OMEGA
225           D  =  K - M*W*W
230           IF ABS(D)  <  EPS THEN ALPHA  =  PI/2
                 ELSE ALPHA  =  ATN(C*W/D)
240           IF ALPHA  <  0 THEN ALPHA  =  PI + ALPHA
250           X  =  B/SQR(D*D + C*C*W*W)
260           PRINT USING
                 "#    #.#####        ##.#####        #.#####";
                 N, X, W, ALPHA
270      NEXT N
280      STOP
290 REM--Compute force coefficients:
300      IF N\2  =  N/2 THEN B  =  0 ELSE B  =  12/(PI*N)
310      RETURN
320      END
```

13. $B_n = 12/\pi n$ for n odd, $B_n = 0$ for n even

$$x_{sp}(t) \approx 1.2725\sin(t - 0.0333) + 0.2542\sin(3t - 3.0817) + 0.0364\sin(5t - 3.1178) + \cdots$$

14. $B_n = 4(-1)^{n+1}/n$ for $n = 1, 2, 3, \cdots$

$$x_{sp}(t) \approx 0.2500\sin(t - 0.0063) - 0.2000\sin(2t - 0.0200)$$

$$+ 4.444\sin(3t - 1.5708) - 0.0714\sin(4t - 3.1130) + \cdots$$

Note the dominance of the $n = 3$ term.

15. $B_n = 8/n^3\pi^3$ for n odd, $B_n = 0$ for n even

$$x_{sp}(t) \approx 0.08150 \sin(\pi t - 1.44692) + 0.00004 \sin(3\pi t - 3.10176) + \cdots$$

16. $F(t) = A_0 + \Sigma A_n \cos(n\pi t/2)$ where $A_0 = 2$, $A_n = -16/\pi^2 n^2$ for n odd, $A_n = 0$ for n even and positive.

$$x_{sp}(t) \approx 0.5000 + 1.0577 \cos(\pi t/2 - 0.0103)$$
$$- 0.0099 \cos(3\pi t/2 - 3.1390) - 0.0011 \cos(5\pi t/2 - 3.1402) \cdots$$

17. $B_n = 60/n\pi$ for n odd, $B_n = 0$ for n even

$$x_{sp}(t) \approx 0.5687 \sin(\pi t - 0.0562) + 0.4271 \sin(3\pi t - 0.3891)$$
$$+ 0.1396 \sin(5\pi t - 2.7899) + 0.0318 \sin(7\pi t - 2.9874) + \cdots$$

$$x_{sp}(5) \approx 0.248 \text{ ft} \approx 2.98 \text{ in.}$$

18. $B_n = (4/\pi n^2)\sin(n\pi/2)$

$$x_{sp}(t) \approx 0.0531 \sin(t - 0.0004) - 0.0088 \sin(3t - 0.0019)$$
$$+ 1.0186 \sin(5t - 1.5708) - 0.0011 \sin(7t - 3.1387) + \cdots$$

Note the dominance of the $n = 5$ term.

SECTION 9.5

HEAT CONDUCTION AND SEPARATION OF VARIABLES

1. From Equation (31) in the text, with $L = \pi$ and $k = 3$, we get

$$u(x,t) = \sum_{n=1}^{\infty} b_n \exp(-3n^2 t)\sin nx.$$

With $b_2 = 4$ and $b_n = 0$ otherwise we get the solution

$$u(x, t) = 4e^{-12t}\sin 2x.$$

2. From Equation (40) with $k = 10$ and $L = 5$ we get

$$u(x, t) = a_0/2 + \Sigma a_n \exp(-10n^2\pi^2 t/25)\cos(n\pi x/5).$$

With $a_0 = 14$ and $a_n = 0$ for $n > 0$ we get the solution $u(x, t) = 7$ (constant).

3. With $L = 1$ and $k = 2$ in Equation (31), we take $b_1 = 5$, $b_3 = -1/5$, and $b_n = 0$ otherwise. The result is the solution

$$u(x, t) = 5 \exp(-2\pi^2 t)\sin \pi x - (1/5)\exp(-18\pi^2 t)\sin 3\pi x.$$

4. From Equation (31) with $k = 1$ and $L = \pi$ we get

$$u(x,t) = \Sigma\, b_n \exp(-n^2 t) \sin nx.$$

But the $\sin A \cos B$ identity yields

$$4 \sin 4x \cos 2x = 2 \sin 2x + 2 \sin 6x.$$

Hence we choose $b_2 = b_6 = 2$ and $b_n = 0$ for $n \neq 2,6$. Thus

$$u(x, t) = 2e^{-4t}\sin 2x + 2e^{-36t}\sin 6x.$$

5. $u(x, t) = 4 \exp(-8\pi^2 t/9) \cos(2\pi x/3) - 2 \exp(-32\pi^2 t/9) \cos(4\pi x/3)$

6. From Equation (31) with $k = 1/2$ and $L = 1$ we get

$$u(x, t) = \Sigma\, b_n \exp(-n^2 \pi^2 t/2) \sin n\pi x.$$

Trigonometric identities yield

$$4 \sin \pi x \cos^3 \pi x = (2 \sin \pi x \cos \pi x)(2 \cos^2 \pi x)$$
$$= (\sin 2\pi x)(1 + \cos 2\pi x) = \sin 2\pi x + (1/2)\sin 4\pi x.$$

Hence we choose $b_2 = 1$, $b_4 = 1/2$, and $b_n = 0$ otherwise to get

$$u(x, t) = \exp(-2\pi^2 t) \sin 2\pi x + (1/2)\exp(-8\pi^2 t) \sin 4\pi x.$$

7. The identity $\cos^2 2\pi x = (1 + \cos 4\pi x)/2$ yields

$$u(x, t) = 1/2 + (1/2)\exp(-16\pi^2 t/3) \cos 4\pi x.$$

8. From Equation (40) with $k = 1$ and $L = 2$ we get

$$u(x, t) = a_0/2 + \Sigma\, a_n \exp(-n^2 \pi^2 t/4) \cos n\pi x/2.$$

But

$$10 \cos \pi x \cos 3\pi x = 5 \cos 2\pi x + 5 \cos 4\pi x.$$

Hence we choose $b_4 = b_8 = 5$ and $b_n = 0$ otherwise to get

$$u(x, t) = 5 \exp(-4\pi^2 t) \cos 2\pi x + 5 \exp(-16\pi^2 t) \cos 4\pi x.$$

9. $$u(x,t) = \frac{100}{\pi} \sum_{n \text{ odd}} \frac{1}{n} \exp\left(\frac{-n^2\pi^2 t}{250}\right) \sin \frac{n\pi x}{5}$$

10.   From Equation (31) with $k = 1/5$ and $L = 10$ we get

$$u(x, t) = \sum b_n \exp(-n^2\pi^2 t/500) \sin n\pi x/10.$$

On the basis of Equation (16) in Section 9.3 we choose $b_n = 80(-1)^{n+1}/\pi n$ for $n = 1, 2, 3, \cdots$.

11. $$u(x,t) = 20 - \frac{160}{\pi^2} \sum_{n \text{ odd}} \frac{1}{n^2} \exp\left(\frac{-n^2\pi^2 t}{500}\right) \cos \frac{n\pi x}{10}$$

12.   From Equation (31) with $k = 1$ and $L = 100$ we get

$$u(x, t) = \sum b_n \exp(-n^2\pi^2 t/10000) \sin n\pi x/100.$$

The $\{b_n\}$ should be the Fourier sine coefficients of $f(x) = x(100 - x)$ on $[0, 100]$. Hence we choose $b_n = 80000/n^3\pi^3$ for n odd and $b_n = 0$ for n even.

13.   **(a)** $$u(x,t) = \frac{400}{\pi} \sum_{n \text{ odd}} \frac{1}{n} \exp\left(\frac{-n^2\pi^2 kt}{1600}\right) \sin \frac{n\pi x}{40}.$$

(b)   With $k = 1.15$ we find that $u(20, 300) \approx 15.16°C$

(c)   About 19 hr 16 min

14.   **(a)**   The boundary value problem is

$$u_t = ku_{xx} \quad (0 < x < 50)$$
$$u_x(0, t) = u_x(50, t) = 0$$
$$u(x, 0) = 2x$$

with $k = 1.15$ cm^2/sec for copper. By Equation (40) in the text the solution is of the form
$$u(x, t) = a_0/2 + \sum a_n \exp(-n^2\pi^2 kt/2500) \cos n\pi x/50.$$

Consulting the Fourier series given in Equation (15) of Section 9.2, we satisfy the initial condition $u(x, 0) = 2x$ by choosing $a_0 = 100$, $a_n = -400/n^2\pi^2$ for n odd, and $a_n = 0$ for n even.

(b) With the aid of the BASIC program

```
100 INPUT "X";X
110 INPUT "T";T
120 SUM  =  50 : N  =  -1 : PI  =   3.141593
130 A  =  400/(PI*PI) : K  =  1.15
140 B  =  PI*PI*K/2500
150 N  =  N + 2
160 TERM  =  A*EXP(-B*N*N*T)*COS(N*PI*X/50)/(N*N)
170 SUM  =  SUM - TERM
180 IF ABS(TERM)  > .001 THEN GOTO 150
190 PRINT SUM
200 END
```

we find that $u(10, 60) \approx 25.15$ (degrees Celsius)

(c) The program above makes a "hit or miss" approach effective. We find that

$$u(10, 300) = 41.60 \qquad u(10, 414.0) = 44.99$$
$$u(10, 400) = 44.67 \qquad u(10, 415.0) = 45.02$$
$$u(10, 410) = 44.90$$

Thus $u = 45$ at $x = 10$ after 6 min 54.3 sec.

16. **(a)** Summing numerically the series in Problem 15 with $k = 0.15$ for iron, we find that $u(25, 1800) \approx 21.92 \approx 22$ (degrees Celsius).

(b) Because for x fixed the temperature is a function of the *product* kt, in the case of concrete slabs with $k = 0.005$ the same temperature will be attained when

$$(0.005)(t) = (0.15)(1800),$$

that is, when $t = 54000$ sec $= 15$ hr.

SECTION 9.6

VIBRATING STRINGS AND THE ONE-DIMENSIONAL WAVE EQUATION

In Problems 1–10 we use the general solution

$$y(x, t) = \Sigma (A_n \cos n\pi at/L + B_n \sin n\pi at/L) \sin n\pi x/L$$

of the string equation $y_{tt} = a^2 y_{xx}$ with endpoint conditions $y(0, t) = y(L, t) = 0$. This form of the solution is obtained by superposition of the solutions in Equations (23) and (33) of Problems

A and B in this section. It remains only to choose the coefficients $\{A_n\}$ and $\{B_n\}$ so as to satisfy given initial conditions $u(x, 0) = f(x)$ and $u_t(x, 0) = g(x)$.

1.　　Here $a = 2$ and $L = \pi$. To satisfy the condition $y(x, 0) = (1/10)\sin 2x$ we choose $A_2 = 1/10$ and $A_n = 0$ otherwise. To satisfy the condition $y_t(x, 0) = 0$ we choose $B_n = 0$ for all n. Thus

$$y(x, t) = (1/10)\cos 4t \sin 2x.$$

2.　　Here $a = L = 1$. To satisfy the condition

$$y(x, 0) = (1/10)\sin \pi x - (1/20)\sin 3\pi x$$

we choose $A_1 = 1/10$, $A_3 = -1/20$, and $A_n = 0$ otherwise. To satisfy the condition $y_t(x, 0) = 0$ we choose $B_n = 0$ for all n. Thus

$$y(x, t) = (1/10)\cos \pi t \sin \pi x - (1/20)\cos 3\pi t \sin 3\pi x.$$

3.　　Here $a = 1/2$ and $L = \pi$. Choosing $A_1 = 1/10$ and $A_n = 0$ otherwise, $B_1 = 1/5$ and $B_n = 0$ otherwise, we get

$$y(x, t) = (1/10)[\cos t/2 + 2 \sin t/2] \sin x.$$

4.　　Here $a = 1/2$ and $L = 2$, so $n\pi x/L = n\pi x/2$ and $n\pi at/L = n\pi t/4$. To satisfy the condition

$$y(x, 0) = (1/5) \sin \pi x \cos \pi x = (1/10)\sin 2\pi x = (1/10)\sin 4\pi x/2,$$

we choose $A_4 = 1/10$ and $A_n = 0$ for $n \neq 4$. To satisfy the condition $y_t(x, 0) = 0$ we choose $B_n = 0$ for all n. Thus

$$y(x, t) = (1/10)\cos \pi t \sin 2\pi x.$$

5.　　Here $a = 5$ and $L = 3$. Choosing $A_3 = 1/4$ and $A_n = 0$ for $n \neq 3$, $B_6 = 1/\pi$ and $B_n = 0$ for $n \neq 6$, we get

$$y(x, t) = (1/4)\cos 5\pi t \sin \pi x + (1/\pi)\sin 10\pi t \sin 2\pi x.$$

6.　　Here $a = 10$ and $L = \pi$. To satisfy the condition $y_t(x, 0) = 0$ we choose $B_n = 0$ for all n, so

$$y(x, t) = \Sigma A_n\cos 10nt \sin nx.$$

To satisfy the condition $y(x, 0) = x(\pi - x)$ we choose $A_n = 8/\pi n^3$ for n odd and $A_n = 0$ for n even.

7.　　Here $a = 10$ and $L = 1$. To satisfy the condition $y(x, 0) = 0$ we choose $A_n = 0$ for all n, so

$$y(x, t) = \Sigma \, B_n \sin 10n\pi t \sin n\pi x.$$

To satisfy the condition $y_t(x, 0) = x$ we choose

$$B_n = (-1)^{n+1}/(5\pi^2 n^2)$$

for $n \geq 1$ (see Equation (16) in Section 9.3).

8. Here $a = 2$ and $L = \pi$. To satisfy the condition $y(x, 0) = \sin x$ we choose $A_1 = 1$ and $A_n = 0$ for $n > 1$, so

$$y(x, t) = \cos 2t \sin x + \Sigma \, B_n \sin 2nt \sin nx,$$

$$y_t(x, t) = -2 \sin 2t \sin x + \Sigma \, 2nB_n \cos 2nt \sin nx.$$

The condition $y_t(x, 0) = 1$ will be satisfied if $2nB_n = 4/\pi n$ for n odd and $b_n = 0$ for n even. We therefore choose $B_n = 2/\pi n^2$ for n odd and $B_n = 0$ for n even.

9. Here $a = 2$ and $L = 1$. To satisfy the condition $y(x, 0) = 0$ we choose $A_n = 0$ for all n, so

$$y(x, t) = \Sigma \, B_n \sin 2n\pi t \sin n\pi x.$$

To satisfy the condition $y_t(x, 0) = x(1 - x)$ we choose $B_n = 4/n^4 \pi^4$ for n odd, and $B_n = 0$ for n even.

10. Here $a = 5$ and $L = \pi$ so

$$y(x, t) = \Sigma \, (A_n \cos 5nt + B_n \sin 5nt) \sin nx.$$

We first compute the Fourier sine series

$$\sin^2 x = \Sigma \, b_n \sin nx$$

and find that $b_n = 0$ if n is even whereas

$$b_n = 2(n^2 + 4) \, / \, \pi n(4 - n^2)$$

if n is odd. To satisfy the condition $y(x, t) = \sin^2 x$ we choose $A_n = b_n$, and to satisfy the condition $y_t(x, t) = \sin^2 x$ we choose $B_n = b_n/5n$.

11. Substitution of $L = 2$ ft, $T = 32$ lb, and

$$\rho = (1/64) \text{ oz/ft} = 1/(32 \cdot 16 \cdot 64) \text{ slug/ft}$$

in Equation (26) in the text yields the fundamental frequency of 256 Hz. The velocity with which waves of this frequency move along the string is $a = 1024$ ft/sec.

18. When we separate variables as in Equations (8)–(12) in this section, we find that $X(x)$ must satisfy the eigenvalue problem

$$X'' + \lambda X = 0, \qquad X(0) = X'(L) = 0.$$

In Example 4 of Section 3.10 we found that the eigenvalues and eigenfunctions of this problem are

$$\lambda_n = (2n - 1)^2 \pi^2 / 4L^2, \qquad X_n(x) = \sin(2n - 1)\pi x / 2L$$

for $n = 1, 2, 3, \cdots$. The function $T_n(t)$ must satisfy the conditions

$$T_n'' + \lambda_n a^2 T_n = 0, \qquad T_n'(0) = 0$$

so it follows that

$$T_n(t) = \cos(2n - 1)\pi a t / 2L.$$

Thus the form of $y(t)$ is

$$y(x, t) = \Sigma A_n \cos(2n - 1)\pi a t / 2L \sin(2n - 1)\pi x / 2L.$$

Finally, in order to satisfy the initial condition $y(x, 0) = f(x)$ we use the odd half-multiple sine series

$$f(x) = \Sigma A_n \sin(2n - 1)\pi x / 2L$$

discussed in Problem 21 of Section 9.3.

22. The eigenvalue problem

$$X'' + \lambda X = 0, \qquad X(0) = X(L) = 0$$

has the usual eigenvalues and eigenfunctions

$$\lambda_n = n^2 \pi^2 / L^2, \qquad X_n(x) = \sin n\pi x / L$$

for $n = 1, 2, 3, \cdots$. The function $T_n(t)$ satisfies the equation

$$T_n'' + (\omega_n)^2 R T_n = 0, \quad (\omega_n)^2 = (n^2 \pi^2 a^2 / L^2) - h^2 > 0,$$

so

$$T_n(t) = A_n \cos \omega_n t + B_n \sin \omega_n t.$$

Thus

$$v(x, t) = \Sigma (A_n\cos \omega_n t + B_n\sin \omega_n t)\sin n\pi x/L.$$

To satisfy the conditions $v(x, 0) = f(x)$ and $v_t(x, 0) = h\,f(x)$ we choose $A_n = b_n$ and $B_n = hb_n/\omega_n$ where

$$f(x) = \Sigma b_n\sin n\pi x/L.$$

Then

$$v(x, t) = \Sigma (b_n/\omega_n)(\omega_n\cos \omega_n t + h \sin \omega_n t) \sin n\pi x/L$$

$$= \Sigma c_n\cos(\omega_n t - \alpha_n) \sin n\pi x/L$$

where

$$c_n = b_n/(\cos \alpha_n) \text{ and } \alpha_n = \tan^{-1}(h/\omega_n).$$

Finally,

$$y(x,t) = e^{-ht}v(x, t) = e^{-ht}\Sigma c_n\cos(\omega_n t - \alpha_n) \sin n\pi x/L.$$

23. If $\pi/4 \leq x \leq 3\pi/4$ then

$$\pi/2 \leq x + \pi/4 \leq \pi \text{ and } 0 \leq x - \pi/4 \leq \pi/2$$

so

$$y(x, \pi/4) = (1/2)[F(x + \pi/4) + F(x - \pi/4)]$$

$$= (1/2)[1 - \cos 2(x + \pi/4) + 1 - \cos 2(x - \pi/4)]$$

$$= (1/2)[1 - \cos (2x + \pi/2) + 1 - \cos (2x - \pi/2)]$$

$$= (1/2)[2 + \sin 2x - \sin 2x]$$

$$y(x, \pi/4) = 1$$

24. (a) $f'(x) = 4 \cos 2x = 0$ if $x = \pi/4$ or $x = 3\pi/4$.

(b)   If $0 \leq t \leq \pi/4$ then $0 \leq \pi/4 \pm t \leq \pi/2$ so

$$y(\pi/4, t) = (1/2)[F(\pi/4 + t) + F(\pi/4 - t)]$$

$$= (1/2)[1 - \cos 2(\pi/4 + t) + 1 - \cos 2(\pi/4 - t)]$$

$$= (1/2)[1 - \cos (\pi/2 + 2t) + 1 - \cos (\pi/2 - 2t)]$$

$$= (1/2)[2 + \sin 2t - \sin 2t]$$

$$y(\pi/4, t) = 1$$

SECTION 9.7

STEADY-STATE TEMPERATURE AND LAPLACE'S EQUATION

1. Because $Y(0) = Y(b) = 0$ we take our separation of variables in the form

$$X'' - \lambda X = 0 = Y'' + \lambda Y$$

with $\lambda > 0$. Then it follows that

$$Y_n(y) = \sin n\pi y/b, \quad \lambda_n = n^2 \pi^2/b^2$$

and thence that

$$X_n(x) = A_n\cosh n\pi x/b + B_n\sinh n\pi x/b.$$

The condition that $X(0) = 0$ implies that $A_n = 0$ so $X_n(x) = C_n\sinh n\pi x/b$, and hence

$$u(x, y) = \Sigma\, C_n(\sinh n\pi x)/(b \sin n\pi y/b).$$

Finally we satisfy the condition $u(a, y) = g(y)$ by choosing $C_n = b_n/(\sinh n\pi a/b)$ where the $\{b_n\}$ are the Fourier sine coefficients of $g(y)$ on $0 \leq y \leq b$.

2. Because $Y(0) = Y(b) = 0$ we take our separation of variables in the form

$$X'' - \lambda X = 0 = Y'' + \lambda Y$$

with $\lambda > 0$. Then it follows that

$$Y_n(y) = \sin n\pi y/b, \quad \lambda_n = n^2 \pi^2/b^2$$

and thence that

$$X_n(x) = A_n\cosh n\pi x/b + B_n\sinh n\pi x/b.$$

The condition $X(a) = 0$ implies that

$$B_n = -(A_n\cosh n\pi a/b)/(\sinh n\pi a/b).$$

It now follows as in Equation (12) in the text that

$$X_n(x) = C_n\sinh n\pi(a - x)/b,$$

so

$$u(x, t) = \Sigma\, C_n\, [\sinh n\pi(a - x)/b] \sin n\pi y/b.$$

Finally we satisfy the condition $u(0, y) = g(y)$ by choosing $C_n = b_n/(\sinh n\pi a/b)$ where the $\{b_n\}$ are the Fourier sine coefficients of $g(y)$ on $0 \le y \le b$.

3. Just as in Example 1 of Section 9.7 we have $X_n(x) = \sin n\pi x/a$ and

$$Y_n(y) = A_n\cosh n\pi y/a + B_n\sinh n\pi y/a.$$

The condition $Y(0) = 0$ now yields $A_n = 0$ so $Y_n(y) = B_n\sinh n\pi y/a$, and hence

$$u(x, y) = \Sigma\, C_n\sin n\pi x/a \sinh n\pi y/a.$$

Finally we satisfy the condition $u(x, b) = f(x)$ by choosing $C_n = b_n/(\sinh n\pi b/a)$ where the $\{b_n\}$ are the Fourier sine coefficients of $f(x)$ on $0 \le x \le a$.

4. We work with the separation of variables

$$X'' + \lambda X = 0 = Y'' - \lambda Y.$$

The eigenvalue problem

$$X'' + \lambda X = 0, \qquad X'(0) = X'(a) = 0$$

has eigenvalues and eigenfunctions $\lambda_0 = 0$, $X_0(x) = 1$ and

$$\lambda_n = n^2\pi^2/a^2, \qquad X_n(x) = \cos n\pi x/a$$

for $n = 1, 2, 3, \cdots$. When $n = 0$, $Y_0'' = 0$ yields $Y_0(y) = Ay + B$. Then $Y_0(0) = 0$ gives $B = 0$, so we take $Y_0(y) = y$. For $n > 0$ we have

$$Y_n(y) = A_n\cosh n\pi y/a + B_n\sinh n\pi y/a,$$

and $Y_n(0) = 0$ gives $A_n = 0$, so

$$u(x, y) = B_0 y + \Sigma\, B_n\cos n\pi x/a \sinh n\pi y/a.$$

Finally

$$u(y, b) = B_0 b + \Sigma\, B_n\sinh n\pi b/a \cos n\pi x/a,$$

so we satisfy the condition $u(x, b) = f(x)$ by taking $B_0 = a_0/2b$ and $B_n = a_n/(\sinh n\pi b/a)$ where

$$f(x) = a_0/2 + \Sigma\, a_n\cos n\pi x/a.$$

5. Now we work with the separation of variables

$$X'' - \lambda X = 0 = Y'' + \lambda Y.$$

The eigenvalue problem

$$Y'' + \lambda Y = 0, \qquad Y'(0) = Y'(b) = 0$$

has eigenvalues and eigenfunctions $\lambda_0 = 0$, $Y_0(y) = 1$ and

$$\lambda_n = n^2\pi^2/b^2, \qquad Y_n(y) = \cos n\pi y/b$$

for $n = 1, 2, 3, \cdots$. When $n = 0$, $X_0'' = 0$ yields $X_0(x) = Ax + B$. Then $X_0(a) = 0$ is satisfied by $X_0(x) = a - x$. For $n > 0$ we have

$$X_n(x) = A_n\cosh n\pi x/b + B_n\sinh n\pi x/b,$$

and $X_n(a) = 0$ is satisfied by the particular linear combination

$$X_n(x) = C_n\sinh n\pi(a - x)/b$$

of $\cosh n\pi x/b$ and $\sinh n\pi x/b$. Therefore

$$u(x, t) = C_0(a - x) + \Sigma C_n\sinh n\pi(a - x)/b \cos n\pi y/b.$$

Finally we satisy the condition $u(0, y) = g(y)$ by choosing

$$C_0 = a_0/2a \quad \text{and} \quad C_n = b_n/(\sinh n\pi a/b)$$

where the $\{a_n\}$ are the Fourier cosine coefficients of $g(y)$ on $0 \le y \le b$.

6. This is the same as Problem 4 except that $Y'(0) = 0$ instead of $Y(0) = 0$, so $Y_0(y) = 1$ and $Y_n(y) = A_n\cosh n\pi y/a$ for $n > 0$. Then

$$u(x, y) = A_0 + \Sigma A_n\cos n\pi x/a \cosh n\pi y/a,$$

so we satisfy the condition $u(x, b) = f(x)$ by choosing $A_0 = a_0/2$ and $A_n = a_n/(\cosh n\pi b/a)$ where $\{a_n\}$ are the Fourier cosine coefficients of $f(x)$ on $[0, a]$.

7. The eigenvalue problem

$$X'' + \lambda X = 0, \qquad X(0) = X(a) = 0$$

yields the eigenvalues and eigenfunctions

$$\lambda_n = n^2\pi^2/a^2, \qquad X_n(x) = \sin n\pi x/a$$

for $n = 1, 2, 3, \cdots$. Then

$$Y_n'' + \lambda_n Y_n = 0$$

yields

$$Y_n(y) = A_n e^{n\pi y/a} + B_n e^{-n\pi y/a}.$$

In order that $Y(y) \to 0$ as $y \to \infty$ we take $A_n = 0$, so

$$u(x, y) = \Sigma B_n e^{-n\pi y/a} \sin n\pi x/a.$$

Finally we satisfy the condition $u(x,0) = f(x)$ by choosing the constants $\{B_n\}$ as the Fourier sine coefficients of $f(x)$ on $0 \le x \le a$.

8. The eigenvalue problem

$$X'' + \lambda X = 0, \qquad X'(0) = X'(a) = 0$$

yields $\lambda_0 = 0$, $X_0(x) = 1$ and

$$\lambda_n = n^2 \pi^2 / a^2, \qquad X_n(x) = \cos n\pi x/a$$

for $n > 0$. Then

$$Y_n'' + \lambda_n Y_n = 0$$

yields $Y_0(y) = Ay + B$ and

$$Y_n(y) = A_n e^{-n\pi y/a} + B_n e^{n\pi y/a}.$$

In order that $Y(y)$ be bounded as $y \to \infty$, we take $A_n = 0$ and $B_n = 0$ for $n > 0$, so

$$u(x, y) = B + \Sigma A_n e^{-n\pi y/a} \cos n\pi x/a.$$

Finally we satisfy the condition $u(x, 0) = f(x)$ by choosing $B = a_0/2$ and $A_n = a_n$ where the $\{a_n\}$ are the Fourier cosine coefficients of $f(x)$ on $[0, a]$.

9. $u(0, 5) \approx 41.53$; $u(5, 5) = 50$; $u(10, 5) \approx 58.47$

10. The boundary value problem is

$$u_{xx} + u_{yy} = 0 \qquad (0 < x < a, \; 0 < y < b)$$
$$u(0, y) = u_x(a, y) = u(x, 0) = 0,$$
$$u(x, b) = f(x).$$

The eigenvalue problem

$$X'' + \lambda X = 0, \qquad X(0) = X'(a) = 0$$

yields (by Example 4 in Section 3.10)

$$\lambda_n = (2n-1)^2 \pi^2/4a^2, \qquad X_n(x) = \sin(2n-1)\pi x/2a$$

for $n = 1, 2, 3, \cdots$. Then

$$Y_n'' - \lambda_n Y_n = 0$$

yields

$$Y_n(y) = A_n \cosh(2n-1)\pi y/2a + B_n \sinh(2n-1)\pi y/2a.$$

Because $Y(0) = 0$, we choose $A_n = 0$, so

$$u(x, y) = \Sigma B_n \sin(2n-1)\pi x/2a \, \sinh(2n-1)\pi y/2a.$$

Finally we satisfy the condition $u(x, b) = f(x)$ by choosing

$$B_n = b_{2n-1}/\sinh(2n-1)\pi b/2a,$$

where the $\{b_{2n-1}\}$ are the odd half-multiple sine coefficients of $f(x)$ on $[0, a]$, as given by Problem 21 in Section 9.3.

11. $u(x, y) = \Sigma C_n \sinh n\pi(a-x)/2b \, \cos n\pi y/2b$

where $C_n = 0$ for n even, whereas if n is odd then $C_n = a_n/(\sinh n\pi a/2b)$ where

$$a_n = \frac{2}{b} \int_0^b g(y) \cos \frac{n\pi y}{2b} \, dy.$$

12. The boundary value problem is

$$u_{xx} + u_{yy} = 0 \qquad (0 < x < 30, \ y > 0)$$

$$u(0, y) = u_x(30, y) = 0$$

$$u(x, y) \quad \text{bounded as} \quad y \to \infty$$

$$u(x, 0) = 25$$

The eigenvalue problem

$$X'' + \lambda X = 0, \qquad X(0) = X'(30) = 0$$

yields (by Example 4 in Section 3.10)

$$\lambda_n = (2n - 1)^2 \pi^2 / 3600, \qquad X_n(x) = \sin(2n - 1)\pi x / 60$$

for $n = 1, 2, 3, \cdots$. Then

$$Y_n'' - \lambda_n Y_n = 0$$

yields

$$Y_n(y) = A_n e^{n\pi y/60} + B_n e^{-n\pi y/60}$$

and we take $A_n = 0$ in order that $Y_n(y)$ be bounded as $y \to \infty$. Hence

$$u(x, y) = \Sigma B_n e^{-n\pi y/60} \sin(2n - 1)\pi x / 60.$$

In order to obtain the formula for $u(x, y)$ given in the text it remains only to compute (Section 9.3, Problem 21) the odd half-multiple Fourier sine coefficients of $u(x, 0) = 25$ on $[0, 30]$.

13. $C_n = b_n / a^n$ where the $\{b_n\}$ are the Fourier sine coefficients of $f(\theta)$ on $0 \leq \theta \leq \pi$.

14. When we introduce the separation of variables $u(r, \theta) = R(r)T(\theta)$, we get

$$T_0(\theta) = 1,$$
$$R_0(r) = C_0 + D_0 \ln r,$$
$$T_n(\theta) = A_n \cos n\theta + B_n \sin n\theta,$$
$$R_n(r) = C_n r^n + D_n r^{-n}$$

just as in Equations (25)–(30) in the text. We choose $B_n = 0$ in order that $T'(0) = T'(\pi) = 0$, and $D_n = 0$ in order that $R(r)$ be continuous at $r = 0$. Hence

$$u(r, \theta) = c_0/2 + \Sigma c_n r^n \cos n\theta,$$

and we satisfy the condition $u(a, \theta) = f(\theta)$ by choosing $c_0 = a_0$, $c_n = a_n / a^n$ where the $\{a_n\}$ are the Fourier cosine coefficients of $f(\theta)$ on $[0, \pi]$.

15. $C_n = \dfrac{2}{\pi a^{n/2}} \displaystyle\int_0^\pi f(\theta) \sin \dfrac{n\theta}{2} d\theta$

16. The only difference between the exterior problem here and the interior problem in the text is that in

$$R_n(r) = C_n r^n + D_n r^{-n}$$

we must choose $C_n = 0$ in order that $R_n(r)$ be bounded as $r \to \infty$.

20.   When we substitute $v(r, t) = r\, u(r, t)$ we get the boundary value problem

$$v_t = k v_{rr} \qquad (r < a, \quad t > 0)$$

$$v(0, t) = v(a, t) = 0$$

$$v(r, 0) = T_0 r$$

that corresponds to a heated rod along the interval $0 \le r \le a$. It therefore follows from Equation (31) in Section 9.5 that

$$v(r, t) = \Sigma\, b_n \exp(-n^2 \pi^2 kt/a^2) \sin n\pi x/a.$$

To get the formula given in the text it remains only to calculate the Fourier sine coefficients $\{b_n\}$ of $f(r) = T_0 r$ on $0 < r < a$, and finally to divide $v(r, t)$ by r to get $u(r, t)$.

21.   (a)   Since we cannot simply substitute $r = 0$, we apply continuity of $u(r, t)$ at $r = 0$ and calculate

$$u(0, t) = \lim_{r \to 0} u(r, t)$$

noting that

$$\lim_{r \to 0} \frac{\sin n\pi r / a}{r} = \frac{n\pi}{a}$$

(using l'Hospital's rule, for instance).

CHAPTER 10

EIGENVALUES AND BOUNDARY VALUE PROBLEMS

SECTION 10.1

STURM-LIOUVILLE PROBLEMS AND EIGENFUNCTION EXPANSIONS

1. In the notation of Equation (9) in Section 10.1 of the text we have $\alpha_1 = \beta_1 = 0$ and $\alpha_2 = \beta_2 = 1$, so Theorem 1 implies that the eigenvalues are all nonnegative. If $\lambda = 0$, then $y'' = 0$ implies that $y(x) = Ax + B$. Then $y'(x) = A$, so the endpoint conditions yield $A = 0$, but B remains arbitrary. Hence $\lambda_0 = 0$ is an eigenvalue with eigenfunction

    $$y_0(x) = 1.$$

    If $\lambda = \alpha^2 > 0$, then the equation $y'' + \alpha^2 y = 0$ has general solution

    $$y(x) = A \cos \alpha x + B \sin \alpha x,$$

    with

    $$y'(x) = -A\alpha \sin \alpha x + B\alpha \cos \alpha x.$$

    Then $y'(0) = 0$ yields $B = 0$ so $A \neq 0$, and then

    $$y'(L) = -A\alpha \sin \alpha L = 0,$$

    so αL must be an integral multiple of π. Thus the nth positive eigenvalue is

    $$\lambda_n = \alpha_n^2 = n^2\pi^2/L^2,$$

    and the associated eigenfunction is

    $$y_n(x) = \cos n\pi x/L.$$

2. In the notation of Equation (9) in this section we have $\alpha_1 = \beta_2 = 1$ and $\alpha_2 = \beta_1 = 0$, so Theorem 1 implies that the eigenvalues are all nonnegative. If $\lambda = 0$, then $y'' = 0$ implies $y(x) = Ax + B$. But then $y(0) = B = 0$ and $y'(L) = A = 0$, so it follows that 0 is not an eigenvalue. We may therefore write $\lambda = \alpha^2 > 0$, so our equation is $y'' + \alpha^2 y = 0$ with general solution

    $$y(x) = A \cos \alpha x + B \sin \alpha x.$$

Now $y(0) = A = 0$, so $y(x) = B \sin \alpha x$ and

$$y'(x) = B\alpha \cos \alpha x.$$

Hence

$$y'(L) = B\alpha \cos \alpha L = 0,$$

so it follows that αL must be an odd multiple of $\pi/2$. Thus

$$\alpha_n = (2n - 1)\pi/2L, \qquad \lambda_n = \alpha_n^2, \qquad y_n(x) = \sin \alpha_n x.$$

3. If $\lambda = 0$ then $y'' = 0$ yields $y(x) = Ax + B$ as usual. But $y'(0) = A = 0$, and then $hy(L) + y'(L) = h(B) + 0 = 0$, so $B = 0$ also. Thus $\lambda = 0$ is not an eigenvalue. If $\lambda = \alpha^2 > 0$ so our equation is $y'' + \alpha^2 y = 0$, then

$$y(x) = A \cos \alpha x + B \sin \alpha x,$$

$$y'(x) = -A\alpha \sin \alpha x + B\alpha \cos \alpha x.$$

Now $y'(0) = 0$ yields $B = 0$, so we may write

$$y(x) = \cos \alpha x, \qquad y'(x) = -\alpha \sin \alpha x.$$

The equation

$$hy(L) + y'(L) = h \cos \alpha L - \alpha \sin \alpha L = 0$$

then gives

$$\tan \alpha L = h/\alpha = hL/\alpha L,$$

so $\beta_n = \alpha_n L$ is the nth positive root of the equation

$$\tan x = hL/x.$$

Thus

$$\lambda_n = \alpha_n^2 = \beta_n^2/L^2, \qquad y_n(x) = \cos \beta_n x/L.$$

Finally, a sketch of the graphs $y = \tan x$ and $y = hL/x$ indicates that $\beta_n \approx (n - 1)\pi$ for n large.

4. Here $\alpha_1 = h > 0$, $\alpha_2 = \beta_1 = 1$, and $\beta_2 = 0$, so by Theorem 1 in Section 10.1 there are no negative eigenvalues. If $\lambda = 0$ and $y(x) = Ax + B$, then the equations

$$hy(0) - y'(0) = hB - A = 0, \qquad y(L) = AL + B = 0$$

imply $h = A/B = -1/L < 0$. Thus 0 is not an eigenvalue. If $\lambda = \alpha^2 > 0$ and

$$y(x) = A \cos \alpha x + B \sin \alpha x,$$

then the condition $hy(0) = y'(0)$ yields $B = hA/\alpha$, so

$$y(x) = (A/\alpha)(\alpha \cos \alpha x + h \sin \alpha x)$$

$$= (A/\beta)(\beta \cos \beta x/L + hL \sin \beta x/L)$$

where $\beta = \alpha L$. Then the condition

$$y(L) = (A/B)(\beta \cos \beta + hL \sin \beta) = 0$$

reduces to $\tan \beta = -\beta/hL$.

6. $y_n(x) = \sin (2n - 1)\pi x/2L$ so Equation (25) in Section 10.1 yields

$$c_n \int_0^L \sin^2 (2n-1)\pi x/2L \, dx = \int_0^L f(x) \sin(2n-1)\pi x/2L \, dx.$$

When we evaluate the integral on the left we immediately get the formula in (29).

7.   The coefficient c_n in Eq. (23) of this section is given by Formula (25) with $f(x) = r(x) = 1$, $a = 0$, $b = L$, and $y_n(x) = \sin \beta_n x/L$. Using the fact that $\tan \beta_n = -\beta_n/hL$, so $(\sin \beta_n)/\beta_n = -(\cos \beta_n)/hL$, we find that

$$\int_0^L \sin^2 \beta_n x/L \, dx = \left(hL + \cos^2 \beta_n\right)/2h$$

and

$$\int_0^L \sin \beta_n x/L \, dx = L(1 - \cos \beta_n)/\beta_n.$$

Hence the desired eigenfunction expansion is

$$1 = 2hL \sum_{n=1}^{\infty} \frac{1 - \cos \beta_n}{\beta_n \left(hL + \cos^2 \beta_n\right)} \sin \frac{\beta_n x}{L}.$$

for $0 < x < L$.

8.   The coefficient c_n in (23) is given by Formula (25) with $f(x) = r(x) = 1$, $a = 0$, $b = L$, and $y_n(x) = \cos \beta_n x/L$. The result is

$$c_n = (4 \sin \beta_n)/(2\beta_n + \sin 2\beta_n)$$

for $n = 1, 2, 3, \cdots$, so the desired eigenfunction expansion is

$$1 = \sum_{n=1}^{\infty} \frac{4\sin\beta_n}{2\beta_n + \sin 2\beta_n} \cos\frac{\beta_n x}{L}.$$

9. The coefficient c_n in (23) is given by Formula (25) with $f(x) = r(x) = 1$, $a = 0$, $b = 1$, and $y_n(x) = \sin\beta_n x$. Using the fact that $\tan\beta_n = -\beta_n/h$, so $h\sin\beta_n = -\beta_n\cos\beta_n$, we find that

$$\int_0^1 \sin^2\beta_n x\, dx = \left(h + \cos^2\beta_n\right)/2h$$

and

$$\int_0^1 x\sin\beta_n x\, dx = \left(\sin\beta_n - \beta_n\cos\beta_n\right)/\beta_n^2 = (1+h)(\sin\beta_n)/\beta_n^2.$$

It follows that the desired expansion is given by

$$x = 2h(1+h)\sum_{n=1}^{\infty} \frac{\sin\beta_n \sin\beta_n x}{\beta_n^2\left(h + \cos^2\beta_n\right)}$$

for $0 < x < 1$.

10. The coefficient c_n in (23) is given by Formula (25) with $f(x) = x$, $r(x) = 1$, $a = 0$, $b = 1$, and $y_n(x) = \cos\beta_n x$. The result is

$$c_n = 4(\beta_n\sin\beta_n + \cos\beta_n - 1) / \beta_n(2\beta_n + \sin 2\beta_n).$$

With this value of c_n for $n = 1, 2, 3, \cdots$ the desired eigenfunction expansion is

$$x = \Sigma\, c_n\cos\beta_n x/L.$$

11. If $\lambda = 0$ then $y'' = 0$ implies that $y(x) = Ax + B$. Then $y(0) = 0$ gives $B = 0$, so $y(x) = Ax$. Hence

$$hy(L) - y'(L) = h(AL) - A = A(hL - 1) = 0$$

if and only if $hL = 1$, in which case $\lambda_0 = 0$ has associated eigenfunction $y_0(x) = x$.

12. If $\lambda = -\alpha^2 < 0$, then the general solution of $y'' - \alpha^2 y = 0$ is

$$y(x) = A\cosh\alpha x + B\sinh\alpha x.$$

But then $y(0) = A = 0$, so we may take $y(x) = \sinh\alpha x$. Now the condition $hy(L) = y'(L)$ yields

$$h \sinh \alpha L = \alpha \cosh \alpha L.$$

It follows that $\beta = \alpha L$ must be a root of the equation

$$\tanh x = x/hL.$$

The curve $y = \tanh x$ passes through the origin with slope 1, and is concave upward for $x < 0$, concave downward for $x > 0$. Hence this curve and the line $y = x/hL$ intersect other than at the origin if and only if the slope of the line is less than 1, that is, if and only if $hL > 1$. In this case, with β_0 the positive root of $\tanh x = x/hL$, we have $\lambda_0 = -\beta_0^2$ and $y_0(x) = \sinh \beta_0 x$.

13. The computation with $\lambda = +\alpha^2 > 0$ is essentially the same as in Problem 12, replacing hyperbolic functions with ordinary trigonometric functions.

14. With $\lambda = 0$, $y'' = 0$, and hence $y(x) = Ax + B$, we have $y(0) = B = 0$, so $y(x) = Ax$. Then the condition $hy(L) = y'(L)$ reduces to the equation $hL = A$, which is satisfied because $hL = 1$. Thus $\lambda_0 = 0$ is an eigenvalue with associated eigenfunction $y_0(x) = x$. Together with the positive eigenvalues and associated eigenfunctions provided by Problem 13, this gives the eigenfunction expansion

$$f(x) = c_0 x + \Sigma c_n \sin \beta_n x/L$$

where $\tan \beta_n = \beta_n$. The given formulas for the coefficients follow readily upon evaluation of the denominator integrals in (25).

18. By Equation (16) in Section 9.3,

$$bx = (2bL/\pi) \Sigma [(-1)^{n+1}/n] \sin n\pi x/L.$$

If $y = \Sigma b_n \sin n\pi x/L$, then

$$EI y^{(4)} = EI \Sigma (n^4 \pi^4 b_n/L^4) \sin n\pi x/L.$$

When we equate the coefficients of $\sin n\pi x/L$ in these two series, we get

$$b_n = 2bL^5(-1)^{n+1}/EIn^5 \pi^5$$

as desired.

20. With $\lambda = \alpha^4$, the general solution of $y^{(4)} - \alpha^4 y = 0$ is

$$y(x) = A \cosh \alpha x + B \sinh \alpha x + C \cos \alpha x + D \sin \alpha x,$$

and then

$$y'(x) = \alpha(A \sinh \alpha x + B \cosh \alpha x - C \sin \alpha x + D \cos \alpha x).$$

The conditions $y(0) = 0$ and $y'(0) = 0$ yield $C = -A$ and $D = -B$, so now

$$y(x) = A(\cosh \alpha x - \cos \alpha x) + B(\sinh \alpha x - \sin \alpha x).$$

The conditions $y''(L) = 0$ and $y^{(3)}(L) = 0$ yield the two linear equations

$$A(\cosh \alpha L + \cos \alpha L) + B(\sinh \alpha L + \sin \alpha L) = 0,$$

$$A(\sinh \alpha L - \sin \alpha L) + B(\cosh \alpha L + \cos \alpha L) = 0.$$

This linear system can have a non-trivial solution for A and B only if its coefficient determinant vanishes,

$$(\cosh \alpha L + \cos \alpha L)^2 - (\sinh^2 \alpha L - \sin^2 \alpha L) = 0.$$

This equation simplifies to

$$\cosh \alpha L \cos \alpha L + 1 = 0,$$

so $\beta = \alpha L = x$ satisfies the equation

$$\cosh x \cos x = -1.$$

The eigenvalue corresponding to the nth root β_n is

$$\lambda_n = \alpha_n^4 = (\beta_n/L)^4.$$

Finally the first equation in the pair above yields

$$B = -A(\cosh \alpha L + \cos \alpha L)/(\sinh \alpha L + \sin \alpha L),$$

so we may take

$$y_n(x) = (\sinh \beta_n + \sin \beta_n)(\cosh \beta_n x/L - \cos \beta_n x/L)$$
$$- (\cosh \beta_n + \cos \beta_n)(\sinh \beta_n x/L - \sin \beta_n x/L)$$

as the eigenfunction associated with the eigenvalue λ_n.

SECTION 10.2

APPLICATIONS OF EIGENFUNCTION SERIES

1. Most of the work required here has already been done in Problem 3 of Section 10.1,

where we saw that the Sturm-Liouville problem

$$X'' + \alpha^2 X = 0, \qquad X'(0) = hX(L) + X'(L) = 0$$

has eigenfunctions

$$X_n(x) = \cos \beta_n x/L$$

for $n = 1, 2, 3, \cdots$, with $\{\beta_n\}$ being the positive roots of the equation $\tan x = hL/x$. For the coefficients in the eigenfunction expansion we need only calculate the integral

$$\int_0^L \cos^2 \beta_n x / L \, dx = \left(hL + \sin^2 \beta_n\right)/2h.$$

2. $\quad u(x, y) = \Sigma c_n \sinh \beta_n(L - y)/L \sin \beta_n x/L$

where the $\{\beta_n\}$ are the positive roots of the equation $\tan x = -x/hL$ and

$$c_n = \frac{4\beta_n}{L(\sinh \beta_n)(2\beta_n - \sin 2\beta_n)} \int_0^L f(x) \sin \frac{\beta_n x}{L} \, dx.$$

3. $\quad u(x, y) = \Sigma c_n \sinh \beta_n(L - x)/L \cos \beta_n y/L$

where the $\{\beta_n\}$ are the positive roots of the equation $x \tan x = hL$ and

$$c_n = \frac{2h}{(\sinh \beta_n)(hL + \sin^2 \beta_n)} \int_0^L g(y) \cos \frac{\beta_n y}{L} \, dy.$$

4. $\quad u(x, y) = \Sigma c_n \exp(-\beta_n y/L) \sin \beta_n x/L$

where the $\{\beta_n\}$ are the positive roots of the equation $\tan x = -x/hL$ and

$$c_n = \frac{4\beta_n}{L(2\beta_n - \sin 2\beta_n)} \int_0^L f(x) \sin \frac{\beta_n x}{L} \, dx.$$

5. $\quad u(x, t) = \Sigma c_n \exp(-\beta_n kt/L^2) X_n(x)$

where the $\{\beta_n\}$ are the positive roots of the equation $\tan x = -x/hL$,

$$X_n(x) = \beta_n \cos \beta_n x/L + hL \sin \beta_n x/L,$$

and

$$c_n \int_0^L [X_n(x)]^2 \, dx = \int_0^L f(x) X_n(x) \, dx.$$

6. $u(x, t) = \Sigma\, c_n[\exp(-\beta_n^2 kt/L^2)][\beta_n\cos\,\beta_n x/L + hL\sin\,\beta_n x/L]$

where the $\{\beta_n\}$ are the roots of the equation

$$\tan x = 2hLx/(x^2 - h^2 L^2).$$

7. Four terms of the series for $u(x, y)$ give $u(1, 1) \approx 31.38°C$.

10. **(a)** With $\delta = 7.75$ gm/cm^3 and $E = 2{\cdot}10^{12}$ in Equation (16), the speed of sound in steel is

$$a = \sqrt{(E/\delta)} \approx 5.08 \times 10^5 \text{ cm/sec} \approx 11364 \text{ mph}.$$

(b) With $\delta = 1$ gm/cm^3 and $K = 2.25{\cdot}10^{10}$ in Equation (16), the speed of sound in water is

$$a = \sqrt{(K/\delta)} \approx 1.50 \times 10^5 \text{ cm/sec} \approx 3355 \text{ mph}.$$

12. The boundary value problem is

$$u_{tt} = a^2 u_{xx} \quad (0 < x < L,\ t > 0)$$
$$u(0, t) = ku(L, t) + AEu_x(L, t) = 0$$
$$u(x, 0) = f(x),$$
$$u_t(x, 0) = 0.$$

Starting with the general solution

$$X(x) = A\cos\,\alpha x + B\sin\,\alpha x$$

of $X'' + \alpha^2 X = 0$, the condition $X(0) = 0$ gives $A = 0$, so

$$X(x) = \sin\,\alpha x, \qquad X'(x) = \alpha\cos\,\alpha x.$$

Then the condition $kX(L) + AEX'(L) = 0$ yields

$$k\sin\,\alpha L + AE\alpha\cos\,\alpha L = 0,$$

which is equivalent to the equation

$$\tan x = -AEx/kL$$

with $x = \alpha L$, $\alpha = x/L$. If $\{\beta_n\}$ are the positive roots of this equation, then the nth eigenvalue is $\lambda_n = \alpha_n^2 = (\beta_n/L)^2$ with associated eigenfunction

$$X_n(x) = \sin \beta_n x/L.$$

The associated function of t is

$$T_n(t) = A_n\cos \beta_n at/L + B_n\sin \beta_n at/L,$$

but the condition $T'(0) = 0$ yields $B_n = 0$. Hence we obtain a solution of the form

$$u(x, t) = \Sigma\, c_n\cos \beta_n at/L \sin \beta_n x/L.$$

16.   When we substitute $v(r, t) = ru_r(r, t)$ we get the boundary value problem

$$v_t = kv_{rr}$$
$$v(0, t) = v(a, t) - av_r(a, t) = 0$$
$$v(r, 0) = r\, f(r).$$

Then $v(r, t) = R(r)T(t)$ yields the equations

$$R'' + \lambda R = 0, \qquad T' = -\lambda kT.$$

If $\lambda_0 = 0$ then $R(r) = Ar + B$. The condition $R(0) = 0$ gives $B = 0$, and $R(r) = Ar$ satisfies the condition $R(a) - aR'(a) = 0$. Thus $\lambda_0 = 0$ is an eigenvalue with eigenfunction

$$R_0(r) = r; \qquad T_0(t) = 1.$$

If $\lambda = \alpha^2 > 0$ then

$$R(r) = A \cos \alpha r + B \sin \alpha r$$

and $R(0) = 0$ gives $A = 0$, so

$$R(r) = \sin \alpha r, \qquad R'(r) = \alpha \cos \alpha r.$$

The condition $R(a) = aR'(a)$ yields $\sin \alpha a = a\alpha \cos \alpha a$, that is,

$$\tan x = x$$

where $x = \alpha a$. If $\{\beta_n\}$ are the roots of this equation, then $\lambda_n = (\beta_n/a)^2$ is an eigenvalue with associated eigenfunction

$$R_n(r) = \sin \beta_n r/a; \qquad T_n(t) = \exp(-(\beta_n^2 kt/a^2).$$

We therefore obtain a solution of the form

$$v(r, t) = c_0 r + \Sigma\, c_n \exp(-\beta_n^2 kt/a^2)\sin \beta_n r/L.$$

The formulas given for the coefficients follow immediately from Problem 14 in Section 10.1, and finally we obtain $u(r, t)$ upon division of $v(r, t)$ by r.

18. The only difference from Example 3 in the text is that the solution of Equation (37) with $T_n{}'(0) = 0$ is $T_n(t) = \sin n^2 \pi^2 a^2 t/L^2$.

20. The fundamental frequency is

$$\omega_1 = \pi^2 a^2/L^2 = (\pi^2/L^2)\sqrt{(EI/\rho)}.$$

With

$$E = 2 \cdot 10^{12} \text{ dyne/cm}^2,$$

$$I = (2.54)^4/12 \approx 3.47 \text{ cm}^4,$$

$$\rho = (7.75)(2.54)^2 \approx 50.00 \text{ gm/cm},$$

$$L = (19)(2.54) \approx 48.26 \text{ cm},$$

we calculate

$$\omega_1 \approx 1578 \text{ rad/sec} \approx 251 \text{ cycles/sec}.$$

Thus we hear middle C (approximately).

SECTION 10.3

STEADY PERIODIC SOLUTIONS AND NATURAL FREQUENCIES

In Problems 1–6 we substitute $u(x, t) = X(x)\cos \omega t$ in

$$u_{tt} = a^2 u_{xx} \qquad\qquad (a^2 = E/\delta)$$

and then cancel the factor $\cos \omega t$ to obtain the ordinary differential equation

$$a^2 X'' + \omega^2 X = 0$$

with general solution

$$X(x) = A \cos \omega x/a + B \sin \omega x/a.$$

It then remains only to apply the given endpoint conditions to determine the natural (circular) frequencies -- the values of ω for which a non-trivial solution exists.

1. With endpoint conditions $X(0) = X(L) = 0$ the nth natural frequency is $\omega_n = (n\pi/L)$ $\sqrt{(E/\delta)}$.

2. Endpoint conditions: $X'(0) = X'(L) = 0$

The condition $X'(0) = 0$ gives $B = 0$, so we have

$$X(x) = \cos \omega x/a, \qquad X'(x) = -(\omega/a)\sin \omega x/a.$$

Hence the condition $X'(L) = 0$ implies that $\omega L/a$ is an integral multiple of π. Thus the nth natural frequency is

$$\omega_n = n\pi a/L = (n\pi/L)\sqrt{(E/\delta)}.$$

3. With endpoint conditions $X(0) = X'(L) = 0$ the nth natural frequency is $\omega_n = [(2n-1)\pi/2L]\sqrt{(E/\delta)}$.

4. Endpoint conditions: $u(0,t) = mu_{tt}(L, t) + AEu_x(L, t) = 0$

The nth natural frequency is

$$\omega_n = (\beta_n/L)\sqrt{(E/\delta)}$$

where β_n is the nth positive root of the equation

$$mx \tan x = M.$$

This is the special case $k = 0$ of Problem 7 below.

5. Endpoint conditions: $u_x(0, t) = ku(L, t) + AEu_x(L, t) = 0$

The nth natural frequency is

$$\omega_n = (\beta_n/L)\sqrt{(E/\delta)}$$

where β_n is the nth positive root of the equation

$$AEx \tan x = kL.$$

6. Endpoint conditions:

$$m_0 u_{tt}(0, t) - AEu_x(0, t) = 0,$$
$$m_1 u_{tt}(L, t) + AEu_x(L, t) = 0$$

When we substitute $u(x, t) = X(t)\cos \omega t$ in the two endpoint conditions and then cancel the cos ωt factor, we get the equations

$$m_0 \omega^2 X(0) + KX'(0) = 0$$

$$m_1 \omega^2 X(L) - KX'(L) = 0$$

where we write $K = AE$ to avoid confusion with the coefficient of $\cos \omega x/a$ in

$$X(x) = A \cos \omega x/a + B \sin \omega x/a.$$

Then

$$X(0) = A,$$

$$X'(0) = B\omega/a$$

$$X(L) = A \cos \omega L/a + B \sin \omega L/a$$

$$X'(L) = (\omega/a)(-A \sin \omega L/a + B \cos \omega L/a).$$

If we write $z = \omega L/a$, then

$$X(0) = A,$$

$$X'(0) = Bz/L$$

$$X(L) = A \cos z + B \sin z$$

$$X'(L) = (z/L)(-A \sin z + B \cos z).$$

When we substitute these values and $\omega = az/L$ in the two endpoint conditions above and collect coefficients of A and B, we get the equations

$$m_0 a^2 z A + KLB = 0,$$

$$A(m_1 a^2 z \cos z + KL \sin z) + B(m_1 a^2 z \sin z - KL \cos z) = 0.$$

In order for this system to have a non-trivial solution for A and B, its determinant of coefficients must vanish,

$$m_0 a^2 z(m_1 a^2 z \sin z - KL \cos z) - KL(m_1 a^2 z \cos z + KL \sin z) = 0.$$

When we substitute $a^2 = E/\delta$, $M = \delta AL$, and $K = AE$, this last equation simplifies finally to the frequency equation

$$(m_0 m_1 z^2 - M^2)\sin z = M(m_0 + m_1)z \cos z.$$

If β_n is the nth positive root, then the nth natural frequency is

$$\omega_n = (\beta_n/L)\sqrt{(E/\delta)}.$$

7. Endpoint conditions:

$$u(0, t) = mu_{tt}(L, t) + AEu_x(L, t) + ku(L, t) = 0$$

The condition $u(0, t) = 0$ implies that

$$X(x) = \sin \omega x/a, \qquad X'(x) = (\omega/a)\cos \omega x/a.$$

When we substitute $u(x, t) = X(x)\cos \omega t$ in the endpoint condition at $x = L$ and cancel the $\cos \omega t$ factor we get

$$-m\omega^2 X(L) + AEX'(L) + kX(L) = 0.$$

Next we substitute

$$z = \omega L/a, \qquad \omega = az/L, \qquad a^2 = E/\delta,$$

$$X(L) = \sin z, \qquad X'(L) = (z/L) \cos z.$$

The result simplifies readily to the frequency equation

$$(mEz^2 - k\delta L^2)\sin z = MEz \cos z.$$

If β_n is the nth positive root, then the nth natural frequency is $\omega_n = (\beta_n/L)\sqrt{(E/\delta)}$.

In Problems 8–14 we substitute $y(x, t) = X(x)\cos \omega t$ in

$$y_{tt} + a^4 y_{xxxx} = 0 \qquad (a^4 = EI/\rho)$$

and then cancel the factor $\cos \omega t$ to obtain the ordinary differential equation

$$a^4 X^{(4)} - \omega^2 X = 0$$

with general solution

$$X(x) = A \cosh \theta x/a + B \sinh \theta x/a + C \cos \theta x/a + D \sin \theta x/a.$$

where $\theta = \sqrt{\omega}$. We then get the natural frequencies of vibration by applying the given endpoint conditions.

8. Endpoint conditions: $y(0, t) = y_{xx}(0, t) = 0, \quad y(L, t) = y_{xx}(L, t) = 0$

Just as in Example 3 of Section 10.2, the conditions $X(0) = X''(0) = 0$ imply that $A = C = 0$, so

$$X(L) = B \sinh \theta L/a + D \sin \theta L/a = 0,$$

$$X''(L) = (\theta^2/a^2)(B \sinh \theta L/a - D \sin \theta L/a) = 0.$$

It follows that

$$B \sinh \theta L/a = D \sin \theta L/a = 0.$$

But $\sinh \theta L/a \neq 0$ so $B = 0$. Hence $D \neq 0$ so $\sin \theta L/a = 0$. Thus $\theta L/a = n\pi$, an integral multiple of π. Therefore the nth natural frequency $\omega = \theta^2$ is given by

$$\omega_n = n^2 \pi^2 a^2/L^2 = (n^2\pi^2/L^2)\sqrt{(EI/\rho)}.$$

10. Endpoint conditions: $y(0, t) = y_x(0, t) = 0,$ $\quad y_{xx}(L, t) = y_{xxx}(L, t) = 0$

Here we have the equation

$$X^{(4)} - \lambda X = 0$$

with $\lambda = \omega^2/a^4$ and endpoint conditions

$$X(0) = X'(0) = X''(L) = X^{(3)}(L) = 0.$$

According to Problem 20 in Section 10.1 the nth eigenvalue is

$$\lambda_n = (\omega_n/a^2)^2 = (\beta_n/L)^4$$

where the $\{\beta_n\}$ are the positive roots of the equation

$$\cosh x \cos x = -1.$$

Thus the nth natural frequency is

$$\omega_n = (\beta_n/L)^2 a^2 = (\beta_n/L)^2\sqrt{(EI/\rho)}.$$

12. This problem is the special case $k = 0$ of Problem 14 which follows.

14. Endpoint conditions:

$$y(0, t) = y_x(0, t) = y_{xxx}(L, t) = 0$$

$$m y_{tt}(L, t) = EI y_{xxx}(L, t) - k y(L, t)$$

With $p = \theta/a,$ $\theta = \sqrt{\omega}$ we may write

$$X(x) = A \cosh px + B \sinh px + C \cos px + D \sin px.$$

The conditions $X(0) = X'(0) = 0$ readily imply that $C = -A$ and $D = -B$, so

$$X \quad = \quad A(\cosh px - \cos px) + \quad B(\sinh px - \sin px),$$
$$X' \quad = \quad pA(\sinh px + \sin px) + pB(\cosh px - \cos px),$$
$$X'' \quad = \quad p^2A(\cosh px + \cos px) + p^2B(\sinh px + \sin px),$$
$$X^{(3)} \quad = \quad p^3A(\sinh px - \sin px) + p^3B(\cosh px + \cos px).$$

The endpoint conditions at $x = L$ are

$$X''(L) = 0,$$
$$(k - m\omega^2)X(L) - EIX^{(3)}(L) = 0.$$

When we substitute the derivatives above and write $z = pL$ we get

$$A\,(\cosh z + \cos z) + B\,(\sinh z + \sin z) = 0,$$

$$A\,[(k - m\omega^2)(\cosh z - \cos z) - EIp^3(\sinh z - \sin z)]$$
$$+ B\,[(k - m\omega^2)(\sinh z - \sin z) - EIp^3(\cosh z + \cos z)] = 0.$$

If Δ denotes the coefficient determinant of these two linear equations in A and B, then the necessary condition $\Delta = 0$ for a non-trivial solution reduces eventually to the equation

$$EIp^3(1 + \cosh z \cos z) - (k - m\omega^2)(\sinh z \cos z - \cosh z \sin z) = 0.$$

Finally we substitute $p = z/L$, $M = \rho L$, and

$$\omega^2 = p^4 a^4 = (z^4/L^4)(EI/\rho)$$

to get the frequency equation

$$MEIz^3(1 + \cosh z \cos z) = (kML^3 - mEIz^4)(\sinh z \cos z - \cosh z \sin z).$$

We may divide by $\cosh z \cos z$ to write this equation in the form

$$MEIz^3(1 + \operatorname{sech} z \sec z) = (kML^3 - mEIz^4)(\tanh z - \tan z).$$

If β_n denotes the nth positive root of this equation, then the nth natural frequency is

$$\omega_n = (\beta_n/L)^2\sqrt{(EI/\rho)}.$$

15. We want to calculate the fundamental frequency of transverse vibration of a cantilever with the numerical parameters

$$L = 400 \text{ cm}$$
$$E = 2 \cdot 10^{12} \text{ gm/cm-sec}^2$$
$$I = (1/12)(30 \text{ cm})(2 \text{ cm})^3 = 20 \text{ cm}^4$$
$$\rho = (7.75 \text{ gm/cm}^3)(60 \text{ cm}^2) = 465 \text{ gm/cm}.$$

When we substitute these values and $\beta_1 = 1.8751$ in the frequency formula

$$\omega_1 = (\beta_1/L)^2 \sqrt{(EI/\rho)}$$

we find that $\omega_1 \approx 6.45$ rad/sec, so the fundamental frequency is $\omega_1/2\pi \approx 1.03$ cycles/sec. Thus the diver should bounce up and down on the end of the diving board about once every second.

16.   When we substitute $y(x, t) = X(x)\cos \omega t$ in the given partial differential equation

$$\rho y_{tt} + P y_{xx} + EI y_{xxxx} = 0$$

and cancel the factor $\cos \omega t$, we get the ordinary differential equation

$$EI X^{(4)} + P X'' - \lambda X = 0$$

where $\lambda = \rho \omega^2$. By solving the characteristic equation

$$EI \, r^4 + P r^2 - \lambda = 0$$

we find the general solution

$$X(x) = A \cosh \alpha x + B \sinh \alpha x + C \cos \beta x + D \sin \beta x$$

where

$$\alpha^2 = [-P + \sqrt{(P^2 + 4\lambda EI)}]/2EI,$$
$$\beta^2 = -[-P - \sqrt{(P^2 + 4\lambda EI)}]/2EI.$$

The endpoint conditions $X(0) = X''(0) = 0$ imply that $A = C = 0$, so

$$X(x) = B \sinh \alpha x + D \sin \beta x.$$

Then the conditions $X(L) = X''(L) = 0$ yield the equations

$$B \sinh \alpha L + D \sin \beta L = 0,$$
$$\alpha^2 B \sinh \alpha L - \beta^2 D \sin \beta L = 0.$$

The determinant of these two linear equations in B and D must vanish in order that a non-trivial solution exist, so

$$(\alpha^2 + \beta^2)\sinh \alpha L \sin \alpha L = 0.$$

It follows that $\sin \alpha L = 0$, so αL must be an integral multiple of π. The definitions of α^2 and β^2 imply that

$$\beta^2 - \alpha^2 = P/EI, \qquad \alpha^2 \beta^2 = \lambda/EI.$$

Hence if $\alpha_n = n\pi/L$, the corresponding value of β_n is

$$\beta_n = (n^2 \pi^2/L^2 + P/EI)^{1/2}.$$

Then the corresponding value of λ is

$$\lambda_n = EI(\alpha_n \beta_n)^2 = EI(n^4 \pi^4/L^4)(1 + PL^2/n^2 \pi^2 EI).$$

Finally, the nth natural frequency is given by

$$\omega_n = \sqrt{(\lambda_n/\rho)} = (n^2 \pi^2/L^2)(1 + PL^2/n^2 \pi^2 EI)^{1/2} \sqrt{(EI/\rho)}.$$

19. We want to determine a steady periodic solution of the form

$$y(x, t) = X(x)\sin \omega t$$

where, with $\theta = \sqrt{\omega}$ and $p = \theta/a$,

$$X(x) = A \cosh px + B \sinh px + C \cos px + D \sin px$$

as usual. The fixed end conditions $X(0) = X'(0) = 0$ imply that $C = -A$ and $D = -B$, so

$$X(x) = A(\cosh px - \cos px) + B(\sinh px - \sin px).$$

It remains only to find A and B. But the endpoint conditions

$$X''(L) = EIX^{(3)}(L) + F_0 = 0$$

yield the linear equations

$$A(\cosh pL + \cos pL) + B(\sinh pL + \sin pL) = 0$$
$$A(\sinh pL - \sin pL) + B(\cosh pL + \cos pL) = -F_0/p^3 EI$$

that can be solved for A and B.

22. When we substitute

$$e(x, t) = E(x)e^{i\omega t}$$

in the partial differential equation

$$e_{xx} = LCe_{tt} + (LG + RC)e_t + RGe$$

and cancel the factor $e^{i\omega t}$, the result is the ordinary differential equation

$$E''(x) - \gamma E(x) = 0$$

where

$$\gamma = (RG - LC\omega^2) + i\,\omega(LG + RC).$$

If $(\alpha + \beta i)^2 = \gamma$, then the general solution is

$$E(x) = Ae^{-\alpha x}e^{-i\beta x} + Be^{\alpha x}e^{i\beta x}.$$

In order that $e(x,t)$ be bounded as $x \to \infty$ we choose $B = 0$, and in order that $e(0, t) = E_0\cos \omega t$ we choose $A = E_0$. Then our steady periodic solution is the real part

$$\mathrm{Re}[E(x)e^{i\omega t}] = \mathrm{Re}[E_0 e^{-\alpha x}e^{-i\beta x}e^{i\omega t}] = E_0 e^{-\alpha x}\cos(\omega t - \beta x).$$

SECTION 10.4

CYLINDRICAL COORDINATE PROBLEMS

2. The boundary value problem we want to solve is

$$u_{tt} = a^2[u_{rr} + (1/r)u_r] \qquad (r < c, \quad t > 0)$$
$$u(c, t) = 0$$
$$u(r, 0) = 0,$$
$$u_t(r, 0) = v_0.$$

The substitution $u(r, t) = R(r)T(t)$ yields the equations

$$rR'' + R' + \alpha^2 rR = 0, \qquad T'' + \alpha^2 a^2 T = 0$$

with separation constant $\lambda = \alpha^2$. The first is the parametric Bessel equation of order zero with general solution

$$R(r) = AJ_0(\alpha r) + BY_0(\alpha r).$$

In order that $R(r)$ be continuous at $r = 0$ we choose $B = 0$, so $R(r) = AJ_0(\alpha r)$. Then

$$R(c) = AJ_0(\alpha c) = 0$$

requires that αc be one of the roots $\{\gamma_n\}$ of $J_0(x) = 0$. With $\alpha_n = \gamma_n/c$ we get

$$R_n(r) = J_0(\gamma_n r/c).$$

The corresponding function $T(t)$ of t is

$$T_n(t) = A_n\cos \gamma_n at/c + B_n\sin \gamma_n at/c,$$

and we choose $A_n = 0$ to satisfy the condition $T(0) = 0$. Thus the displacement function $u(r, t)$ is of the form

$$u(r, t) = \Sigma\, c_n J_0(\gamma_n r/c) \sin \gamma_n at/c,$$

with

$$u_t(r, 0) = \Sigma\, (c_n\gamma_n a/c)\, J_0(\gamma_n r/c).$$

In order to satisfy the initial condition $u_t(r, 0) = v_0$ we apply Equation (22) in the text and finally choose

$$c_n = \frac{c}{\gamma_n a} \cdot \frac{2}{c^2 J_1(\gamma_n)^2} \int_0^c rv_0 J_0\!\left(\frac{\gamma_n r}{c}\right) dr = \frac{2cv_0}{a\gamma_n^3 J_1(\gamma_n)^2} \int_0^{\gamma_n} x J_0(x)\, dx$$

$$= \frac{2cv_0}{a\gamma_n^3 J_1(\gamma_n)^2}\left[x J_1(x)\right]_0^{\gamma_n} = \frac{2cv_0}{a\gamma_n^2 J_1(\gamma_n)}.$$

3. (a) As in Problem 2,

$$u(r, t) = \Sigma\, c_n J_0(\gamma_n r/c)\sin \gamma_n at/c.$$

In order to satisfy the given initial condition we must choose

$$c_n = \frac{2}{\gamma_n ac J_1(\gamma_n)^2} \int_0^\varepsilon \left(\frac{P_0}{\rho\pi\varepsilon^2}\right) r J_0\!\left(\frac{\varepsilon_n r}{c}\right) dr = \frac{2P_0 c}{\rho\pi\varepsilon^2 \gamma_n^3 a J_1(\gamma_n)^2} \int_0^{\gamma_n \varepsilon/c} x J_0(x)\, dx$$

$$= \frac{2P_0 c}{\rho\pi\varepsilon^2 \gamma_n^3 a J_1(\gamma_n)^2} \cdot \frac{\gamma_n \varepsilon}{c} J_1\!\left(\frac{\gamma_n \varepsilon}{c}\right) = \frac{2cv_0}{a\gamma_n^2 J_1(\gamma_n)}.$$

$$c_n = \frac{2aP_0}{\pi c\rho a^2 \gamma_n J_1(\gamma_n)^2} \cdot \frac{J_1(\gamma_n \varepsilon/c)}{\gamma_n \varepsilon/c}.$$

(b) The final formula given in the text for $u(r, t)$ now follows because $\rho a^2 = T$ and

$J_1(x)/x \to 1/2$ as $x \to 0$.

6.   **(a)**   We start with the boundary value problem

$$u_{rr} + (1/r)u_r + u_{zz} = 0 \quad (r < c, \ 0 < z < L)$$

$$u_r(c, z) = 0$$

$$u(r, 0) = 0,$$

$$u(r, L) = f(r).$$

The substitution $u(r, z) = R(r)Z(z)$ yields the equations

$$rR'' + R' + \alpha^2 rR = 0, \qquad Z'' - \alpha^2 Z = 0$$

with separation constant $\lambda = \alpha^2$. The homogeneous endpoint conditions are

$$R'(c) = Z(0) = 0.$$

If $\lambda = \alpha^2 = 0$ then $rR'' + R = 0$ implies

$$R(r) = A + B \ln r.$$

We choose $B = 0$ for continuity at $r = 0$, so $R(r) = A$. Then $R'(c) = 0$, so $\lambda_0 = 0$ is an eigenvalue, and we may take $R_0(r) = 1$. The equation $Z''(z) = 0$ implies $Z(z) = Az + B$, but $Z(0) = 0$ implies $B = 0$, so we take $Z_0(z) = z$.

If $\lambda = \alpha^2 > 0$ then we have the parametric Bessel equation with general solution

$$R(r) = A J_0(\alpha r) + B Y(\alpha r).$$

In order that $R(r)$ be continuous at $r = 0$ we choose $B = 0$, so $R(r) = A J_0(\alpha r)$. Then

$$R'(c) = \alpha A J_0'(\alpha c) = 0$$

requires that $\gamma = \alpha c$ be a root of the equation

$$J_0'(x) = 0.$$

If $\alpha_n = \gamma_n/c$ where γ_n is the nth positive root of this equation, then

$$R_n(r) = J_0(\gamma_n r/c).$$

The corresponding function $Z(z)$ of z is

$$Z_n(z) = A_n \cosh \gamma_n z/c + B_n \sinh \gamma_n z/c,$$

and we choose $A_n = 0$ because $Z(0) = 0$. Thus we get the solution

$$u(r, z) = c_0 z + \Sigma\, c_n J_0(\gamma_n r/c)\sinh \gamma_n z/c$$

where $J_0'(\gamma_n) = 0$. To satisfy the condition $u(r, L) = f(r)$ we apply the formulas in (24) in the text and choose

$$c_0 = \frac{2}{Lc^2}\int_0^c r f(r)\, dr,$$

$$c_n = \frac{2}{c^2 \sinh(\gamma_n L/c)J_0(\gamma_n)^2}\int_0^c r f(r)J_0\left(\frac{\gamma_n r}{c}\right)dr.$$

(b)   If $f(r) = u_0$ (constant), then the coefficient formulas above readily yield $c_0 = u_0/L$ and $c_n = 0$ for $n > 0$, the latter because

$$\int x J_0(x)\, dx = x J_1(x) + C = -x J_0'(x) + C.$$

Hence the series reduces to the solution $u(r, z) = u_0 z/L$ that one might well guess without all these computations.

7.   We want to solve the boundary value problem

$$u_{rr} + (1/r)u_r + u_{zz} = 0 \qquad (r < 1,\, z > 0)$$

$$hu(1, z) + u_r(1, z) = 0$$

$$u(r, z) \text{ bounded as } z \to \infty$$

$$u(r, 0) = u_0.$$

We start with the separation of variables in Problem 6,

$$rR'' + R' + \alpha^2 rR = 0, \qquad Z'' - \alpha^2 Z = 0$$

and readily see that $\alpha = 0$ is not an eigenvalue. When we impose the condition

$$hR(1) + R'(1) = 0$$

on $R(r) = J_0(\alpha r)$, we find that α must satisfy the equation

$$hJ_0(x) + xJ_0'(x) = 0$$

that corresponds to Case 2 with $n = 0$ in Figure 10.4.2 of the text. If $\{\gamma_n\}$ are the positive roots of this equation then

$$R_n(r) = J_0(\gamma_n r).$$

The general solution of $Z'' = \gamma_n^2 Z$ is

$$Z_n(z) = A_n \exp(-\gamma_n z) + B_n \exp(\gamma_n z),$$

and we choose $B_n = 0$ so that $Z_n(z)$ will be bounded as $z \to \infty$. Thus we obtain a solution of the form

$$u(r, z) = \Sigma \, c_n \exp(-\gamma_n z) J_0(\gamma_n r)$$

where

$$h J_0(\gamma_n) + \gamma_n J_0'(\gamma_n) = 0.$$

We readily calculate the coefficients to get the final formula given in the text.

11. When we substitute $u(r, t) = R(r)\sin \omega t$ in the given partial differential equation and cancel the factor $\sin \omega t$, we get the ordinary differential equation

$$R'' + (1/r)R' + (\omega^2/a^2)R = -F_0/\omega^2.$$

The solution that is continuous at $r = 0$ is

$$R(r) = A J_0(\omega r/a) - F_0/\omega^2.$$

The condition $R(b) = 0$ yields

$$A = F_0/\omega^2 J_0(\omega b/a)$$

so it follows that

$$u(r, t) = [F_0/\omega^2 J_0(\omega b/a)][J_0(\omega r/a) - J_0(\omega b/a)] \sin \omega t.$$

12. When we substitute $y(x, t) = X(x)\sin \omega t$ in the partial differential equation

$$y_{tt} = (g/w)(wxy_x)_x = g(y_x + xy_{xx}),$$

we get the ordinary differential equation

$$x^2 X'' + xX' + (\omega^2 x/g)X = 0.$$

This is of the form of Equation (3) in Section 8.6 with $A = 1$, $B = 0$, $C = \omega^2/g$, and $q = 1$, so its general solution is given by

$$X(x) = A J_0(2\omega\sqrt{(x/g)}) + B Y_0(2\omega\sqrt{(x/g)}).$$

We choose $B = 0$ for continuity at $x = 0$, and the condition $X(L) = 0$ then requires that $2\omega\sqrt{(L/g)}$ be one of the roots $\{\gamma_n\}$ of the equation $J_0(x) = 0$. Hence the nth natural frequency of vibration of the hanging cable is

$$\omega_n = (\gamma_n/2)\sqrt{(g/L)}.$$

13.   With $w(x) = wx$ and $h(x) = h$ (where w and h on the right are constants) the given partial differential equation reduces to

$$xy_{tt} = gh(y_x + y_{xx}).$$

When we substitute $y(x, t) = X(x)\cos \omega t$ we get the parametric Bessel equation

$$x^2 X'' + xX' + (\omega^2 x^2/gh)X = 0$$

with (finite) solution

$$X(x) = A J_0(\omega x/\sqrt{(gh)}).$$

The condition $X = y_0$ implies that $A = y_0/J_0(\omega L/\sqrt{(gh)})$, so

$$y(x, t) = [y_0/J_0(\omega L/\sqrt{(gh)})] J_0(\omega x/\sqrt{(gh)})\cos \omega t.$$

14.   With $w(x) = w$ and $h(x) = kx$ the given partial differential equation reduces to

$$y_{tt} = gh(y_x + xy_{xx}).$$

When we substitute $y(x, t) = X(x)\cos \omega t$ we get the ordinary differential equation

$$x^2 X'' + xX' + (\omega^2 x/gh)X = 0.$$

This has the form of Equation (3) in Section 8.6 with $A = 1$, $B = 0$, $C = \omega^2/gh$, and $q = 1$, so its (bounded) solution is given by

$$X(x) = A J_0(2\omega\sqrt{(x/gh)}).$$

The condition $X(L) = y_0$ now implies that

$$A = y_0/J_0(2\omega\sqrt{(L/gh)}).$$

16.   With $\lambda = \alpha^2$ the general solution is

$$y(x) = A J_0(\alpha x) + B Y_0(\alpha x).$$

The endpoint conditions $y(a) = y(b) = 0$ yield the linear equations

$$A\, J_0(\alpha a) + B\, Y_0(\alpha a) = 0,$$

$$A\, J_0(\alpha b) + B\, Y_0(\alpha b) = 0$$

in A and B. In order for there to exist a non-trivial solution for A and B the coefficient determinant must vanish. Hence α must be one of the solutions $\{\gamma_n\}$ of the equation

$$J_0(ax)\,Y_0(bx) - J_0(bx)\,Y_0(ax) = 0.$$

With $\alpha = \gamma_n$, $A = Y_0(\gamma_n a)$ and $B = -J_0(\gamma_n a)$, both conditions above are satisfied and we have the eigenfunction

$$R_n(x) = Y_0(\gamma_n a)\,J_0(\gamma_n x) - J_0(\gamma_n a)\,Y_0(\gamma_n x).$$

18. We start with the substitution $u(r,t) = R(r)\,T(t)$ in the heat equation. The result is given in Equations (25) and (26):

$$r^2 R'' + r R' + \alpha^2 r^2 R = 0, \quad T' = -\alpha^2 kT.$$

The first of these equations, together with the endpoint conditions

$$R(a) = R(b) = 0,$$

comprise the regular Sturm-Liouville problem of Problem 16. Hence its eigenvalues are given by $\alpha_n = \gamma_n$ where $\{\gamma_n\}$ are the positive roots of the equation in Eq.(41) in the text. The nth eigenfunction is the function $R_n(r)$ defined in (42). Finally the solution of $T_n' = -\gamma_n^2 kT_n$ is

$$T_n(t) = \exp(-\gamma_n^2 kt),$$

so we get a solution of the form

$$u(r,t) = \Sigma\, c_n \exp(-\gamma_n^2 kt)\,R_n(r).$$

SECTION 10.5

HIGHER-DIMENSIONAL PHENOMENA

This section provides the interested student with an opportunity to study several applications at greater depth than is afforded by the usual textbook exercises. The problem sets outlined in Section 10.5 can serve as the basis for several fairly substantial computational projects. Because these problem sets and projects are rather heavily annotated in the text, further outlines of solutions are not included in this manual. However, additional discussion -- particularly regarding computer implementations -- may be found in the *Computing Projects Manual* that accompanies the text.

APPENDIX

EXISTENCE AND UNIQUENESS OF SOLUTIONS

In Problems 1–12 we apply the iterative formula

$$y_{n+1} = b + \int_a^x f(t, y_n(t)) \, dt$$

to compute successive approximations $\{y_n(x)\}$ to the solution of the initial value problem

$$y' = f(x, y), \qquad\qquad y(a) = b.$$

starting with $y_0(x) = b$.

1. $y_0(x) = 3$

$y_1(x) = 3 + 3x$

$y_2(x) = 3 + 3x + 3x^2/2$

$y_3(x) = 3 + 3x + 3x^2/2 + x^3/2$

$y_4(x) = 3 + 3x + 3x^2/2 + x^3/2 + x^4/8$

$y(x) = 3 - 3x + 3x^2/2 + x^3/2 + x^4/8 + \cdots = 3e^x$

2. $y_0(x) = 4$

$y_1(x) = 4 - 8x$

$y_2(x) = 4 - 8x + 8x^2$

$y_3(x) = 4 - 8x + 8x^2 - (16/3)x^3$

$y_4(x) = 4 - 8x + 8x^2 - (16/3)x^3 + (8/3)x^4$

$y(x) = 4 - 8x + 8x^2 - (16/3)x^3 + (8/3)x^4 - \cdots = 4e^{-2x}$

3. $y_0(x) = 1$

$y_1(x) = 1 - x^2$

$y_2(x) = 1 - x^2 + x^4/2$

$y_3(x) = 1 - x^2 + x^4/2 - x^6/6$

$y_4(x) = 1 - x^2 + x^4/2 - x^6/6 + x^8/24$

$y(x) = 1 - x^2 + x^4/2 - x^6/6 + x^8/24 - \cdots = \exp(-x^2)$

4. $\quad y_0(x) = 2$

$\quad\quad y_1(x) = 2 + 2x^3$

$\quad\quad y_2(x) = 2 + 2x^3 + x^6$

$\quad\quad y_3(x) = 2 + 2x^3 + x^6 + (1/3)x^9$

$\quad\quad y_4(x) = 2 + 2x^3 + x^6 + (1/3)x^9 + (1/12)x^{12}$

$\quad\quad y(x) = 2 + 2x^3 + x^6 + (1/3)x^9 + (1/12)x^{12} + \cdots = 2\exp(x^3)$

5. $\quad y_0(x) = 0$

$\quad\quad y_1(x) = 2x$

$\quad\quad y_2(x) = 2x + 2x^2$

$\quad\quad y_3(x) = 2x + 2x^2 + 4x^3/3$

$\quad\quad y_4(x) = 2x + 2x^2 + 4x^3/3 + 2x^4/3$

$\quad\quad y(x) = 2x + 2x^2 + 4x^3/3 + 2x^4/3 + \cdots = e^{2x} - 1$

6. $\quad y_0(x) = 0$

$\quad\quad y_1(x) = (1/2)x^2$

$\quad\quad y_2(x) = (1/2)x^2 + (1/6)x^3$

$\quad\quad y_3(x) = (1/2)x^2 + (1/6)x^3 + (1/24)x^4$

$\quad\quad y_4(x) = (1/2)x^2 + (1/6)x^3 + (1/24)x^4 + (1/120)x^5$

$\quad\quad y(x) = (1/2!)x^2 + (1/3!)x^3 + (1/4!)x^4 + (1/5!)x^5 + \cdots = e^x - x - 1$

7. $\quad y_0(x) = 0$

$\quad\quad y_1(x) = x^2$

$\quad\quad y_2(x) = x^2 + x^4/2$

$\quad\quad y_3(x) = x^2 + x^4/2 + x^6/6$

$\quad\quad y_4(x) = x^2 + x^4/2 + x^6/6 + x^8/24$

$\quad\quad y(x) = x^2 + x^4/2 + x^6/6 + x^8/24 + \cdots = \exp(x^2) - 1$

8. $\quad y_0(x) = 0$

$\quad\quad y_1(x) = 2x^4$

$\quad\quad y_2(x) = 2x^4 + (4/3)x^6$

$\quad\quad y_3(x) = 2x^4 + (4/3)x^6 + (2/3)x^8$

$\quad\quad y_4(x) = 2x^4 + (4/3)x^6 + (2/3)x^8 + (4/15)x^{10}$

$\quad\quad y(x) = 2x^4 + (4/3)x^6 + (2/3)x^8 + (4/15)x^{10} + \cdots = \exp(2x^2) - 2x^2 - 1$

9. $y_0(x) = 1$

$y_1(x) = (1 + x) + x^2/2$

$y_2(x) = (1 + x + x^2) + x^3/6$

$y_3(x) = (1 + x + x^2 + x^3/3) + x^4/24$

$y(x) = 1 + x + x^2 + x^3/3 + x^4/12 + \cdots = 2e^x - 1 - x$

10. $y_0(x) = 0$

$y_1(x) = x + (1/2)x^2 + (1/6)x^3 + (1/24)x^4 + \cdots = e^x - 1$

$y_2(x) = x + \quad x^2 + (1/3)x^3 + (1/12)x^4 + \cdots = 2e^x - x - 2$

$y_3(x) = x + \quad x^2 + (1/2)x^3 + (1/8)x^4 + \cdots = 3e^x - (1/2)x^2 - 2x - 3$

$y(x) = x + \quad x^2 + (1/2)x^3 + (1/6)x^4 + \cdots = xe^x$

11. $y_0(x) = 1$

$y_1(x) = 1 + x$

$y_2(x) = (1 + x + x^2) + x^3/3$

$y_3(x) = (1 + x + x^2 + x^3) + 2x^4/3 + x^5/3 + x^6/9 + x^7/63$

$y(x) = 1 + x + x^2 + x^3 + x^4 + \cdots = 1/(1 - x)$

12. $y_0(x) = 1$

$y_1(x) = 1 + (1/2)x$

$y_2(x) = 1 + (1/2)x + (3/8)x^2 + (1/8)x^3 + (1/64)x^4$

$y_3(x) = 1 + (1/2)x + (3/8)x^2 + (5/16)x^3 + (13/64)x^4 + \cdots$

$y(x) = 1 + (1/2)x + (3/8)x^2 + (5/16)x^3 + (35/128)x^4 + \cdots = (1 - x)^{-1/2}$

13. $\begin{bmatrix} x_0(t) \\ y_0(t) \end{bmatrix} = \begin{bmatrix} 1 \\ -1 \end{bmatrix}$

$\begin{bmatrix} x_1(t) \\ y_1(t) \end{bmatrix} = \begin{bmatrix} 1 + 3t \\ -1 + 5t \end{bmatrix}$

$$\begin{bmatrix} x_2(t) \\ y_2(t) \end{bmatrix} = \begin{bmatrix} 1+3t+\frac{1}{2}t^2 \\ -1+5t-\frac{1}{2}t^2 \end{bmatrix}$$

$$\begin{bmatrix} x_3(t) \\ y_3(t) \end{bmatrix} = \begin{bmatrix} 1+3t+\frac{1}{2}t^2+\frac{1}{3}t^3 \\ -1+5t-\frac{1}{2}t^2+\frac{5}{6}t^3 \end{bmatrix}$$

14.

$$\mathbf{x}(t) = \left[\sum_{n=0}^{\infty} \frac{1}{n!} \begin{bmatrix} 1 & n \\ 0 & 1 \end{bmatrix} t^n \right] \begin{bmatrix} 1 \\ 1 \end{bmatrix}$$

$$= \begin{bmatrix} \sum_{n=0}^{\infty} \dfrac{t^n}{n!} & \sum_{n=0}^{\infty} \dfrac{t^n}{(n-1)!} \\ 0 & \sum_{n=0}^{\infty} \dfrac{t^n}{n!} \end{bmatrix} \begin{bmatrix} 1 \\ 1 \end{bmatrix}$$

$$= \begin{bmatrix} e^t & te^t \\ 0 & e^t \end{bmatrix} \begin{bmatrix} 1 \\ 1 \end{bmatrix}$$

$$\mathbf{x}(t) = \begin{bmatrix} e^t + te^t \\ e^t \end{bmatrix}$$

16.

$y_0(x) = 0$
$y_1(x) = (1/3)x^3$
$y_2(x) = (1/3)x^3 + (1/63)x^7$
$y_3(x) = (1/3)x^3 + (1/63)x^7 + (2/2079)x^{11} + (1/59535)x^{15}$

Then $y_3(1) \approx 0.350185$, which differs by only 0.0134% from the Runge-Kutta approximation $y(1) \approx 0.350232$. As a denouement we may recall from the result of Problem 16 in Section 8.6 that the exact solution of our initial value problem here is

$$y(x) = x \cdot \frac{J_{3/4}\left(\frac{1}{2}x^2\right)}{J_{-1/4}\left(\frac{1}{2}x^2\right)}$$

so the exact value at $x = 1$ is

$$y(1) = \frac{J_{3/4}\left(\frac{1}{2}\right)}{J_{-1/4}\left(\frac{1}{2}\right)} \approx 0.35023\ 18443.$$